T H E

Intelligent Man's Guide

T O

SCIENCE

BOOKS BY ISAAC ASIMOV

BIOCHEMISTRY AND HUMAN METABOLISM *(with B. S. Walker and W. C. Boyd)*

RACES AND PEOPLE *(with W. C. Boyd)*

CHEMISTRY AND HUMAN HEALTH *(with B. S. Walker and M. K. Nicholas)*

THE CHEMICALS OF LIFE

INSIDE THE ATOM

BUILDING BLOCKS OF THE UNIVERSE

ONLY A TRILLION

THE CLOCK WE LIVE ON

THE WORDS OF SCIENCE

THE REALM OF NUMBERS

THE LIVING RIVER

KINGDOM OF THE SUN

THE WELLSPRINGS OF LIFE

THE

Intelligent Man's Guide

TO

SCIENCE

ISAAC ASIMOV

VOLUME ONE

The Physical Sciences

BASIC BOOKS, INC. NEW YORK

Introduction

by

GEORGE W. BEADLE

W<small>HY SHOULD THE INTELLIGENT MAN</small> — and woman, and boy, and girl — want to know about science?

As Professor Asimov says, man wants to know and understand everything possible simply because he is born with curiosity — a curiosity more highly developed and more persistent than that of any other species on earth. His indulgence in satisfying this curiosity, plus his ability to remember, reason, and communicate, has made possible his entire culture, which of course includes science.

What are the laws by which the heavens above go about their ceaseless business? What are the ultimate particles of which the universe is built, where do they come from, how do men probe their mysteries? What is life? How does it evolve? Does it exist on Mars — or elsewhere in the universe? These are but a few of the countless questions that man in his insatiable curiosity asks about himself and the universe in which he lives.

There is the same satisfaction in knowing and understanding science that there is in knowing and understanding religion, history, art, music, or literature. It is one of the ways of appreciating order and beauty — the order and beauty of nature. The purpose of science is to find this order, by searching for basic knowledge.

Such knowledge, when applied to our everyday problems, can affect the food we eat, the clothing we wear, the houses that shelter us; our modes of travel, of entertainment, of education; our religious creeds and moral judgments; and even our national survival. Modern medicine, with its remarkable achievements in preventing, correcting, and circumventing man's many ills and defects, depends on science. So does modern agriculture and much of industry. But the function of science itself is not to make applications. Science consists of principles and laws; the *things* that grow out of it — medicines and medical procedures, the faster-germinating seed, the hardier livestock, the telephone, the radio, television, airplanes, missiles, satellites, moon shots, man-in-space devices, nuclear reactors, and nuclear weapons — are not themselves science. They are the products of engineering or technology.

This is not to say that the applications of science are unimportant. They have in fact changed the world so profoundly that we could not continue to live as we do, and in such numbers, without them. Both science and technology are so much a part of the cultural, economic, and political affairs of all modern nations that lack of understanding of either, by government officials or the general citizenry, can have foolish or even dangerous consequences. But to many people the differing purposes of science and technology are unclear. All too often, at present, far-reaching decisions of a technological nature are made without adequate appreciation of either the possibilities or the limitations of the underlying science.

How, then, do we go about the task of more widely satisfying the intelligent man's curiosity about science and increasing his appreciation and understanding of it?

Clearly one of the most effective ways is through our systems of formal education. Needed at all levels are teachers who know the body of facts that science has discovered and organized. An even greater need is for teachers who recognize the important difference between merely transmitting the facts of science and inspiring in their pupils an awareness of their significance. The latter ability is a rare skill, for it requires deep insights and a high degree of competence in the arts of communication.

Our textbooks, like teachers, too often serve merely as sources of facts. Scientists have earnestly sought to explain modern science through their non-technical writings; however, they often lack communication skills at the desired level. Professional science writers, on the other hand, not infrequently lack the requisite understanding of the subject matter. What we need are more of the rare persons who combine extraordinary writing ability with wide knowledge and understanding of science. Thomas Henry Huxley, the eloquent and effective champion of Darwinism, was such a man. His many writings have become classics, well worth reading or re-reading today. But the Huxleys, like the master teachers, are uncommon.

Professor Asimov is one of the rare ones. He knows and understands science in both its history and its substance, and he writes about it simply, clearly, and with infectious enthusiasm. He is classified professionally as a biochemist — a person who investigates the chemistry of living things like viruses, tomato plants, or guinea pigs. But his knowledge and interest extend far beyond biochemistry to all the main areas of modern science.

I believe that this book will delight and instruct all intelligent persons — students, teachers, and laymen — who want to know what science is all about, how it came to be, and who were some of the people responsible for its development. Scientists, after all, *are* people; the story of science, therefore, is a very human story.

I hope *The Intelligent Man's Guide to Science* will find a place on the shelves of the home and school libraries of America and beyond, and that it will be widely read in many nations. Those who read it should find in it both intellectual satisfaction and enjoyment.

Acknowledgments

"No man is an island," says John Donne—and, I add, no book either. The more complex the book, the more clearly it is "a part of the main."

No doubt, were I cursed with total recall I would find that every incident of my life, every person I met, every book I read, contributed in one way or another to the condition of life that made it possible for me to write these volumes. Consequently I am grateful for the custom that limits acknowledgment only to those directly involved, for all of us thereby avoid an impossible task—I to write a complete acknowledgment and you to read one.

First among those who should be mentioned are those who kindly allowed themselves to be imposed upon to read part or all the manuscript in order that their experience and wisdom might strain out those errors of fact and deduction that had been allowed entry by my own fallibility. Any mistakes that remain are by no means to be attributed to these reviewers, of course, but are my own responsibility and perhaps a tribute to my ingenuity in hiding them where my readers couldn't find them.

These readers include, first, George W. Beadle, who, in addition, was so kind as to write the introduction (in which his opinion of myself, so flatteringly expressed, must remain his own responsibility entirely). Then there are Harry C. Stubbs, William A. Baum, Bruce C. Heezen, Selma B. Brody, David Bardack, E. Joseph Shoben, Jr., Miriam Schapiro, and Francis J. Ryan, whose expert knowledge in their respective fields helped to clarify many knotty points.

Secondly, there is my editor, Leon Svirsky, who in the spring of 1959 managed, by some arcane hypnotic effect concerning which he refuses to elaborate, to persuade me to write this book. I was halfway through before I came out of the spell, and by then it was too late to stop. Mr. Svirsky, in editing the manuscript, succeeded in inserting many a felicitous phrase and not a few useful paragraphs. He also endured with phenomenal patience my invariable anguish (eloquently expressed) upon those occasions when he "tightened the manuscript." I was lost in mingled admiration and exasperation at the manner in which he succeeded in soothing me without ever ceasing to "tighten."

Thirdly, there are, in the more general background, those friends who encouraged me, in important ways, to engage in science writing. These include William C. Boyd, Burnham S. Walker, John W. Campbell, Jr., and Robert P. Mills.

Fourthly, it is impossible not to mention the important contribution of my wife and two children. They let me work! This might seem an easy task, but writers are unreasonable by nature and in the course of major composition become intensely so. I am grateful for their endurance.

Farther than this I must not go. As I indicated at the start, there remain contributions with which I could deal in great detail and with great enthusiasm if the rest of this volume were placed at my disposal for the purpose. But this book is a guide to science and not to my life-history, and I shall stop here.

Contents

VOLUME ONE
The Physical Sciences

INTRODUCTION — GEORGE W. BEADLE   **v**

1. WHAT IS SCIENCE?   3

2. THE UNIVERSE   21
   - THE SIZE OF THE UNIVERSE   21
   - THE BIRTH OF THE UNIVERSE   42
   - THE DEATH OF THE SUN   53
   - THE WINDOWS TO THE UNIVERSE   64

3. THE EARTH   77
   - BIRTH OF THE SOLAR SYSTEM   77
   - OF SHAPE AND SIZE   84
   - THE LAYERS OF THE PLANET   91
   - THE OCEAN   102
   - THE ICE CAPS   110

4. THE ATMOSPHERE   123
   - THE SHELLS OF AIR   123
   - THE GASES IN AIR   134
   - MAGNETS   141
   - METEORS   153
   - THE ORIGIN OF AIR   159

5. THE ELEMENTS ... 167
 THE PERIODIC TABLE ... 167
 RADIOACTIVE ELEMENTS ... 177
 ELECTRONS ... 186
 GASES ... 203
 METALS ... 213

6. THE PARTICLES ... 223
 THE NUCLEAR ATOM ... 223
 ISOTOPES ... 228
 NEW PARTICLES ... 235
 PARTICLE ACCELERATORS ... 243
 STRANGE PARTICLES ... 252
 INSIDE THE NUCLEUS ... 263

7. THE WAVES ... 267
 LIGHT ... 267
 RELATIVITY ... 278
 HEAT ... 289
 MASS TO ENERGY ... 297
 PARTICLES AND WAVES ... 300

8. THE MACHINE ... 309
 FIRE AND STEAM ... 309
 ELECTRICITY ... 315
 ELECTRICAL GADGETS ... 323
 INTERNAL-COMBUSTION ENGINES ... 329
 RADIO ... 333

9. THE REACTOR ... 347
 FISSION ... 347
 THE ATOM BOMB ... 356
 NUCLEAR POWER ... 366
 RADIOACTIVITY ... 371
 FUSION POWER ... 379

CONTENTS

VOLUME TWO
The Biological Sciences

10. THE MOLECULE   389
    ORGANIC MATTER   389
    THE DETAILS OF STRUCTURE   396
    ORGANIC SYNTHESIS   407
    POLYMERS AND PLASTICS   420
    FIBERS   436
    RUBBERS   440

11. THE PROTEINS   445
    KEY MOLECULES OF LIFE   445
    AMINO ACIDS IN THE CHAIN   457
    ENZYMES   465
    METABOLISM   476
    TRACERS   482
    PHOTOSYNTHESIS   489

12. THE CELL   497
    CHROMOSOMES   497
    GENES   506
    NUCLEIC ACIDS   524
    THE ORIGIN OF LIFE   535
    LIFE IN OTHER WORLDS   545

13. THE MICROORGANISM   553
    BACTERIA   553
    VIRUSES   568
    IMMUNITY   581
    CANCER   592

14. THE BODY   603
    FOOD   603
    VITAMINS   607

xiii

CONTENTS

MINERALS	623
HORMONES	632
DEATH	648

15. THE SPECIES — 653
VARIETIES OF LIFE — 653
EVOLUTION — 664
THE DESCENT OF MAN — 678
MAN'S PRESENT AND FUTURE — 690

16. THE MIND — 703
THE NERVOUS SYSTEM — 703
HUMAN BEHAVIOR — 716
FEEDBACK — 726
THINKING MACHINES — 732

APPENDIX. MATHEMATICS IN SCIENCE — 747
GRAVITATION — 747
RELATIVITY — 758

BIBLIOGRAPHY — 769

ILLUSTRATIONS — 781

INDEX OF NAMES — 791

INDEX OF SUBJECTS — 805

VOLUME ONE

The Physical Sciences

CHAPTER

I

WHAT IS SCIENCE?

Almost in the beginning was curiosity.

Curiosity, the overwhelming desire to know, is not characteristic of dead matter. It is also not characteristic of some forms of living organisms, which, for that very reason, we can scarcely bring ourselves to consider alive.

A tree does not display curiosity about its environment in any way we can recognize; nor does a sponge or an oyster. The wind, the rain, the ocean currents bring them what is needful and from it they take what they can. If the chance of events is such as to bring them fire, poison, predators or parasites, they die as stoically and as undemonstratively as they lived.

Early in the scheme of life, however, independent motion was developed by some organisms. It meant a tremendous advance in their control of the environment. A moving organism no longer had to wait in stolid rigidity for food to come its way; it went out after it.

This meant that adventure had entered the world — and curiosity. The individual that hesitated in the competitive hunt for food, that was overly conservative in its investigation, starved. As early as that, curiosity concerning the environment was enforced as the price of survival.

The one-celled paramecium, moving about in a searching way, cannot have conscious volitions and desires in the sense that we do, but it has a drive, even if only a "simple" physical-chemical one, which causes it to behave as if it were investigating its surroundings for food. And this "act of curiosity" is what we most easily recognize as being inseparable from the kind of life that is most akin to ours.

As organisms grew more intricate, their sense organs multiplied and became both more complex and more delicate. More messages of greater variety were received from and about the external environment. Along with that (whether as cause or effect we can't tell) there developed an increasing complexity of the nervous system, the living instrument which interpreted and stored the data collected by the sense-organs.

THERE COMES A POINT where the capacity to receive, store, and interpret messages from the outside world may outrun sheer necessity. An organism may for the moment be sated with food, and there may, at the moment, be no danger in sight. What does it do then?

It might lapse into an oyster-like stupor. But the higher organisms, at least, still show a strong instinct to explore the environment. Idle curiosity, we may call it. Yet, though we may sneer at it, we judge intelligence by it. The dog, in moments of leisure, will sniff idly here and there, pricking up its ears at sounds we cannot hear; and so we judge it to be more intelligent than the cat, which in its moments of leisure grooms itself or quietly and luxuriously stretches out and falls asleep. The more advanced the brain, the greater the drive to explore, the greater the "curiosity-surplus." The monkey is a by-word for curiosity. Its busy little brain must and will be kept going on whatever is handy. And in this respect, as in many others, man is but a super-monkey.

The human brain is the most magnificently organized lump of matter in the known universe, and its capacity to receive, organize and store data is far in excess of the ordinary requirements of life. It is to this excess that we owe our ability to be afflicted by that supremely painful disease, boredom. A human being forced into a situation where he has no opportunity to utilize his brain except for minimal survival will gradually experience a variety of unpleasant symptoms, up to and including serious mental disorganization.

What it amounts to, then, is that the normal human being has an intense and overwhelming curiosity. If he lacks the opportunity to satisfy it in ways immediately useful to him, he will satisfy it in other ways — even regrettable ways to which we have attached admonitions such as: "Curiosity killed the cat," "Mind your own business."

The overriding power of curiosity, even with harm as the penalty, is reflected in the myths and legends of the human race. The Greeks had the tale of Pandora and her box. Pandora, the first woman, was given a box which she was forbidden to open. Quickly and naturally enough she opened it and found it full of the spirits of disease, famine, hate, and all kinds of evil — which escaped and have plagued the world ever since.

In the Biblical story of the temptation of Eve, it seems fairly certain (to me, at any rate) that the serpent had the world's easiest job. He might have saved his tempting words: Eve's curiosity would have driven her to taste the forbidden fruit even without temptation. If you are of a mind to interpret the Bible allegorically, you may think of the Serpent as simply the representation of this inner compulsion; in the conventional cartoon picturing Eve standing under the tree with the forbidden fruit in her hand, the Serpent coiled around the branch might be labeled "Curiosity."

5

If curiosity, like any other human drive, can be put to ignoble use — the prying invasion of privacy that has given the word its cheap and unpleasant connotation — it nevertheless remains one of the noblest properties of the human mind. For its simplest definition is "the desire to know."

This desire finds its first expression in answers to the practical needs of human life — how best to plant and cultivate crops, how best to fashion bows and arrows, how best to weave clothing — in short, the "applied arts." But after these comparatively limited skills have been mastered, or the practical needs fulfilled, what then? Inevitably the desire to know leads on to less limited and more complex activities.

It seems clear that the "fine arts" (designed to satisfy inchoate and boundless and spiritual needs) were born in the agony of boredom. To be sure, one can easily find more mundane uses and excuses for the fine arts. Paintings and statuettes were used as fertility charms and as religious symbols, for instance. But one can't help suspecting that the objects existed first and the use second.

To say that the fine arts arose out of a sense of the beautiful may also be putting the cart before the horse. Once the fine arts were developed, their extension and refinement in the direction of beauty would have followed inevitably, but even if this had not happened, the fine arts would have developed nevertheless. Surely the fine arts antedate any possible need or use for them, other than the elementary need to occupy the mind as fully as possible.

Not only does the production of a work of fine art occupy the mind satisfactorily; the contemplation or appreciation of the work supplies a similar service to the audience. A great work of art is great precisely because it offers a kind of stimulation which cannot readily be found elsewhere. It contains enough data of sufficient complexity to cajole the brain into exerting itself past the usual needs, and unless a person is hopelessly ruined by routine or stultification, that exertion is pleasant.

But if the practice of the fine arts is a satisfactory solution to the problem of leisure, it has this disadvantage: it requires, in addition to

6

an active and creative mind, a physical dexterity. It is just as interesting to pursue mental activities that involve only the mind, without the supplement of manual skill. And, of course, such an activity is available. It is the pursuit of knowledge itself, not in order to do something with it but for its own sake.

Thus the desire to know seems to lead into successive realms of greater etherealization and more efficient occupation of the mind — from knowledge of accomplishing the useful, to knowledge of accomplishing the esthetic, to "pure" knowledge.

Knowledge for itself alone seeks answers to such questions as "How high is the sky?" or "Why does a stone fall?" This is sheer curiosity — curiosity at its idlest and therefore perhaps at its most peremptory. After all, it serves no apparent purpose to know how high the sky is or why the stone falls. The lofty sky does not interfere with the ordinary business of life, and as for the stone, knowing why it falls does not help us to dodge it more skillfully, or soften the blow if it happens to hit us. Yet there have always been people who ask such apparently useless questions and try to answer them out of the sheer desire to know — out of the absolute necessity of keeping the brain working.

The obvious method of dealing with such questions is to make up an esthetically-satisfying answer: one that has sufficient analogies to what is already known to be comprehensible and plausible. The expression "to make up" is rather bald and unromantic. The ancients liked to think of the process of discovery as the inspiration of the muses, or a revelation from heaven. In any case, whether it was inspiration, revelation or the kind of creative thinking that goes into story-telling, their explanations depended heavily on analogy. The lightning-bolt is destructive and terrifying, but it appears, after all, to be hurled like a weapon and does the damage of a hurled weapon — a fantastically violent one. Such a weapon must have a wielder similarly enlarged in scale, and so the thunderbolt becomes the hammer of Thor or the flashing spear of Zeus. The more-than-natural weapon is wielded by a more-than-natural man.

Thus a myth is born. The forces of nature are personified and become gods. The myths react upon one another, are built up and improved by generations of myth-tellers until the original point may be obscured. Some may degenerate into pretty stories (or ribald ones), while others may gain an ethical content important enough to make them meaningful within the framework of a major religion.

Just as art may be fine or applied, so may mythology. Myths may be maintained for their esthetic charm, or they may be bent to the physical uses of mankind. For instance, the earliest farmers would be intensely concerned with the phenomenon of rain and why it fell so capriciously. The fertilizing rain falling from the heavens upon the earth presented an obvious analogy to the sex act, and by personifying both heaven and earth, man found an easy explanation of the release or withholding of the rains. The earth-goddess, or the sky-god, was either pleased or offended, as the case might be. Once this myth was accepted, farmers had a plausible basis for bringing rain: namely, appeasing the god by appropriate rites. These rites might well be orgiastic in nature — an attempt to influence heaven and earth by example.

THE GREEK MYTHS are among the prettiest and most sophisticated in our literary and cultural heritage. But it was the Greeks also who, in due course, introduced the opposite way of looking at the Universe — that is, as something impersonal and inanimate. To the myth-makers, every aspect of nature was essentially human in its unpredictability. However mighty and majestic the personification, however superhuman Zeus or Marduk or Odin might be in powers, they were also — like mere men — frivolous, whimsical, emotional, capable of outrageous behavior for petty reasons, susceptible to childish bribes. As long as the universe was in the control of such whimsical and unpredictable deities, there was no hope of understanding it, only the shallow hope of appeasing it. But in the new view of the later Greek thinkers, the Universe was a machine governed by inflexible laws. The Greek philosophers now devoted themselves to the exciting intellectual exercise of trying to discover just what the laws of nature might be.

8

In engaging in this intellectual exercise, the Greeks assumed, of course, that nature would play fair; that, if attacked in the proper manner, it would yield its secrets and would not change position or attitude in mid-play. (Thousands of years later Albert Einstein expressed this feeling when he said, "God may be subtle, but he is not malicious.") There was also the feeling that the natural laws, when found, would be comprehensible. This Greek optimism has never entirely left the human race.

With confidence in the fair play of nature, man needed to work out an orderly system for learning how to determine the underlying laws from the observed data. To progress from one point to another by established rules of argument is to use "reason." A reasoner may use "intuition" to guide his search for answers, but he must rely on sound logic to test his theories. To take a simple example: if brandy and water, whiskey and water, vodka and water, and rum and water are all intoxicating beverages, one may jump to the conclusion that the intoxicating factor must be the ingredient these drinks hold in common — namely, water. There is something wrong with this reasoning, but the fault in the logic is not immediately obvious, and in more subtle cases the error may be hard indeed to discover.

The tracking-down of errors or fallacies in reasoning has amused thinkers from Greek times to the present. And of course we owe the earliest foundations of systematic logic to Aristotle of Stagira, who in the fourth century B.C. first summarized the rules of rigorous reasoning.

The essentials of the intellectual game of man-against-nature are three. First, you must collect observations about some facet of nature. Second, you must organize these observations into an orderly array. (The organization does not alter them but merely makes them easier to handle. This is plain in the game of bridge, for instance, where arranging the hand in suits and order of value does not change the cards or show the best course of play, but makes it easier to arrive at the logical plays.) Third, you must derive from your orderly array of observations some principle that summarizes the observations.

For instance, we may observe that marble sinks in water, wood floats, iron sinks, a feather floats, mercury sinks, olive oil floats, and so on. If we put all the sinkable objects in one list and all the floatable ones in another, and look for a characteristic that differentiates all the objects in one group from all in the other, we will conclude: Heavy objects sink in water and light objects float.

The Greeks named their new manner of studying the Universe *philosophia* ("philosophy") meaning "love of knowledge," or in free translation, "the desire to know."

THE GREEKS ACHIEVED their most brilliant successes in geometry. These successes can be attributed mainly to their development of two techniques: (1) abstraction and (2) generalization.

Here is an example. Egyptian land surveyors had found a practical way to form a right angle: they divided a rope into 12 equal parts and made a triangle in which three parts formed one side, four parts another and five parts the third side — the right angle lay where the three-unit side joined the four-unit side. There is no record of how the Egyptians discovered this method, and apparently their interest went no farther than to make use of it. But the curious Greeks went on to investigate why such a triangle should contain a right angle. In the course of their analysis, they grasped the point that the physical construction itself was only incidental: it did not matter whether the triangle was made of rope or linen or wooden slats. It was simply a property of "straight lines" meeting at angles. In conceiving of ideal straight lines, which were independent of any physical visualization and could exist only in imagination, they originated the method called abstraction — stripping away non-essentials and considering only those properties necessary to the solution of the problem.

The Greek geometers made another advance by seeking general solutions for classes of problems, instead of treating individual problems separately. For instance, one might discover by trial that a right angle appeared in triangles not only with sides three, four, and five feet long but also in those of 5, 12, and 13 feet and of 7, 24, and 25 feet. But these were merely numbers without meaning. Could some common property be found that would describe all right triangles? By careful reasoning the Greeks showed that a triangle was a right triangle if, and only if, the lengths of the sides had the relation $x^2 + y^2 = z^2$, z being the length of the longest side. The right angle lay where the sides of lengths x and y met. Thus for the triangle with sides of 3, 4, and 5 feet, squaring the sides gives $9 + 16 = 25$; similarly, squaring the sides of 5, 12, and 13 gives $25 + 144 = 169$; and squaring 7, 24, and 25 gives $49 + 576 = 625$. These are only three cases out of an infinity of possible ones, and as such, trivial. What intrigued the Greeks was the discovery of a proof that the relation must hold in all cases. And they pursued geometry as an elegant means of discovering and formulating generalizations.

Various Greek mathematicians contributed proofs of relationships existing among the lines and points of geometric figures. The one involving the right angle was reputedly worked out by Pythagoras of Samos about 525 B.C. and is still called the Pythagorean theorem in his honor.

About 300 B.C. Euclid gathered the mathematical theorems known in his time and arranged them in a reasonable order, such that each theorem could be proved through the use of theorems proved previously. Naturally, this system eventually worked back to something unprovable: if each theorem had to be proved with the help of one already proved, how could one prove theorem No. 1? The solution was to begin with a statement of truths so obvious and acceptable to all as to need no proof. Such a statement is called an "axiom." Euclid managed to reduce the accepted axioms of the day to a few simple statements. From these axioms alone, he built an intricate and majestic system of "Euclidean geometry." Never was so much constructed so well from so little, and Euclid's reward is that his textbook has remained in use, with but minor modification, for more than 2,000 years.

WORKING OUT a body of knowledge as the inevitable consequence of a set of axioms ("deduction") is an attractive game. The

Greeks fell in love with it, thanks to the success of their geometry — enough in love with it to commit two serious errors.

First, they came to consider deduction as the only respectable means of attaining knowledge. They were well aware that for some kinds of knowledge deduction was inadequate; for instance, the distance from Corinth to Athens could not be deduced from abstract principles but had to be measured. The Greeks were willing to look at nature when necessary; however, they were always ashamed of the necessity and considered that the highest type of knowledge was that arrived at by cerebration. They tended to undervalue knowledge which was too directly involved with everyday life. There is a story that a student of Plato, receiving mathematical instruction from the master, finally asked impatiently: "But what is the use of all this?" Plato, deeply offended, called a slave and ordered him to give the student a coin. "Now," he said, "you need not feel your instruction has been entirely to no purpose." With that, the student was expelled.

There is a well-worn belief that this lofty view arose from the Greeks' slave-based culture, in which all practical matters were relegated to the slaves. Perhaps so, but I incline to the view that the Greek attitude toward philosophy *was* a sport, an intellectual game. We regard the amateur in sports as a gentleman socially superior to the professional who makes his living at it. In line with this concept of purity, we take almost ridiculous precautions to make sure that the contestants in the Olympic games are free of any taint of professionalism. The Greek rationalization for the "cult of uselessness" may similarly have been based on a feeling that to allow mundane knowledge (such as the distance from Athens to Corinth) to intrude upon abstract thought was to allow imperfection to enter the Eden of true philosophy. Whatever the rationalization, the Greek thinkers were severely limited by their attitude. Greece was not barren of practical contributions to civilization, but even its great engineer, Archimedes of Syracuse, refused to write about his practical inventions and discoveries; to maintain his amateur status, he broadcast only his achievements in pure mathematics. And lack of interest in earthly things — in invention, in experiment, in the study of nature — was but one of the factors that put bounds upon Greek thought. The Greeks' emphasis upon purely abstract and formal study — indeed, their very success in geometry — led them into a second great error, and eventually to a dead end.

Seduced by the success of the axioms in developing a system of geometry, the Greeks came to think of the axioms as "absolute truths" and to suppose that other branches of knowledge could be developed from similar "absolute truths." Thus in astronomy they took as self-evident axioms the notions that (1) the earth was motionless and the center of the Universe, and (2) whereas the earth was corrupt and imperfect, the heavens were eternal, changeless, and perfect. Since the Greeks considered the circle the perfect curve, and since the heavens were perfect, it followed that all the heavenly bodies must move in circles around the earth. In time their observations (arising from navigation and calendar-making) showed that the planets did not move in perfectly simple circles, and so they were forced to allow planets to move in ever more complicated combinations of circles, which eventually were formulated as a ludicrously complex system by Claudius Ptolemaeus (Ptolemy) about 150 A.D. at Alexandria. Similarly, Aristotle worked up fanciful theories of motion from "self-evident" axioms, such as the proposition that the speed of an object's fall was proportional to its weight (anyone could see that a stone fell faster than a feather).

Now this worship of deduction from self-evident axioms was bound to wind up at the edge of a precipice, with no place to go. After the Greeks had worked out all the implications of the axioms, further important discoveries in mathematics or astronomy seemed out of the question. Philosophic knowledge appeared complete and perfect, and for nearly 2,000 years after the Golden Age of Greece, when questions involving the material universe arose there was a tendency to settle matters to the satisfaction of all by saying, "Aristotle says . . . ," or "Euclid says . . ."

HAVING SOLVED the problems of mathematics and astronomy, the Greeks turned to more subtle and challenging fields of knowledge. One was the field of the human soul.

Plato was far more interested in questions such as "What is justice?" or "What is virtue?" than in why rain fell or how the planets moved. As the supreme moral philosopher of Greece, he superseded Aristotle, the supreme natural philosopher. The Greek thinkers of the Roman period found themselves drawn more and more to the subtle delights of moral philosophy and away from the apparent sterility of natural philosophy. The last classical development in philosophy was an exceedingly mystical "neo-Platonism" formulated by Plotinus about 250 A.D.

Christianity, with its emphasis on the nature of God and His relation to man, introduced an entirely new dimension into the subject-matter of moral philosophy and increased its superiority as an intellectual pursuit over natural philosophy. From 200 A.D. to 1200 A.D., Europeans concerned themselves almost exclusively with moral philosophy, in particular with theology. Natural philosophy was nearly forgotten.

The Arabs, however, managed to preserve Aristotle and Ptolemy through the Middle Ages, and from them, Greek natural philosophy eventually filtered back to Western Europe. By 1200 Aristotle had been rediscovered. Further infusions came from the dying Byzantine Empire, which was the last area in Europe that maintained a continuous cultural tradition from the great days of Greece.

The first and most natural consequence of the rediscovery of Aristotle was the application of his system of logic and reason to theology. About 1250 the Italian theologian Thomas Aquinas established the system called "Thomism," based on Aristotelian principles, which still represents the basic theology of the Roman Catholic Church. But men soon began to apply the revival of Greek thought to secular fields as well.

Because the leaders of the Renaissance shifted emphasis from matters concerning God to the works of humanity, they were called

"humanists," and the study of literature, art, and history is still referred to as "the humanities."

To the Greek natural philosophy, the Renaissance thinkers brought
a fresh outlook, for the old views no longer entirely satisfied. In 1530
the Polish astronomer Nicholas Copernicus went so far as to reject
a basic axiom of astronomy: he proposed that the sun, not the earth,
be considered the center of the universe. (He retained the notion of
circular orbits for the earth and other planets, however.) This new
axiom allowed a much simpler explanation of the observed motions
of heavenly bodies. Yet the Copernican axiom of a moving earth
was far less "self-evident" than the Greek axiom of a motionless
earth, and so it is not surprising that it took nearly a century for the
Copernican theory to be accepted.

In a sense, the Copernican system itself was not a crucial change.
Copernicus had merely switched axioms; and Aristarchus of Samos
had already anticipated this switch to the sun as the center 2,000
years earlier. This is not to say that the changing of an axiom is a
minor matter. When mathematicians of the nineteenth century chal-
lenged Euclid's axioms and developed "non-Euclidean geometries"
based on other assumptions, they influenced thought on many matters in a most profound way: today the very history and form of the
Universe are thought to conform to a non-Euclidean (Riemannian)
geometry rather than the "commonsense" geometry of Euclid. But
the revolution initiated by Copernicus entailed not just a shift in
axioms but a whole new approach to nature. This revolution was
carried through in the person of the Italian Galileo Galilei.

THE GREEKS, by and large, had been satisfied to accept
the "obvious" facts of nature as starting points for their reasoning.
It is not on record that Aristotle ever dropped two stones of different weight to test his assumption that the speed of fall was proportional to an object's weight. To the Greeks, experimentation seemed
irrelevant. It interfered with and detracted from the beauty of pure
deduction. Besides, if an experiment disagreed with a deduction,

could one be certain that the experiment was correct? Was it likely that the imperfect world of reality would agree completely with the perfect world of abstract ideas, and, if it did not, ought one to adjust the perfect to the demands of the imperfect? To test a perfect theory with imperfect instruments did not impress the Greek philosophers as a valid way to gain knowledge.

Experimentation began to become philosophically respectable in Europe with the support of such philosophers as Roger Bacon (a contemporary of Thomas Aquinas) and his later namesake Francis Bacon. But it was Galileo who overthrew the Greek view and effected the revolution. He was not only an inspired experimentalist and a convincing logician but also a genius as a publicist. He described his experiments so clearly and so dramatically that he won over the European learned community. And they accepted his methods along with his results.

According to the best-known story about him, Galileo tested Aristotle's theories of falling bodies by asking the question of nature in such a way that all Europe could hear the answer. He is supposed to have climbed to the top of the Leaning Tower of Pisa and dropped a ten-pound sphere and a one-pound sphere simultaneously: the thump of the two balls hitting the ground in the same split-second killed Aristotelian physics.

Actually Galileo probably did not perform this particular experiment, but the story is so typical of his dramatic methods that it is no wonder it has been widely believed through the centuries.

Galileo undeniably did roll balls down inclined planes and measure the distance they traveled in given times. He was the first to conduct time experiments, the first to use measurement in a systematic way, the first to apply mathematics to physical phenomena.

His revolution consisted in elevating "induction" above deduction as the logical method of science. Instead of building conclusions upon an assumed set of generalizations, the inductive method starts with observations and derives generalizations (axioms, if you will) from them. Of course, even the Greeks obtained their axioms from observation; Euclid's axiom that a straight line is the shortest distance between two points was an intuitive judgment based on experience. But whereas the Greek philosophers minimized the role played by induction, Galileo looked upon induction as the essential process of gaining knowledge, the only way of justifying generalizations. Moreover, he realized that no generalization could be allowed to stand unless it was repeatedly tested by newer and still newer experiments — unless it withstood the continuing test of further induction.

Galileo's general viewpoint was just the reverse of the Greeks'. Far from considering the real world an imperfect representation of ideal truth, Galileo considered generalizations to be only imperfect representations of the real world. No amount of inductive testing could render a generalization completely and absolutely valid. Even though billions of observations tend to bear out a generalization, a single observation that contradicts or is inconsistent with it must force its modification. And no matter how many times a theory meets its tests successfully, there can be no certainty that it will not be overthrown by the next observation.

This, then, is a cornerstone of modern natural philosophy. It makes no claim of attaining ultimate truth. In fact, the phrase "ultimate truth" becomes meaningless, because there is no way in which enough observations can be made to make truth certain, and therefore "ultimate." The Greek philosophers recognized no such limitation. Moreover, they saw no difficulty in applying exactly the same method of reasoning to the question "What is justice?" as to the question "What is matter?" The new natural philosophy inaugurated by Galileo, on the other hand, made a sharp distinction between the two types of questions. The inductive method cannot make generalizations about what it cannot observe, and since the nature of the human soul, for example, is not observable by any direct means yet known, this subject lies outside the realm of the inductive method.

The new natural philosophy came in time to be called "science" (from the Latin word meaning "to know"). It is generally taken to mean specifically the inductive method. The older term "natural philosophy" lingered on as a synonym for science through the nineteenth century, and it is still recognized in the highest degree given to scientists — the Ph.D., or "Doctor of Philosophy."

THE VICTORY of modern science did not become complete until it established one more essential principle — namely, free and cooperative communication among all scientists. Although this necessity seems obvious to us now, it was not obvious to the philosophers of ancient and medieval times. The Pythagoreans of ancient Greece were a secret society who kept their mathematical discoveries to themselves. The alchemists of the Middle Ages deliberately obscured their writings to keep their so-called findings within as small an inner circle as possible. In the sixteenth century the Italian mathematician Niccolo Tartaglia, who discovered a method of solving cubic equations, saw nothing wrong in attempting to keep it a secret. When Geronimo Cardano, a fellow mathematician, wormed the secret out of Tartaglia and published it as his own, Tartaglia naturally was outraged, but aside from Cardano's trickery in claiming the credit, he was certainly correct in his reply that such a discovery had to be published.

Nowadays no scientific discovery is reckoned a discovery if it is kept secret. And it is not considered valid, even after publication, until at least one other investigator has repeated the observation and "confirmed" it. Science is the product not of individuals but of a "scientific community."

One of the first groups (and certainly the most famous) to represent such a scientific community was the Royal Society of London for Improving Natural Knowledge, usually called simply the "Royal Society." It grew out of informal meetings, beginning about 1645, of a group of gentlemen interested in the new scientific methods originated by Galileo. In 1660 the Society was formally chartered by King Charles II.

The members of the Royal Society met and discussed their findings openly, wrote letters describing them, and pursued their experiments with vigor and vivacity. Nevertheless, through most of the seventeenth century they remained in a defensive position. The attitude of many of their learned contemporaries might be expressed by a cartoon, after the modern fashion, showing the lofty shades of Pythagoras, Euclid and Aristotle staring down haughtily at children playing with marbles, labeled "Royal Society."

All this was changed by the work of Isaac Newton, who became a member of the society. From the observations and conclusions of Galileo, of the Danish astronomer Tycho Brahe, and of the German astronomer Johannes Kepler, who figured out the elliptical nature of the orbits of the planets, Newton arrived by induction at his three simple laws of motion and his great fundamental generalization — the law of universal gravitation. The educated world at once was so impressed with this discovery that Newton was idolized, almost deified, in his own lifetime. This majestic new Universe, built upon a few simple assumptions, now made the Greek philosophers look like boys playing with marbles. The revolution that Galileo had initiated at the beginning of the seventeenth century was triumphantly completed by Newton at the century's end.

IT WOULD BE PLEASANT to be able to say that science and man have lived happily ever since. But the truth is that the real difficulties of both were only beginning. As long as science had remained deductive, natural philosophy could be part of the general culture of all educated men. But inductive science became an immense labor — of observation, learning, and analysis. It was no longer a game for amateurs. And the complexity of science grew with each decade. During the century after Newton, it was still possible for a man of unusual attainments to master all fields of scientific knowledge. But by 1800 this had become entirely impracticable. As time went on, it was increasingly necessary for a scientist to limit himself to a portion of the field if he intended an intensive concern with it. Specialization was forced upon science by its own inexorable growth. And with each generation of scientists, specialization has grown more and more intense.

The publications of scientists concerning their individual work have never been so copious — and so unreadable for anyone but their fellow specialists. This has been a great handicap to science itself, for basic advances in scientific knowledge often spring from the cross-fertilization of knowledge from different specialties. What is even more ominous is that science has increasingly lost touch with non-scientists. Under such circumstances scientists come to be regarded almost as magicians — feared rather than admired. And the impression that science is incomprehensible magic, to be understood only by a chosen few who are suspiciously different from ordinary mankind, is bound to turn many youngsters away from science.

Yet modern science need not be so complete a mystery to non-scientists. Much could be accomplished toward bridging the gap if scientists accepted the responsibility of communication — explaining their own fields of work as simply and to as many as possible — and if non-scientists, for their part, accepted the responsibility of listening. To gain a satisfactory appreciation of the developments in a field of science, it is not essential to have a total understanding of the science. After all, no one feels that he must be capable of writing a great work of literature in order to appreciate Shakespeare. To listen to a Beethoven symphony with pleasure does not require the listener to be capable of composing an equivalent symphony of his own. By the same token, one can appreciate and take pleasure in the achievements of science even though he does not himself have a bent for creative work in science.

But what, you may ask, would be accomplished? The first answer is that no one can really feel at home in the modern world unless he has some intelligent notion of what science is up to. But beyond this, initiation into the magnificent world of science brings great esthetic satisfaction, inspiration to youth, fulfillment of the desire to know, and a deeper appreciation of the wonderful potentialities and achievements of the human mind.

It is with this in mind that I have undertaken to write these volumes.

CHAPTER

2

THE UNIVERSE

THE SIZE OF THE UNIVERSE

THERE IS NOTHING about the sky that makes it look particularly distant to a casual observer. Young children have no great trouble in accepting the fantasy that "the cow jumped over the moon" — or "he jumped so high, he touched the sky." The ancient Greeks, in their myth-telling stage, saw nothing ludicrous in allowing the sky to rest upon the shoulders of Atlas. Of course, Atlas might have been astronomically tall, but another myth suggests otherwise. Atlas was enlisted by Hercules to help him with the eleventh of his famous 12 labors — fetching the golden apples (oranges?) of the Hesperides ("the far west" — Spain?). While Atlas went off to fetch the apples, Hercules stood on a mountain and held up the sky. Granted that Hercules was a large specimen, he was nevertheless not a giant. It follows then that the early Greeks took quite calmly to the notion that the sky cleared the mountain tops by only a few feet.

It is natural to suppose, to begin with, that the sky is simply a hard canopy in which the shining heavenly bodies are set like diamonds. (Thus the Bible refers to the sky as the "firmament," from the same Latin root as the word "firm.") As early as the sixth to fourth centuries B.C., Greek astronomers realized that there must be more than one canopy. For while the "fixed" stars moved around the earth in a body, apparently without changing their relative positions, this was not true of the sun, the moon, and five bright star-like objects (Mercury, Venus, Mars, Jupiter and Saturn) — in fact, each moved in a separate path. These seven bodies were called planets (from a Greek word meaning "wanderer"), and it seemed obvious that they could not be attached to the vault of the stars.

The Greeks assumed that each planet was set in an invisible vault of its own, and that the vaults were nested one above the other, the nearest belonging to the planet that moved fastest. The quickest motion belonged to the moon, which circled the sky in about 29 and a half days. Beyond it lay in order (so thought the Greeks) Mercury, Venus, the sun, Mars, Jupiter, and Saturn.

The first scientific measurement of any cosmic distance came about 240 B.C. Eratosthenes of Cyrene, the head of the Library at Alexandria, then the most advanced scientific institution in the world, pondered the fact that on June 21, when the noonday sun was exactly overhead at the city of Syene in Egypt, it was not quite at the zenith at noon in Alexandria, 500 miles north of Syene. Eratosthenes decided that the explanation must be that the surface of the earth curved away from the sun. From the length of the shadow in Alexandria at noon on the solstice, straightforward geometry could yield an answer as to the amount by which the earth's surface curved in the 500-mile distance from Syene to Alexandria. From that one could calculate the circumference and the diameter of the earth, assuming that the earth was spherical in shape — a fact which Greek astronomers of the day were ready to accept.

Eratosthenes worked out the answer (in Greek units), and as

nearly as we can judge, his figures in our units came out at about 8,000 miles for the diameter and 25,000 miles for the circumference of the earth. This, as it happens, is just about right. (Later astronomers, for some reason, got much lower, incorrect results, which persisted for 1,700 years until the first circumnavigation of the globe in 1521–1523 definitely re-established Eratosthenes' correct value.)

With the benefit of Eratosthenes' measurement of the earth's diameter, Hipparchus of Nicaea about 150 B.C. worked out the distance to the moon. He used a method that had been suggested much earlier by Aristarchus of Samos, the most daring of all Greek astronomers. The Greeks had already surmised that eclipses of the moon were caused by the earth coming between the sun and the moon. Aristarchus saw that the curve of the earth's shadow as it crossed the moon should indicate the relative sizes of the earth and the moon. From this, geometric methods offered a way to calculate how far distant the moon was in terms of the diameter of the earth. Hipparchus, on this basis, calculated that the moon's distance from the earth was 30 times the earth's diameter. Taking Eratosthenes' figure of 8,000 miles for the earth's diameter, that meant the moon must be about 240,000 miles from the earth. This again happens to be about correct.

But finding the moon's distance was as far as Greek astronomy managed to carry the problem of the size of the universe — at least correctly. Aristarchus had made a heroic attempt to determine the distance to the sun. The geometric method he used was absolutely correct in theory, but it involved measuring such small differences in angles that, without the use of modern instruments, he was unable to get a good value. He decided that the sun was about 20 times as far as the moon (actually it is about 400 times). Although his figures were wrong, Aristarchus nevertheless did deduce from them that the sun must be much larger than the earth. Pointing out that it was illogical to suppose that the large sun circled the small earth, he decided that the earth must be revolving around the sun.

Unfortunately, no one listened to him. Later astronomers, beginning with Hipparchus and ending with Claudius Ptolemy, worked out all the heavenly movements on the basis of a motionless earth at the center of the universe, with the moon 240,000 miles away and other objects an undetermined distance farther. This scheme held sway until 1543, when Nicholas Copernicus published a book which returned to the viewpoint of Aristarchus and forever dethroned Earth's position as the center of the Universe.

THE MERE FACT that the sun was placed at the center of the solar system did not in itself help determine the distance of the planets. Copernicus adopted the Greek value for the distance of the moon but had no notion of the distance of the sun.

In 1609, however, the German astronomer Johannes Kepler opened the way to accurate distance determinations with his discovery that the orbits of the planets were ellipses, not circles. For the first time it became possible to calculate planetary orbits accurately, and, furthermore, to plot a scale map of the solar system. That is, the relative distances and orbit-shapes of all the known bodies in the system could be plotted. This meant that if the distance between any two bodies in the system could be determined in miles, all the other distances could be calculated at once.

One method by which cosmic distances can be calculated involves the use of parallax. It is easy to illustrate what this term means. Hold your finger about three inches before your eyes and look at it first with just the left eye and then with just the right. Your finger will shift position against the background, because you have changed your point of view. Now if you repeat this procedure with your finger farther away, say at arm's length, the finger again will shift against the background, but this time not so much. Thus the amount of shift can be used to determine the distance of the finger from your eye.

Of course, for an object 50 feet away the shift in position from one eye to the other begins to be too small to measure; we need a wider "baseline" than just the distance between our two eyes. But all we have to do to widen the change in point of view is to look at the object from one spot, then move 20 feet to the right and look at it again. Now the parallax is large enough to be measured easily and the distance can be determined. Surveyors make use of just this method for determining the distance across a stream or ravine, for instance.

The same method, precisely, can be used to measure the distance of the moon, with the stars playing the role of background. Viewed from an observatory in California, for instance, the moon will be in one position against the stars. Viewed at the same instant from an observatory in England, it will be in a slightly different position. From this change in position, and the known distance between the two observatories (in a straight line through the earth), the distance of the moon can be calculated. Of course, we can, in theory, enlarge the baseline by making observations from observatories at directly opposite sides of the earth; the length of the baseline is then 8,000 miles. The resulting angle of parallax, divided by two, is called the "geocentric parallax."

The shift in position of a heavenly body is measured in degrees or subunits of a degree — minutes and seconds. One degree is one 360th of the circuit around the sky; each degree is split into 60 minutes of arc, and each minute into 60 seconds of arc. A minute of arc is therefore $1/(360 \times 60)$ or $1/21,600$ of the circuit of the sky, while a second of arc is $1/(21,600 \times 60)$ or $1/1,296,000$ of the circuit of the sky.

By trigonometry, Claudius Ptolemy was able to measure the distance of the moon from its parallax, and his result agreed with the earlier figure of Hipparchus. It turned out that the geocentric parallax of the moon is 57 minutes of arc (nearly a full degree). The shift is about equal to the width of a 25-cent piece as seen at a distance of five feet. This is easy enough to measure even with the naked eye. But when it came to measuring the parallax of the sun or a planet, the angles involved were too small. The only conclusion that could be reached was that the other bodies were much farther than the moon. How much farther, no one could tell.

Trigonometry alone, in spite of its refinement by the Arabs during the Middle Ages and by European mathematicians of the sixteenth century, could not give the answer. But measurement of small angles of parallax became possible with the invention of the telescope (which Galileo first built and turned to the sky in 1609, after hearing of a magnifying tube that had been made some months earlier by a Dutch spectacle-maker).

The first real breakthrough in measuring the distances of the solar system came in 1761. It was known that the planet Venus would pass across the sun's disk, and plans were made to observe this event from widely separated points, in accordance with a suggestion made years earlier by the English astronomer Edmund Halley. The time that Venus took to cross the sun's disk, as observed from different stations, could be used to calculate its parallax and, therefore, its distance. From that, all other distances in the solar system (and parallaxes) could be calculated. The solar parallax, for instance, turned out to be just under nine seconds of arc, or equal to the diameter of a 25-cent piece as seen from a distance of 2,000 feet.

Since then, various parallaxes in the solar system have been measured with increasing accuracy. In 1931 a vast international project was made out of the determination of the parallax of a small planetoid named Eros, which happened then to approach more closely to earth than any heavenly body except the moon. Eros on this occasion showed a large parallax which could be measured with considerable precision, and the scale of the solar system was determined more accurately than ever before. From these calculations, the distance of the sun from the earth is now known to average approximately 92,870,000 miles. (Because the earth's orbit is elliptical, the actual distance varies from 91,400,000 to 94,600,000 miles.)

This average distance is called an "astronomical unit" (A. U.), and other distances in the solar system are given in this unit. Saturn, for instance, turned out to be, on the average, 887 million miles from the sun, or 9.54 A. U. As the outer planets — Uranus, Neptune and Pluto — were discovered, the boundaries of the solar system were successively enlarged. The extreme diameter of Pluto's orbit is 7,300 million miles, or 79 A. U. And some comets are known to recede to even greater distances from the sun.

By 1830 the solar system was known to stretch across billions of miles of space, but this was obviously by no means the full size of the universe. There were still the stars.

Astronomers felt certain that the stars were spread throughout space and that some were closer than others, if only because some were so much brighter than others. This should mean that the nearer stars would show a parallax when compared with the more distant ones. However, no such parallax could be detected. Even when the astronomers used as their baseline the full diameter of the earth's orbit around the sun (186 million miles), looking at the stars from the opposite ends of the orbit at half-year intervals, they still could observe no parallax. This meant, of course, that even the nearest stars must be extremely distant. As better and better telescopes failed to show a stellar parallax, the estimated distance of the stars had to be increased more and more. That they were visible at all at the vast distances to which they had to be pushed made it quite plain that they must be tremendous balls of flame like our own sun.

But telescopes continued to improve. In the 1830's the German astronomer Friedrich Wilhelm Bessel built one with which he finally succeeded in measuring the parallax of a star. He chose a small

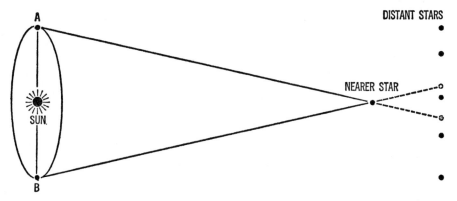

PARALLAX *of a star measured from opposite points on the earth's orbit around the sun.*

star in the constellation Cygnus, called 61 Cygni. His reason for choosing it was that it showed an unusually large shift in position from year to year against the background of the other stars, which could only mean that it was nearer than the others. (This steady motion across the sky, called "proper motion," should not be confused with the back-and-forth shift against the background that indicates parallax.) Bessel pinpointed the successive positions of 61 Cygni against the "fixed" neighboring stars (presumably much more distant) and continued his observations for more than a year. Then, in 1838, he reported that 61 Cygni had a parallax of 0.31 second of arc — the width of a 25-cent piece as seen from a distance of 10 miles! This parallax, observed with the diameter of the earth's orbit as the baseline, meant that 61 Cygni was about 64 trillion (64,000,-000,000,000) miles away. That is 9,000 times the width of our solar system. Thus, compared to the distance of even the nearest stars, the solar system shrinks to an insignificant dot in space.

Because distances in the trillions of miles are inconvenient to handle, astronomers shrink the numbers by giving the distances in terms of the speed of light — 186,282 miles per second. In a year, light travels 5,880,000,000,000 (nearly six trillion) miles. That distance is therefore called a "light-year." In terms of this unit, 61 Cygni is about 11 light-years away.

Two months after Bessel's success (so narrow a margin by which to lose the honor of being the first!), the British astronomer Thomas Henderson obtained the distance of the star Alpha Centauri. This star, located low in the southern skies and not visible from the United States or Europe, is the third brightest in the heavens. It turned out that Alpha Centauri had a parallax of 0.75 second of arc, more than twice that of 61 Cygni. Alpha Centauri was therefore correspondingly closer. In fact, it is only 4.3 light-years from the solar system, and is our nearest stellar neighbor. Actually it is not a single star but a cluster of three.

In 1840 the German-born Russian astronomer Friedrich Wilhelm von Struve announced the parallax of Vega, the fourth brightest star in the sky. He was a little off in his determination, as it turned out, but this was understandable, because Vega's parallax was very small and it was much farther away — 27 light-years.

By 1900 the distances of about 60 stars had been determined by the parallax method. One hundred light-years was about the limit of the distance that could be measured with any accuracy, even with the best instruments. And beyond this lay countless stars at immeasurable distances. Man's universe was growing.

With the naked eye we can see about 6,000 stars. The invention of the telescope made plain at once that this was only a fragment of the universe. When Galileo raised his telescope to the heavens in 1609, he not only found new stars previously invisible, but, on turning to the Milky Way, received an even more profound shock. To the naked eye, the Milky Way is merely a luminous band of foggy light. Galileo's telescope broke down this foggy light into myriads of stars, as numerous as the grains in talcum powder.

The first man to try to make sense out of this was the German-born English astronomer William Herschel. In 1785 Herschel suggested that the stars of the heavens were arranged in a lens-shape. If we look toward the Milky Way, we see a vast number of stars, but when we look out to the sky at right angles to this wheel, we see relatively few stars. Herschel deduced that the heavenly bodies formed a flattened system, with the long axis in the direction of the Milky Way. We now know that, within limits, this picture is correct, and we call our star system the Galaxy, which is actually another term for Milky Way, because galaxy comes from the Greek word for "milk."

Herschel tried to estimate the size of the Galaxy. He assumed that all the stars had about the same intrinsic brightness, so that one could tell the relative distance of a star by its brightness. (By a well-known law, brightness decreases as the square of the distance, so if star A is one-ninth the brightness of star B, it should be three times as far as star B.)

By counting samples of stars in various spots of the Milky Way, Herschel estimated that there were about 100 million stars in the Galaxy altogether. From the levels of their brightness, he decided that the diameter of the Galaxy was 850 times the distance to the bright star Sirius, and that its thickness was 155 times that distance.

We now know that the distance to Sirius is 8.8 light-years, so Herschel's estimate was equivalent to a Galaxy about 7,500 light-years in diameter and 1,300 light-years thick. This turned out to be far too conservative. But like Aristarchus's over-conservative measure of the distance to the sun, it was a step in the right direction.

Beginning in 1906 the Dutch astronomer Jacobus Cornelis Kapteyn conducted another survey of the Milky Way. He had photography at his disposal and knew the true distance of the nearer stars, so he was able to make a better estimate than Herschel had. Kapteyn decided that the dimensions of the Galaxy were 23,000 light-years by 6,000. Thus Kapteyn's model of the Galaxy was four times as wide and five times as thick as Herschel's — but it was still over-conservative.

To sum up, by 1900 the situation with respect to stellar distances was the same as that with respect to planetary distances in 1700. In 1700 the moon's distance was known but the distance of the farther planets could only be guessed at. In 1900 the distance of the nearer stars was known, but that of the more distant stars could only be guessed at.

THE NEXT MAJOR STEP forward was the discovery of a new measuring rod — certain variable stars which fluctuated in brightness. This part of the story begins with a fairly bright star called Delta Cephei, in the constellation Cepheus. On close study the star was found to have a cycle of varying brightness: from its dimmest stage it rather quickly doubled in brightness, then slowly faded to its dim point again. It did this over and over with great regularity. Astronomers found a number of other stars which varied in the same regular way, and in honor of Delta Cephei all were named "Cepheid variables," or simply "Cepheids."

The Cepheids' periods (the time from dim point to dim point) vary from less than a day to as long as nearly two months. Those nearest our sun seem to have a period in the neighborhood of a week. The period of Delta Cephei itself is 5.3 days, while the nearest Cepheid of all (the Pole Star, no less) has a period of four days.

The importance of the Cepheids to astronomers involves their brightness, and that is a subject which requires a small digression.

Ever since Hipparchus, the brightness of stars has been measured by the term "magnitude." The brighter the star, the lower the magnitude. The dimmest stars visible to the naked eye are said to be of the 6th magnitude. A star of magnitude 5 is 2.5 times brighter than one of magnitude 6; magnitude 4 is 2.5 times brighter still, and so on. A star of magnitude 1 is $2.5 \times 2.5 \times 2.5 \times 2.5 \times 2.5$ or 100 times as bright as a star of magnitude 6. And the measure goes on to still greater brightnesses which are designated by magnitude 0 and beyond this by negative numbers. The planet Venus attains a magnitude of —4; the full moon, —12; the sun —26.

Among the stars, 61 Cygni is a dim star with a magnitude of 5.0 (modern astronomical methods allow magnitudes to be fixed to the nearest tenth and even to the nearest hundredth in some cases). Capella is a bright star, with a magnitude of 0.9; Alpha Centauri still brighter, with a magnitude of 0.1. Sirius, the brightest star in the sky, has a magnitude of —1.6.

These are the "apparent magnitudes" of the stars as we see them — not their absolute luminosities independent of distance. But if we know the distance of a star and its apparent magnitude, we can calculate its actual luminosity. Astronomers base the scale of "absolute magnitudes" on the brightness at a standard distance, which has been established at 10 "parsecs," or 32.6 light-years. (The "parsec" is the distance at which a star would show a parallax of one second of arc; it is equal to a little more than 19 trillion miles, or 3.26 light-years.)

Although Capella looks dimmer than Alpha Centauri and Sirius, actually it is a far more powerful emitter of light than either of them. It merely happens to be a great deal farther away. If all were at the standard distance, Capella would be much the brightest of the three. Capella has an absolute magnitude of —0.1, Serius 1.3, and Alpha Centauri 4.8. Our own sun is just about as bright as Alpha Centauri.

with an absolute magnitude of 4.86. It is an ordinary, medium-sized star.

Now to get back to the Cepheids. In 1912 Miss Henrietta Leavitt, an astronomer at the Harvard Observatory, was studying the smaller of the Magellanic Clouds — the huge star systems in the Southern Hemisphere named after Ferdinand Magellan although he was not their discoverer. Among the stars of the Small Magellanic Cloud, Miss Leavitt detected 25 Cepheids. She recorded the period of variation of each and found to her surprise that the longer the period, the brighter the star.

This was not true of the Cepheid variables in our own neighborhood; why should it be true of the Small Magellanic Cloud? Well, in our own neighborhood, we know only the apparent magnitudes of the Cepheids; not knowing their distances or absolute brightnesses, we have no scale for relating the period of a star to its brightness. But in the Small Magellanic Cloud, all the stars are effectively at about the same distance from us, because the Cloud itself is so far away. It is as if a person in New York were trying to calculate his distance from each person in Chicago. He would conclude that all the Chicagoans were about equally distant from himself—what is a difference of a few miles in a total distance of a thousand? Similarly, a star at the far end of the Cloud is not significantly farther away than one at the near end.

With the stars in the Small Magellanic Cloud all at about the same distance from us, their apparent magnitude could be taken as a measure of their comparative absolute magnitude. So Miss Leavitt could consider the relationship she saw a true one: that is, the period of the Cepheid variables increased smoothly with the absolute magnitude. She was thus able to establish a "period-luminosity curve" — a graph which showed what period a Cepheid of any absolute magnitude must have, and conversely what absolute magnitude a Cepheid of a given period must have.

If Cepheids everywhere in the universe behaved as they did in the Small Magellanic Cloud (a reasonable assumption), then astronomers had a *relative* scale for measuring distances, out as far as Cepheids could be detected in the best telescopes. If they spotted two Cepheids with equal periods, they could assume that both were equal in absolute magnitude. If Cepheid A seemed four times as bright as Cepheid B, Cepheid B must be twice as distant from us. In this way the relative distances of all the observable Cepheids could be plotted on a scale map. Now if the actual distance of just one of the Cepheids could be determined, so could the distances of all the rest.

Unfortunately, even the nearest Cepheid, the Pole Star, is about 300 light-years away, much too far to measure its distance by parallax. Astronomers had to use less direct methods. One usable clue was proper motion: on the average, the more distant a star is, the smaller its proper motion. (Recall that Bessel decided 61 Cygni was relatively close because it had a large proper motion.) A number of devices were used to determine the proper motions of groups of stars, and statistical methods were brought to bear. The procedure was complicated, but the results gave the approximate distances of various groups of stars which contained Cepheids. From the distances and the apparent magnitudes of those Cepheids, their absolute magnitudes could be determined, and these could be compared with the periods.

In 1913 the Danish astronomer Ejnar Hertzsprung found that a Cepheid of absolute magnitude —2.3 had a period of 6.6 days. From that, and using Miss Leavitt's period-luminosity curve, he could determine the absolute magnitude of any Cepheid. (It turned out, incidentally, that Cepheids generally were large, bright stars, much more luminous than our sun. Their variations in brightness are probably the result of pulsations. The stars seem to expand and contract steadily, as though they are ponderously breathing in and out.)

A few years later the American astronomer Harlow Shapley repeated the work and decided that a Cepheid of absolute magnitude —2.3 had a period of 5.96 days. The agreement was close enough to allow astronomers to go ahead. They had their yardstick.

IN 1918 Shapley began observing the Cepheids of our own Galaxy in an attempt to determine the Galaxy's size by this new

3 3

method. He concentrated on the Cepheids found in groups of stars called "globular clusters" — densely packed spherical aggregates of tens of thousands to tens of millions of stars. There are about 100 known globular clusters in our Galaxy, and probably as many again that have not yet been detected.

Shapley calculated the distance of the various globular clusters at from 20,000 to 200,000 light-years from us. He found that they were distributed in a large sphere which the plane of the Milky Way cut in half; they surrounded a portion of the main body of the Galaxy like a halo. Shapley made the natural assumption that they encircled the center of the Galaxy. His calculations placed the central point of this halo of globular clusters within the Milky Way in the direction of the constellation Sagittarius and about 50,000 light-years from us. This meant that our solar system, far from being at the center of the Galaxy, as Herschel and Kapteyn had thought, was far out toward one edge.

Shapley's model pictured the Galaxy as a giant lens about 300,000 light-years in diameter. This time its size was overestimated, as another method of measurement soon showed.

From the fact that the Galaxy had a disk shape, astronomers from William Herschel onward assumed that it was rotating in space. In 1926 the Dutch astronomer Jan Oort set out to measure this rotation. Since the Galaxy is not a solid object, but is composed of numerous individual stars, it is not to be expected that it rotates in one piece, as a wheel does. Instead, stars close to the gravitational center of the disk must revolve around it faster than those farther away (just as the planets closest to the sun travel fastest in their orbits). This means that the stars toward the center of the Galaxy (*i.e.*, in the direction of Sagittarius) should tend to be drifting ahead of our sun, while those farther from the center (in the direction of the constellation Gemini) should tend to lag behind us in their revolution. And the farther a star is from us, the greater this difference in speed should be.

On these assumptions, it became possible to calculate the rate of rotation around the Galactic center from the relative motions of the

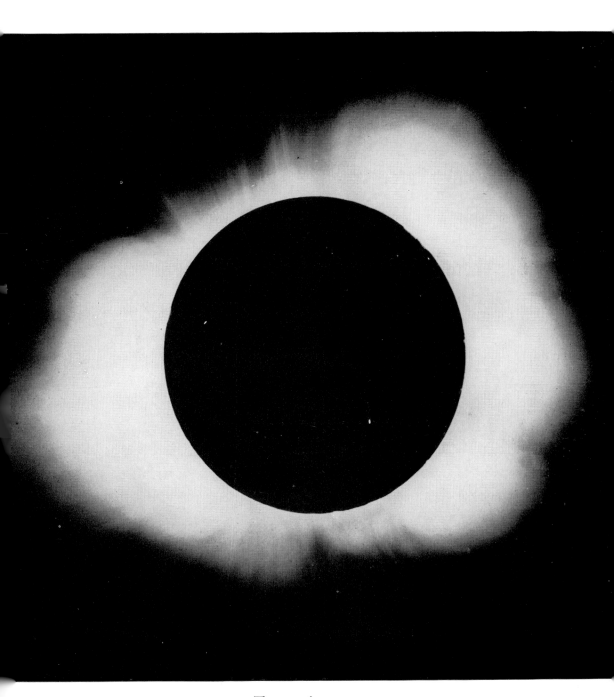

THE SUN'S CORONA.

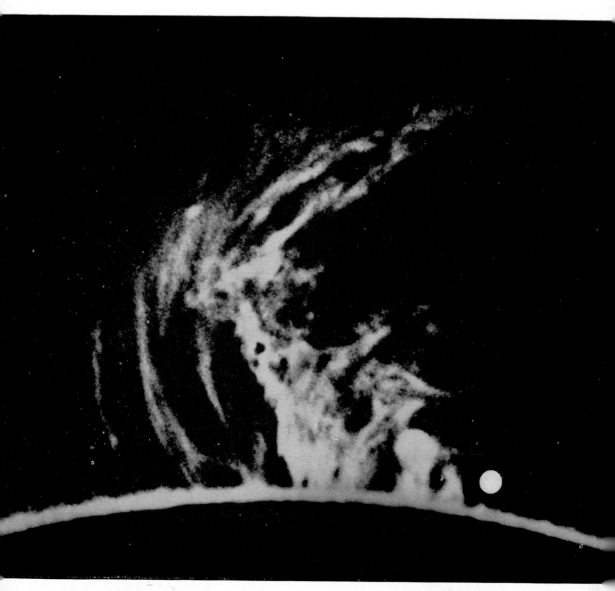

A SOLAR FLARE, *stretching 140,000 miles from the sun, photographed in the light of calcium.*

DANIEL'S COMET, *photographed July 17, 1907. The streaks are stars.*

THE COAL SACK, *a huge cloud of dust and gas in the Southern Cross.*

stars. The sun and nearby stars, it turned out, travel at about 150 miles a second relative to the Galactic center and make a complete revolution around the center in approximately 200 million years.

Having a value for the rate of rotation, astronomers were then able to calculate the strength of the gravitational field of the Galactic center and, therefore, its mass. The Galactic center (which contains most of the mass of the Galaxy) turns out to be well over 100 billion times as massive as our sun. Since our sun is a star of average mass, our Galaxy therefore contains perhaps 200 billion stars — 2,000 times the number estimated by Herschel.

From the curve of the orbits of the revolving stars, it is also possible to locate the center around which they are revolving. The center of the Galaxy in this way has been confirmed to be in the direction of Sagittarius, as Shapley found, but only 30,000 light-years from us, and the total diameter of the Galaxy comes to 100,000 light-years instead of 300,000. In this new model, now believed to be correct, the thickness of the disk is some 20,000 light-years at the center and falls off toward the edge: at the location of our sun, which is two-thirds of the way out toward the extreme edge, the disk is perhaps 3,000 light-years thick. But these are only rough figures, because the Galaxy has no sharply definite boundaries.

If the sun is so close to the edge of the Galaxy, why isn't the Milky Way much brighter in the direction toward the center than in the opposite direction, where we look toward the edge? Looking toward Sagittarius, we face the main body of the Galaxy, with nearly 100 billion stars, whereas out toward the edge there is only a scattering of some millions. Yet in each direction the band of the Milky Way seems of about the same brightness. The answer appears to be that huge clouds of obscuring dust hide much of the center of the Galaxy from us. Probably we see no more than one ten-thousandth (at most) of the light of the Galactic center.

This explains why Herschel and other early students of the Galaxy thought our solar system was at the center, and also, it seems, why Shapley originally overestimated the size of the Galaxy. Some of the clusters he studied were dimmed by the intervening dust, so that the Cepheids in them seemed dimmer and therefore more distant than they really were.

EVEN BEFORE the size and mass of the Galaxy itself had been determined, the Cepheid variables of the Magellanic Clouds (where Miss Leavitt had made the crucial discovery of the period-luminosity curve) were used to determine the distance of the clouds. They proved to be more than 100,000 light-years away. The best modern figures place the Large Magellanic Cloud at about 150,000 light-years from us and the Small Magellanic Cloud at 170,000 light-years. The Large Cloud is no more than half the size of our Galaxy in diameter; the Small Cloud, no more than a fifth. Besides, they seem to be less densely packed with stars. The Large Magellanic Cloud contains five billion stars (only 1/20 the number in our Galaxy), while the Small Magellanic Cloud has only 1.5 billion.

That was the situation as it stood in the early 1920's. The known Universe was less than 200,000 light-years in diameter and consisted of our Galaxy and its two neighbors. The question then arose as to whether anything existed outside that.

Suspicion rested upon certain small patches of luminous fog, called nebulae (from the Greek word for "cloud"), which astronomers had long noted. The French astronomer Charles Messier had catalogued a number of them about 1800. (Many are still known by the numbers he gave them, preceded by the letter M for Messier.) The most spectacular of these patches, known as M31 or the Andromeda Nebula, because it is in the constellation Andromeda, is an elongated oval of dim light about half the size of the full moon.

Now were these nebulosities merely clouds in the Galaxy or were they distant, outside collections of stars? Some, such as the Orion Nebula, seemed definitely to be clouds of gas and dust illumined by hot stars contained within them. But what of the luminous Andromeda Nebula? There seemed to be no stars within it to account for its glow. In 1924 the American astronomer Edwin Powell Hubble turned the new 100-inch telescope at Mount Wilson in California

A MODEL OF OUR GALAXY seen edgewise. Globular clusters are arrayed around the central portion of the galaxy. The position of our sun is indicated by +.

on the Andromeda Nebula. The powerful new instrument resolved portions of the Nebula's outer edge into individual stars. This meant at once that the Andromeda Nebula, or parts of it at least, resembled the Milky Way. Might it be a second galaxy, independent of our own?

Among the stars at the edge of the Andromeda Nebula were Cepheid variables. With these measuring rods it was found that the Nebula was nearly a million light-years away! So the Andromeda Nebula was far, far outside our Galaxy. Allowing for its distance, its apparent size showed that it must be a huge conglomeration of stars, almost rivalling our own Galaxy.

Other nebulosities, too, turned out to be conglomerations of stars, even farther away than the Andromeda Nebula. These "extra-galactic nebulae" all had to be recognized as galaxies — new universes which reduced our own to just one of many in space. Once again the Universe had expanded. It was larger than ever — not merely hundreds of thousands of light-years across but perhaps hundreds of millions.

THROUGH THE 1930's, astronomers wrestled with several nagging puzzles about these galaxies. For one thing, on the basis of their assumed distances all of them turned out to be much smaller than our own. It seemed an odd coincidence that we should be inhabiting by far the largest galaxy in existence. For another thing, globular clusters surrounding the Andromeda galaxy seemed to be only one-half or one-third as luminous as those of our own galaxy. For still another, the distances of the galaxies seemed to imply that the Universe was only about two billion years old (for reasons I shall discuss later in this chapter). This was puzzling, for the earth itself was considered by geologists to be older than that, on what was thought to be the very best kind of evidence.

The beginning of an answer came during World War II, when the German-born American astronomer Walter Baade discovered

that the yardstick by which the galaxies' distances had been measured was wrong.

In 1942 Baade took advantage of the wartime blackout of Los
Angeles, which cleared the night sky at Mount Wilson, to make a
detailed study of the Andromeda galaxy with the 100-inch telescope.
With the improved seeing, he was able to resolve some of the stars
in the inner regions of the galaxy. He immediately noted some striking differences between these stars and those in the outskirts of the
galaxy. The brightest stars in the interior were reddish, whereas
those of the outskirts were bluish. Moreover, the red giants of the
interior were not nearly as bright as the blue giants of the outskirts:
the latter had up to 100,000 times the luminosity of our sun, while
the internal red giants had only up to 1,000 times that luminosity.
Finally, the outskirts of the Andromeda galaxy, where the bright
blue stars were found, was loaded with dust, whereas the interior,
with its somewhat less bright red stars, was free of dust.

To Baade, it seemed that here were two sets of stars with different
structure and history. He called the bluish stars of the outskirts
Population I and the reddish stars of the interior, Population II.

When the new 200-inch Hale Telescope was set up on Palomar
Mountain after the war, Baade continued his investigations. He
found certain regularities in the distribution of the two populations,
and these depended on the nature of the galaxies involved. Galaxies
of the class called "elliptical" (systems with the shape of an ellipse
and rather uniform internal structure) apparently were made up
mainly of Population II stars. On the other hand, in "spiral galaxies"
(that is, with arms which make them look like a pinwheel) the spiral
arms were composed of Population I.

It is estimated that only about 2 per cent of the stars in the Universe are of the Population I type. But our own sun and the familiar
stars in our neighborhood fall in this class. From this fact alone we
can deduce that ours is a spiral galaxy and that we lie in one of the
spiral arms. (This explains why there are so many dust clouds, both
light and dark, in our neighborhood: the spiral arms of a galaxy are

39

clogged with dust.) Photographs show that the Andromeda galaxy also is of the spiral type.

Now to get back to the yardstick. Baade began to compare the Cepheid stars found in globular clusters (Population II) with those found in our spiral arm (Population I). It turned out that the Cepheids in the two populations were really of two different types, as far as the relation between period and luminosity was concerned. Cepheids of Population II followed the period-luminosity curve set up by Leavitt and Shapley. With this yardstick, Shapley had accurately measured the distances to the globular clusters and the size of our galaxy. But the Cepheids of Population I, it now developed, were a different yardstick altogether! A Population I Cepheid was four or five times as luminous as a Population II Cepheid of the same period. This meant that use of the Leavitt scale would result in miscalculation of the absolute magnitude of a Population I Cepheid from its period. And if the absolute magnitude was wrong, the calculation of distance must be wrong; the star would actually be much farther away than the calculation indicated.

Hubble had gauged the distance of the Andromeda galaxy from the Cepheids (of Population I) in its outskirts — the only ones that could be resolved at the time. Now, with the revised yardstick, the galaxy proved to be more than two million light-years away, instead of less than one million. And other galaxies had to be moved out in proportion.

At one stroke, the size of the known Universe was more than doubled. This instantly solved the problems that had plagued the 1930's. Our galaxy was no longer larger than all the others; the Andromeda galaxy, for instance, was four or five times as massive as ours. Secondly, it now appeared that the Andromeda galaxy's globular clusters were as luminous as ours; they had seemed less bright only because of the misjudgment of their distance. Finally, for reasons I will explain later, the new scale of distances allowed the Universe to be considered much older — at least five billion years old — which brought it into line with the geologists' estimates of the age of the earth.

40

DOUBLING THE DISTANCE of the galaxies does not end the problem of size. We must now consider the possibility of still larger systems — of clusters of galaxies and supergalaxies.

Actually, modern telescopes have shown that clusters of galaxies do exist. For instance, in the constellation of Coma Berenices there is a large, ellipsoidal cluster of galaxies about eight million light-years in diameter. The "Coma Cluster" contains about 11,000 galaxies, separated by an average distance of only 300,000 light-years (as compared with an average of something like three million light-years between galaxies in our own vicinity).

The French astronomer Gérard de Vaucouleurs suggests that much larger conglomerations also exist, and that our own galaxy is part of a "local cluster" which includes the Magellanic Clouds, the Andromeda galaxy, and three small "satellite galaxies" near it, plus some other small galaxies. The cluster, he goes on, may be part of a "local supergalaxy" spread out in ellipsoidal shape over a volume of space 40 million light-years in diameter and several million light-years thick, with our own galaxy far on the outskirts.

If supergalaxies, why not super-supergalaxies, super-super-super-galaxies and so on? In 1959 Fritz Zwicky at the California Institute of Technology began preparation of a catalogue of galaxies and clusters of galaxies to replace the "New General Catalogue" (which, despite the name, is now quite old). Such a catalogue, when completed, may go far toward answering this question.

If galaxies do form clusters and clusters of clusters, does that mean the Universe goes on forever and that space is infinite? Or is there some end, both to the Universe and to space? Well, the 200-inch telescope can make out objects up to an estimated two billion light-years away, and there is no sign of an end of the Universe — yet. New instruments are already in view to extend this range. The human mind, of course, will not stop even there. At the theoretical level, there are arguments both for an end of space and for no end, for a beginning in time and for no beginning. Having considered space, let's consider time next.

THE BIRTH OF THE UNIVERSE

MYTH-MAKERS have invented many fanciful creations of the Universe (usually concentrating on the earth itself, with all the rest dismissed quickly as "the sky" or the "heavens"). Generally, the time of creation is set not very far in the past (although we should remember that to people in the pre-literate stage, a time of a thousand years was even more impressive than a billion years is today).

The creation story with which we are most familiar is, of course, that given in the first chapters of Genesis, which, some people hold, is an adaptation of Babylonian myths, intensified in poetic beauty and elevated in moral grandeur.

Various attempts have been made to work out the date of the Creation on the basis of the data given in the Bible (the reigns of the various kings, the time from the Exodus to the dedication of Solomon's temple, the ages of the patriarchs both before and after the flood). Medieval Jewish scholars put the date of the Creation at 3760 B.C., and the Jewish calendar still counts its years from that date. About 1650 A.D. Archbishop James Ussher of the Anglican Church calculated the date of the Creation to be 4004 B.C. — a date still recorded in most editions of the King James Bible. Some theologians of the Greek Orthodox Church put Creation as far back as 5508 B.C.

As late as the eighteenth century, the Biblical version was accepted by the learned world, and the age of the Universe was considered to be only six or seven thousand years at most. But this view received its first major blow in 1785 in the form of a book entitled "Theory of the Earth," by a Scotch naturalist named James Hutton. Hutton started with the proposition that the slow natural processes working on the surface of the earth (mountain-building and erosion, the cutting of river channels, and so on) had been working at about the same rate throughout the earth's history. This "uniformitarian principle" implied that the processes must have been working for a stupendously long time to produce the observed phenomena. Therefore the earth must be not thousands but many millions of years old.

Hutton's views were immediately derided. But the ferment worked. In the early 1830's the British geologist Charles Lyell reaffirmed Hutton's views, and in a three-volume work entitled "Principles of Geology" presented the evidence with such clarity and force that the world of science was won over. The modern science of geology can be dated from that work.

ATTEMPTS were made to calculate the age of the earth on the basis of the uniformitarian principle. For instance, if one knew the amount of sediment laid down by the action of water each year, one could calculate the age of a layer of sedimentary rock from its thickness. It soon became obvious that this approach could not determine the earth's age, because the record of the rocks was obscured by processes of erosion, crumbling, upheavals, and other forces. Nevertheless, even the incomplete evidence indicated that the earth must be at least 100 million years old.

Another way of measuring the age of the earth was to estimate the rate of accumulation of salt by the oceans. Rivers steadily washed salt into the sea; since only fresh water left it by evaporation, the salt concentration rose. Assuming that the ocean had started as fresh water, the time necessary for the rivers to have endowed the oceans with their salt content of over 3 per cent could have been as long as one billion years.

This great age was very agreeable to the biologists, who during the latter half of the nineteenth century were trying to trace the slow development of living organisms from primitive one-celled creatures to the complex higher animals. They needed long eons for the development to take place, and a billion years gave them time enough.

However, by the mid-nineteenth century astronomical considerations brought in sudden complications. For instance, the principle of the "conservation of energy" raised an interesting problem with respect to the sun. The sun was pouring out energy in colossal quantities and had been doing so throughout recorded history. If the earth had existed for countless eons, where had all this energy come from? It could not have come from the usual sources familiar to mankind. If the sun had started as solid coal, for instance, it would have been reduced to a cinder (at the rate it was delivering energy) in the space of a few thousand years.

The German physicist Hermann Ludwig Ferdinand von Helmholtz, one of the first to enunciate the law of conservation of energy, was particularly interested in the problem of the sun. In 1854 he pointed out that if the sun were contracting, its mass would gain energy as it fell toward its center of gravity, just as a rock gains energy when it falls. This energy could be converted into radiation. Helmholtz calculated that a contraction of the sun by a mere ten-thousandth of its radius could provide it with a 2,000-year supply of energy.

The British physicist William Thomson (later Lord Kelvin) did more work on the subject and decided that on this basis the earth could not be more than 50 million years old, for at the rate the sun had spent energy, it must have contracted from a gigantic size, originally as large as the earth's orbit around the sun. (This meant, of course, that Venus must be younger than the earth and Mercury still younger.) Lord Kelvin went on to estimate that if the earth itself had started as a molten mass, the time needed to cool to its present temperature, and therefore its age, would be about 20 million years.

By the 1890's the battle-lines seemed drawn between two invincible armies. The physicists seemed to have shown conclusively that the earth could not have been solid for more than a few million years, while the geologists and biologists seemed to have proved just as conclusively that the earth must have been solid for not less than a billion years.

And then something new and completely unexpected turned up, and the physicists found themselves with their case crumbling.

44

In 1896 the discovery of radioactivity made it clear that the earth's uranium and other radioactive substances were liberating large quantities of energy and had been doing so for a very long time. This finding made Kelvin's calculations meaningless. There is no point in trying to decide how long it would take the earth to cool if you don't take into account the fact that heat is being constantly supplied by radioactive substances. With this new factor, it might take the earth billions of years, rather than millions, to cool from a molten mass to its present temperature.

Actually, radioactivity itself eventually gave the most conclusive evidence of the earth's age, for it allowed geologists and geochemists to calculate the age of rocks directly from the quantity of uranium and lead they contain. By the clock of radioactivity, some of the earth's rocks are about 3.3 billion years old, and there is every reason to think that the earth is somewhat older than that. An age of five billion years is now accepted as likely.

And what of the sun? Radioactivity and discoveries concerning the atomic nucleus introduced a new source of energy, much larger than any previously known. In 1930 the British physicist Sir Arthur Eddington set a train of thought working when he suggested that the temperature and pressure at the center of the sun must be outrageously high: the temperature might be as high as 30,000,000 degrees. At such temperatures and pressures, the nuclei of atoms could undergo reactions which could not take place in the bland mildness of Earth's environment. The sun is known to consist largely of hydrogen. If four hydrogen nuclei combined (forming a helium atom), they would liberate large amounts of energy.

Then in 1938 the German-born American physicist Hans Albrecht Bethe worked out the possible ways in which this combination of hydrogen to helium could take place. There were two processes by which this could occur under the conditions at the center of stars like the sun. Either would convert mass to energy. (Einstein, in his Special Theory of Relativity, had shown that mass and

45

energy were different aspects of the same thing and could be interconverted, and furthermore that a great deal of energy could be liberated by the conversion of a small amount of mass.)

The rate of radiation of energy by the sun requires the disappearance of solar mass at the rate of 4.2 million tons per second. At first blush this seems a frightening loss, but the total mass of the sun is 2,200,000,000,000,000,000,000,000,000 tons, so the sun loses only 0.0000000000000000002 per cent of its mass each second. The sun could easily continue to radiate energy at its present rate for billions of years to come, and could easily have been doing so for billions of years in the past.

By 1940, then, an age of five billion years for both the earth and the sun seemed reasonable. The whole matter of the age of the Universe might have been settled, but astronomers had thrown another monkey wrench into the machinery. Now the Universe as a whole seemed too youthful to account for the age of the solar system.

The trouble arose from an examination of the distant galaxies by the astronomers and from a phenomenon first discovered in 1842 by an Austrian physicist named Christian Johann Doppler.

The "Doppler effect" is familiar enough; it is most commonly illustrated by the whistle of a passing locomotive, which rises in pitch as it approaches and drops in pitch as it recedes. The change in pitch is due simply to the fact that the number of sound waves striking the eardrum per second changes because of the source's motion.

As Doppler suggested, the Doppler effect applies to light waves as well as to sound. When light from a moving source reaches the eye, there is a shift in frequency — that is, color — when the source is moving fast enough. For instance, if the source is traveling toward us, more light waves are crowded into each second and the light perceived shifts toward the high-frequency end of the visible spectrum: it looks bluer than the source actually is. On the other hand, if the source is moving away, fewer waves arrive per second and the light looks redder. This is known as the "red-shift."

Now astronomers have been studying the spectra of stars for a long time, and they are well acquainted with the normal picture —

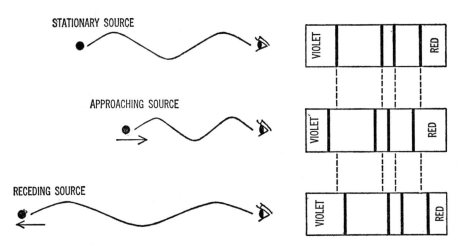

THE DOPPLER-FIZEAU EFFECT. *The lines in the spectrum shift toward the violet end* (left) *when the light source is approaching. When the source recedes, the spectral lines shift toward the red end* (right).

a pattern of bright lines against a dark background or dark lines against a bright background showing the emission or absorption of light by atoms at certain wavelengths, or colors. They have been able to calculate the velocity of stars moving toward or away from us (*i.e.*, radial velocity) by measuring the displacement of the usual spectral lines toward the violet or red end of the spectrum.

It was Armand H. L. Fizeau of France, not Doppler, who first demonstrated the Doppler effect on light, and this is sometimes called the "Doppler-Fizeau effect," in honor of both scientists. However, things do not always work out with perfect justice, and nowadays the light shift is usually called simply the Doppler effect, unfairly depriving Fizeau of his share of the credit.

In 1868 the British astronomer Sir William Huggins measured the radial velocity of Sirius and announced it was moving away from us at 29 miles per second. (We have better figures now, but he came reasonably close for a first try.) Radial velocity, in fact, became a more important tool for astronomers than proper motion (across the line of sight). The radial velocity could be determined quickly from a star's spectrum, and it could be found for distant stars whose proper motions were undetectable. Hertzsprung used radial velocities as the key observations in determining the absolute magnitudes of Cepheids, and Oort in exploring the rotation of the galaxy.

In 1912 the American astronomer Vesto Melvin Slipher found, on measuring the radial velocity of the Andromeda galaxy, that it was moving toward us at approximately 125 miles per second. But when he went on to examine other galaxies, he discovered that most of them were moving away from us. By 1914 Slipher had figures on 15 galaxies, and of these, 13 were receding, all at the healthy clip of several hundred miles per second.

As research along these lines continued, the situation grew more remarkable. Except for a few of the nearest galaxies, all were fleeing from us. What's more, as techniques improved so that fainter, more distant galaxies could be tested, the red-shift increased.

In 1929 Hubble at Mount Wilson suggested that there was a regular increase in these velocities of recession in proportion to the distance of the galaxy involved. If galaxy A was twice as far from us as galaxy B, then galaxy A receded at twice the velocity of galaxy B. This is sometimes known as "Hubble's Law."

Hubble's Law certainly continued to be borne out by observations. Beginning in 1929, Milton L. Humason at Mount Wilson used the 100-inch telescope to obtain spectra of dimmer and dimmer galaxies. The most distant galaxies he could test were receding at 25,000 miles per second. When the 200-inch telescope came into use, still more distant galaxies could be studied, and by 1957 William A. Baum had found recession velocities as high as 75,000 miles per second, or two-fifths the speed of light.

Why should this be? Well, imagine a balloon with small dots painted on it. When the balloon is inflated, the dots move apart. To a manikin standing on any one of the dots, all the other dots would seem to be receding, and the further away from him a particular dot was, the faster it would be receding. It would not matter on which particular dot he was standing; the effect would be the same.

The galaxies behave as if the Universe is expanding like a balloon.

Astronomers have now generally accepted the fact of this expansion, and Einstein's "field equations" in his General Theory of Relativity can be construed to fit an expanding Universe.

But this raises profound questions. Does the Universe have a limit? The farthest galaxies we can now see (about two billion light-years away) are receding from us at two-fifths the speed of light. If Hubble's law of the increase in recession velocity holds, at about five billion light-years from us the galaxies are receding with the speed of light. But the speed of light is the maximum possible velocity, according to Einstein's theory. Does that mean there can be no galaxies more distant?

There is also the age question. If the Universe has been expanding constantly, it is logical to suppose that it was smaller in the past than it is now, and that at some time in the distant past it began as a dense core of matter. And that is where the conflict over the age of the Universe lay in the 1940's. From its rate of expansion and the distance of the galaxies, it appeared that the Universe could not be more than two billion years old. But the geologists, thanks to radioactivity, were now certain that the earth must be nearly four billion years old, at least.

Fortunately, the revision of the Cepheid yardstick in 1952 saved the situation. By doubling, possibly tripling, the size of the Universe, it doubled or tripled its age, and so the rocks and the red-shift now agreed that both the solar system and the galaxies were five or six billion years old.

In 1959 the situation was thrown into some confusion again. The British astronomer Fred Hoyle, after analyzing the probable composition of Population I and Population II stars, decided that, of the two processes by which stars burn hydrogen to form helium, the slower one was predominant. On that basis, he estimated that some stars must be at least ten, perhaps 15, billion years old. Then the Mount Wilson astronomer Allan Sandage found that stars in a cluster called NGC 188 appeared to be at least 24 billion years old. "We are in trouble," said Sandage. Such an age would not conflict with the rocks' evidence on the age of the earth, for the earth could certainly be younger than the Universe, but if the Universe has been expanding at the present rate for 24 billion years, it would seem that it should be more spread out than it is. So the astronomers have a new problem to resolve.

ASSUMING that the Universe expands and that Einstein's field equations agree with that interpretation, the question still arises inexorably: Why? The easiest, and almost inevitable, explanation is that the expansion is the result of an explosion at the beginning. In 1927 the Belgian mathematician Abbé Georges Edouard Lemâitre suggested that all matter came originally from a tremendously dense "cosmic egg" which exploded and so gave birth to the Universe as we know it. Fragments of the original sphere of matter formed galaxies, which are still rushing outward in all directions as a result of that unimaginably powerful multibillion-year-old explosion.

The Russian-born American physicist George Gamow has elaborated this notion. His calculations led him to believe that the various elements as we know them were formed in the first half hour after the explosion. For 250 million years after the explosion, radiation predominated over matter, and the Universe's matter, as a consequence, remained dispersed as a thin gas. After a critical point in the expansion, however, matter came into predominance and began to condense into the beginnings of galaxies. Gamow believes the expansion will probably continue until all the galaxies, except for those in our own local cluster, have receded beyond the reach of our most powerful instruments. We will then be alone in the Universe.

And where did the matter in the "cosmic egg" come from? Some astronomers suggest that the Universe started as an extremely thin gas, gradually contracted under the force of gravitation to a super-dense mass, and then exploded. In other words, it began an eternity ago in the form of almost complete emptiness, went through a contracting stage to the "cosmic egg," exploded, and is going through an expanding stage back to an eternity of almost complete emptiness. We just happen to be living during the very temporary period (an instant in eternity) of the fullness of the Universe.

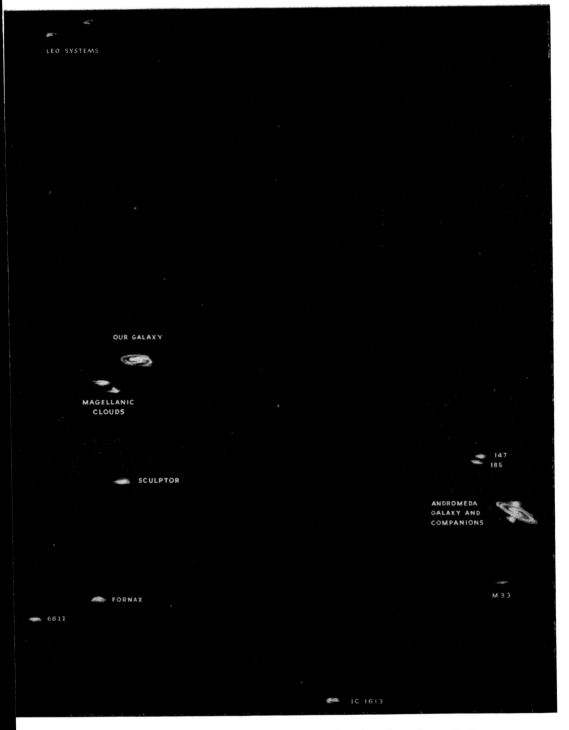

LEO SYSTEMS

OUR GALAXY

MAGELLANIC
CLOUDS

147
185

SCULPTOR

ANDROMEDA
GALAXY AND
COMPANIONS

FORNAX

M 33

6822

IC 1613

OUR REGION OF THE UNIVERSE—*a drawing showing the other galaxies in our neighborhood.*

THE SPIRAL GALAXY IN ANDROMEDA.

STELLAR POPULATIONS I AND II. At the left a spiral arm of the Andromeda galaxy, photographed in blue light, shows giant and super-giant stars of Population I; at the right the galaxy NGC 205, a companion of the Andromeda galaxy, photographed in yellow light, shows stars of Population II, the brightest of which are red stars one-hundredth as bright as the blue giants of Population I. (The large stars in both pictures are foreground stars belonging to our own Milky Way.)

A SPIRAL GALAXY *in Coma Berenices, seen edge on.*

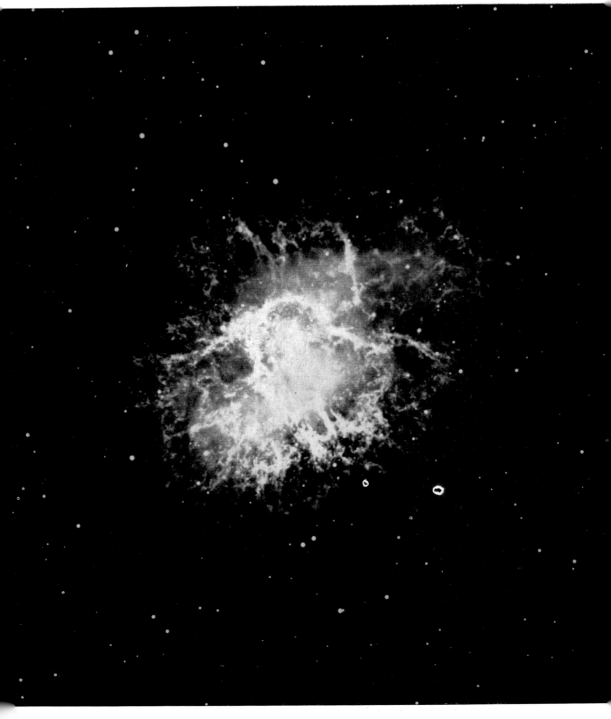

THE CRAB NEBULA, *the remains of a supernova, photographed in red light.*

A SPIRAL GALAXY *in broadside view—the "whirlpool nebula" in Canes Venatici.*

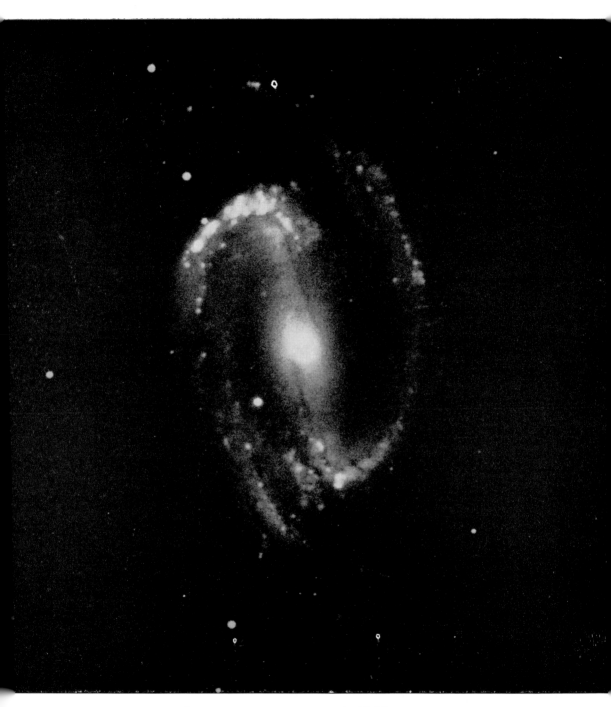

A BARRED SPIRAL GALAXY *in Eridanus*.

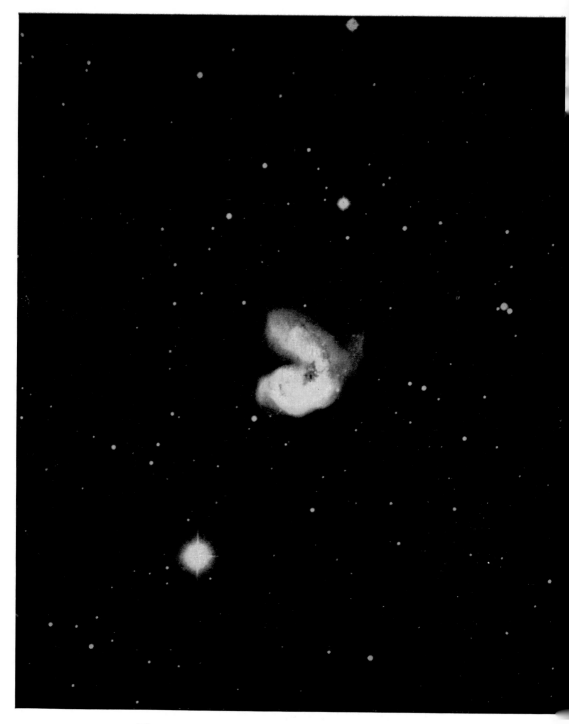

Two colliding galaxies—*NGC 4038 and 4039*.

Other astronomers, notably W. B. Bonnor of England, argue that the Universe has gone through an unending series of such cycles, each lasting perhaps tens of billions of years — in other words, an "oscillating Universe."

Whether the Universe is simply expanding, or contracting and expanding, or oscillating, all these theories have in mind an "evolutionary Universe."

In 1948 the British astronomers Hermann Bondi and Thomas Gold put forward an opposite theory, since extended and popularized by another British astronomer, Fred Hoyle. Their universe is called the "steady-state Universe." They agree that the galaxies are receding and the Universe is expanding. When the farthest galaxies reach the speed of light, so that no light from them can reach us, they may be said to have left our Universe. However, while the galaxies and clusters of galaxies of our Universe move apart, new galaxies are continually forming among the old ones. For every galaxy that leaves us over the speed-of-light edge of the Universe, another joins our midst. Therefore the Universe remains in a steady state, with galaxies always at the same density in space.

Of course, new matter has to be created continually to replace the galaxies that leave. The Bondi-Gold-Hoyle school contends that we simply have no instruments that could detect this creation. But where does this new matter come from? What happens to the law of conservation of mass-energy? Surely matter cannot be made out of nothing. Hoyle replies that the energy for the creation of new matter may be siphoned from the energy of the expansion. In other words, the Universe may be expanding a bit more slowly than it would be if matter were not being formed, and the matter being formed could be manufactured at the expense of the energy being pumped into expansion.

The question remains, why should the Universe be expanding at all? In 1959 Bondi and the British astronomer R. A. Lyttleton suggested a new physical theory to account for it. The Universe is made up mostly of hydrogen atoms, each consisting of a proton and an electron. Bondi and Lyttleton suggest that the positive charge of the proton and the negative charge of the electron are not quite equal: the proton's charge is slightly greater than the electron's. The difference is so slight (one part in a million trillion) that it can't be measured by our instruments, they say. But on the scale of a galaxy or cluster of galaxies, the excess of positive charge is sufficient to make the galaxies and clusters repel one another strongly, since all are positively charged and like repels like. This would account for the expansion of the Universe without an explosion.

The argument between the proponents of the evolutionary and steady-state views has been hot. Most astronomers seem to favor the evolutionary view at the moment. Proponents of the evolutionary view ask: if new galaxies are continually forming among the old ones, why don't we see both old and new ones among the nearby galaxies that we can analyze? All of them seem to be at about the same stage of development. But this is not decisive; it may be just chance that our sample of the Universe is so uniform.

Perhaps the best hope of deciding between the two views at the moment lies in getting accurate measurements of the velocity of the most distant galaxies. Those at the limit of the 200-inch telescope are two billion light-years away, which means that we are seeing them as they were two billion years ago. At that time, if the evolutionary view is correct, all the galaxies were closer together than now and were moving apart faster, because the time was closer to that of the original explosion. Consequently the remote galaxies, in the two-billion-year-old picture we are now seeing, should be receding more rapidly than Hubble's Law would predict for their distance. On the other hand, if the steady-state view is correct, galaxies have always receded from one another at the same velocity, and Hubble's Law should hold as far as our telescopes can reach.

In the middle 1950's the measured red-shifts of the most distant galaxies began to suggest that they were in fact moving a trifle faster than in straight proportion to the Hubble formula, and this seemed to lend support to the evolutionary theory. But the spectra are hard to observe and the differences are small. We need better instruments to settle the matter definitely.

THE DEATH OF THE SUN

Whether the Universe is evolutionary or steady-state is a point that does not affect individual galaxies or clusters of galaxies directly. Even if all the distant galaxies recede and recede until they are out of range of the best possible instruments, our own galaxy will remain intact, its component stars held firmly within its gravitational field. Nor will the other galaxies of the local cluster leave us. But changes within our galaxy, possibly disastrous to our planet and its life, are by no means excluded.

The whole conception of changes in heavenly bodies is a modern one. The ancient Greek philosophers, Aristotle in particular, believed that the heavens were perfect and unchangeable. All change, corruption, and decay were confined to the imperfect regions that lay below the nethermost heavenly sphere — the moon. This seemed only common sense, for certainly from generation to generation and century to century there was no important change in the heavens. To be sure, there were the mysterious comets that occasionally materialized out of nowhere — erratic in their comings and goings, ghost-like as they shrouded stars with a thin veil, baleful in appearance, for the filmy tail looked like the streaming hair of a distraught creature prophesying evil (in fact, the word "comet" comes from the Latin word for "hair"). Aristotle tried to reconcile these apparitions with the perfection of the heavens by insisting that they belonged to the atmosphere of the corrupt and changing earth. This view prevailed until late in the sixteenth century. But in 1577 the Danish astronomer Tycho Brahe attempted to measure the parallax of a bright comet and discovered that it could not be measured (this was before the days of the telescope). Since the moon's parallax *was* measurable, Tycho Brahe was forced to conclude that the comet lay far beyond the moon, and that there was change and imperfection in the heavens.

Actually, changes even in the stars had been noticed much earlier, but apparently they had aroused no great curiosity. For instance, there are the variable stars that change noticeably in brightness from night to night, even to the naked eye. No Greek astronomer made any reference to variations in the brightness of any star. It may be that we have lost the records of such references; on the other hand, perhaps the Greek astronomers simply chose not to see these phenomena. One interesting case in point is Beta Persei, the second brightest star in the constellation Perseus, which suddenly loses two-thirds of its brightness, then regains it, and does this regularly every 69 hours. (We know now that Beta Persei has a dim companion star which eclipses it and diminishes its light at 69-hour intervals.) The Greek astronomers made no mention of the dimming of Beta Persei, nor did the Arab astronomers of the Middle Ages. Nevertheless, the Arab name for the star, Algol, meaning "the ghoul" (nowadays translated into the "Demon Star"), shows that they must have noticed something strange about it.

A star in the constellation Cetus, called Omicron Ceti, varies irregularly. Sometimes it is as bright as the Pole Star; sometimes it vanishes from sight. Neither the Greeks nor the Arabs said a word about it, and the first man to report it was a Dutch astronomer, David Fabricius, in 1596. He named it Mira (Latin for "wonderful"), astronomers having grown less frightened of heavenly change by then.

Even more remarkable was the sudden appearance of "new stars" in the heavens. This the Greeks could not altogether ignore. Hipparchus is said to have been so impressed by the sighting of such a "new star" in the constellation Scorpio in 134 B.C. that he designed the first star map, in order that "new stars" in the future might be more easily detected.

In 1054 A.D., in the constellation Taurus, another new star was sighted — a phenomenally bright one, in fact. It surpassed Venus in brightness, and for weeks it was visible in broad daylight. Chinese and Japanese astronomers recorded its position accurately, and their records have come down to us. In the Western world, however, the state of astronomy was so low at the time that no European record of this remarkable occurrence has survived, probably because none was kept.

It was different in 1572, when a new star as bright as that of 1054 appeared in the constellation Cassiopeia. European astronomy was reviving from its long sleep. The young Tycho Brahe carefully observed the new star and wrote a book entitled *De Nova Stella*. It is from the title of that book that the word "nova" was adopted for any new star.

In 1604 still another remarkable nova appeared, in the constellation Serpens. It was not quite as bright as that of 1572, but it was bright enough to outshine Mars. Johannes Kepler observed this one, and he too wrote a book about the subject.

After the invention of the telescope, novae became less mysterious. They were not new stars at all, of course; merely faint stars which had suddenly brightened to visibility.

Increasing numbers of novae were discovered with time. They would brighten many thousand-fold, sometimes within the space of a few days, and then dim slowly over a period of months to their previous obscurity. Novae showed up at the average rate of 20 per year per galaxy (including our own).

From an investigation of the Doppler-Fizeau shifts that took place during nova-formation and from certain other fine details of their spectra, it became plain that the novae were exploding stars. In some cases the star material blown into space could be seen as a shell of expanding gas, illuminated by the remains of the star.

This sort of nova-formation does not necessarily signify the death of a star. It is a tremendous catastrophe, of course. (If our sun were to become a nova, it would destroy all life on the earth and possibly vaporize the planet.) But the explosion apparently ejects only 1 or 2 per cent of the star's mass, and afterward the star settles back to a reasonably normal life. In fact, some stars seem to undergo such explosions every generation or so and still survive.

The most remarkable nova that appeared after the invention of the telescope was one in the Andromeda galaxy of 1885. It was just below visibility to the naked eye; in the telescope it looked one-tenth as bright as the entire Andromeda galaxy. At the time, no one realized how distant the Andromeda galaxy was, or how large, and so the brightness of its nova occasioned no particular excitement. But after Hubble worked out the distance of the Andromeda galaxy, the brilliance of that nova of 1885 suddenly staggered astronomers. Hubble eventually discovered a number of novae in the Andromeda galaxy, but none even approached the 1885 nova in brightness. The nova of 1885 must have been 10,000 times as bright as ordinary novae. It was a "supernova."

Looking back now, we realize that the novae of 1054, 1572, and 1604 also were supernovae. What's more, they must have been in our own galaxy, which would account for their extreme brightness.

Supernovae apparently are quite different in physical behavior from ordinary novae, and astronomers are eager to study their spectra in detail. The main difficulty is that they are so rare. About three per thousand years is the average for any one galaxy. Although astronomers have managed to spot about 50 so far, all these are in distant galaxies and cannot be studied in detail. The 1885 supernova of Andromeda, the closest to us in the last 350 years, appeared a couple of decades before photography in astronomy had been fully developed, so no permanent record of its spectrum exists.

The brightness of a supernova (absolute magnitudes range from —14 to an occasional —17) could only come about as a result of a complete explosion — a star literally tearing itself to pieces. What would happen to such a star? Well, let's go back a little. . . .

As EARLY AS 1834, Bessel (the astronomer who was later to be the first to measure the parallax of a star) noticed that Sirius and Procyon shifted position very slightly from year to year in a manner which did not seem related to the motion of the earth. Their motions were not in a straight line but wavy, and Bessel decided that each must actually be moving in an orbit around something.

From the manner in which Sirius and Procyon were moving in these orbits, the "something" in each case had to have a powerful gravitational attraction which could belong to nothing less than a star. Sirius's companion, in particular, had to be as massive as our own sun to account for the bright star's motions. So the companions were judged to be stars, but since they were invisible in telescopes of the time, they were referred to as "dark companions." They were believed to be old stars growing dim with time.

Then in 1862 the American astronomer Alvan Clark, testing a new telescope, sighted a dim star near Sirius and, sure enough, on further observation this turned out to be the companion. Sirius and the dim star circled about a mutual center of gravity in a period of about 50 years. The companion of Sirius ("Sirius B" it is now called, with Sirius itself as "Sirius A") has an absolute magnitude of only 11.2, and so it is only about 1/400 as bright as our sun, though it is just as massive.

This seemed to check with the notion of a dying star. But in 1914 the American astronomer Walter Sydney Adams, after studying the spectrum of Sirius B, decided that the star had to be as hot as Sirius A itself, and hotter than our sun. The atomic vibrations that gave rise to the particular absorption lines found in its spectrum could only be taking place at very high temperatures. But if Sirius B was so hot, why was its light so faint? The only possible answer was that it was considerably smaller than our sun. Being hotter, it radiated more light per unit of surface, but to account for the small total amount of light, its total surface had to be small. In fact, the star could not be more than 16,000 miles in diameter — only twice the earth's diameter. Yet Sirius B had a mass equal to that of our sun! Adams found himself trying to imagine this mass mashed down into a volume as small as that of Sirius B. The star's density would have to be nearly 3,000 times that of platinum.

This represented nothing less than a completely new state of matter. Fortunately, by this time physicists had no trouble in suggesting the answer. They knew that in ordinary matter the atoms are composed of very tiny particles, so tiny that most of the volume of an atom is "empty" space. Under extreme pressure the subatomic particles could be forced together into a superdense mass, known as a "degenerate gas." In short, Sirius B could be considered a mass of crushed atomic nuclei. Even greater density is possible; in fact, stars have since been discovered with densities 15 times that of Sirius B.

The companion of Procyon ("Procyon B") also was found to be a superdense star, and, as the years passed, more examples were found. These stars are called "white dwarfs," because they combine small size with high temperature and white light. (There are also "red dwarfs," low in temperature and not superdense.)

The year after Sirius B was found to have its astonishing properties, Albert Einstein presented his General Theory of Relativity, which was mainly concerned with new ways of looking at gravity. Einstein's views of gravity led to the prediction that light emitted by a source possessing a very strong gravitational field should be displaced toward the red. Adams, fascinated by the white dwarfs he had discovered, carried out careful studies of the spectrum of Sirius B and found that there was indeed the red-shift predicted by Einstein. This was not only a point in favor of Einstein's theory but also a point in favor of the superdensity of Sirius B, for in an ordinary star the red-shift effect would be too slight to be detected.

But what have white dwarfs to do with supernovae, the subject that prompted this discussion? To answer that, let's go back to the supernova of 1054. In 1844 the British astronomer William Parson (3rd Earl of Rosse), investigating the location in Taurus where the oriental astronomers had reported finding the 1054 supernova, came across a small cloudy object. Because of its irregularity and its claw-like projections, the object was named the "Crab Nebula." Continued observation over decades showed that the patch of gas was slowly expanding. The actual rate of expansion could be calculated from the Doppler-Fizeau effect, and this, combined with the apparent rate of expansion, made it possible to compute the distance of the Crab Nebula as 4,000 light-years from us. From the expansion rate it was also determined that the gas had started its expansion from a central explosion point nearly 900 years ago, which agrees well with the date 1054. So there can be little doubt that the Crab Nebula represents the remnants of the 1054 supernova. At the center of the

Nebula is a dim star, of magnitude 16. By the 1920's astronomers had established that this star is a white dwarf.

The Crab Nebula is the only supernova whose aftermath we are in a position to see. What is left is a white dwarf and a cloud of gas. Are the other white dwarfs also remnants of stars that exploded? If so, why don't they have clouds of gas around them? Will our own sun some day explode and become a white dwarf? These queries lead us into the problem of the evolution of stars.

OF THE STARS near us, the bright ones seem to be hot and the dim ones cooler, according to a fairly regular brightness-temperature scale. If the surface temperatures of various stars are plotted against their absolute magnitudes, most of the familiar stars fall within a narrow band, increasing steadily from dim coolness to bright hotness. This band is called the "main sequence." It was first plotted in 1913 by the American astronomer Henry Norris Russell, following work along similar lines by Hertzsprung (the astronomer who first determined the absolute magnitudes of the Cepheids). A graph showing the main sequence is therefore called a Hertzsprung-Russell diagram, or H-R diagram.

Not all stars belong in the main sequence. There are some red stars which, despite their rather low temperature, have large absolute magnitudes, because of their tremendous size. Among these "red giants," the best-known are Betelgeuse and Antares. On the other hand, the high-temperature white dwarfs also fall outside the main sequence.

Shortly after the establishment of the main sequence, Sir Arthur Eddington pointed out that the interior of any star must be very hot. Because of a star's great mass, its gravitational force is immense. If the star is not to collapse, this huge force must be balanced by an equal internal pressure — from radiation energy. The more massive the star, the higher the central temperature required to balance the gravitational force. To maintain this high temperature and radiation pressure, the more massive stars must be burning energy faster, and therefore must be brighter, than less massive ones. This is the "mass-luminosity law."

It follows that the massive stars are spendthrift with their hydrogen fuel and have a shorter life. Our sun has enough hydrogen to last it at its present radiation rate for many billions of years. A bright star such as Capella must burn out in about 20 million years, and some of the brightest stars — for example, Rigel — cannot possibly last more than one or two million years. This means that the very brightest stars must be very youthful. New stars are perhaps even now being formed in regions where space is dusty enough to supply the raw material.

The next advance in the study of the evolution of stars came from analysis of the stars in globular clusters. The stars in a cluster are all about the same distance from us, so their apparent magnitude is proportional to their absolute magnitude (as in the case of the Cepheids in the Magellanic Clouds). Therefore, with their magnitude known, an H-R diagram of these stars can be prepared. It is found that the cooler stars (burning their hydrogen slowly) are on the main sequence, but the hotter ones depart from it. In accordance with their high rate of burning, and with their rapid aging, they follow a definite line showing various stages of evolution, first toward the red giants and then back, across the main sequence again, and down toward the white dwarfs.

From this and from certain theoretical considerations as to the manner in which subatomic particles can combine at certain high temperatures and pressures, Fred Hoyle has drawn a detailed picture of the course of a star's evolution. According to Hoyle, in its early stages a star changes very little in size or temperature. (This is the position our sun is in now and will continue to be for a long time.) As it burns its hydrogen in the interior, converting it into helium, the helium accumulates at the center of the star. When this helium core reaches a certain size, the star starts to change its size and temperature dramatically. It becomes cooler and expands enormously. In other words, it leaves the main sequence and moves in the red-giant direction. The more massive the star, the more quickly it

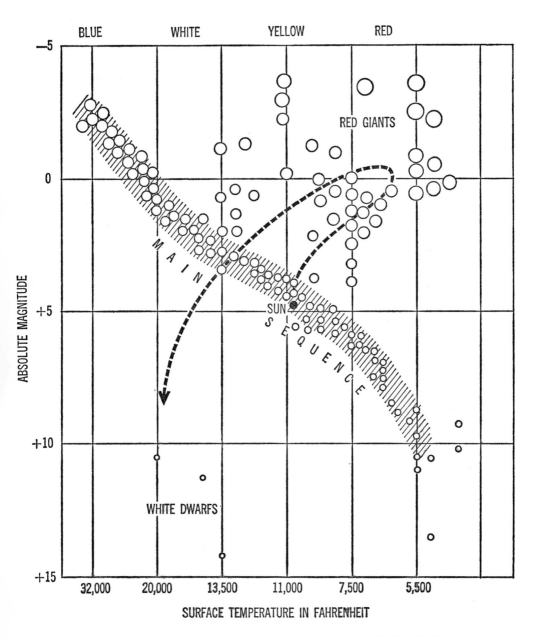

THE HERTZSPRUNG-RUSSELL DIAGRAM. *The dotted line indicates the evolution of a star. The relative sizes of the stars are given only schematically, not according to scale.*

reaches this point. In the globular clusters, the more massive ones have progressed varying lengths along the road.

The expanded giant releases more heat, because of its larger surface area. In the far distant future, when the sun leaves the main sequence, or even somewhat before, it will have heated to the point where life will be impossible on the earth. That point, however, is still at least a billion years in the future.

Until recently the hydrogen-to-helium conversion was the only source of energy recognized in stars, and that raised a problem with respect to the red giants. By the time a star has reached the red-giant stage, most of its hydrogen is gone. How, then, can it go on radiating energy in such large quantities? Hoyle suggested that the helium core itself contracts, and as a result it rises to a temperature at which the helium nuclei can fuse to form carbon, with the liberation of additional energy. In 1959 the American physicist David E. Alburger showed in the laboratory that this reaction actually can take place. It is a very rare and unlikely sort of reaction, but there are so many helium atoms in a red giant that enough such fusions can occur to supply the necessary quantities of energy.

Hoyle goes further. The new carbon core heats up still more, and now it builds more complicated atoms, such as oxygen and neon. While this is happening, the star is contracting and getting hotter again; it moves back toward the main sequence. By now the star has begun to acquire a series of layers, like an onion. It has an oxygen-neon core, then a layer of carbon, then one of helium, and the whole is enveloped in a skin of unconverted hydrogen.

As the temperature at the center continues to increase, more and more complex types of reactions can go on. The neon in the new core can combine further to magnesium, which can combine in turn to form silicon, and then, in turn, iron. At a late stage in its life, the star may be built up of more than half a dozen concentric shells, in each of which a different fuel is being consumed.

However, in comparison with its long life as a hydrogen-consumer, the star is on a quick toboggan slide through the remaining fuels. Its life off the main sequence is a merry one, but short. Once the star begins to form iron, it has reached a dead end. Iron cannot be converted to any other type of atom unless energy is pumped into it. There is no way of making iron yield a net gain of energy.

And so, as Hoyle says, "the stage is set for catastrophe." As the central temperature continues to rise, there comes a point where the iron is converted back to helium. But for this to happen, as I have just said, energy must be poured into the atoms. The only place the star can get this energy from is its gravitational field. When the star shrinks, the energy it gains can be used to convert iron to helium. The amount of energy needed is so great, however, that the star must shrink drastically to a tiny fraction of its former volume, and this must happen, according to Hoyle, "in about a second."

In the blink of an eye, then, the ordinary star is gone and a white dwarf takes its place. That is the fate the far, far future holds in store for our sun.

All this purports to explain the formation of a white dwarf without an explosion. It may be the story of dwarfs such as Sirius B and Procyon B. But where do supernovae come in? What is the story of the white dwarf at the center of the Crab Nebula?

The Indian astronomer Subrahmanyan Chandrasekhar, working at Yerkes Observatory, calculated that no star more than 1.4 times the mass of our sun (now called "Chandrasekhar's limit") could become a white dwarf by the "normal" process Hoyle described. And in fact all the white dwarfs so far observed turn out to be below Chandrasekhar's limit in mass. But it also develops that the white dwarf at the center of the Crab Nebula, though itself less than 1.4 times the mass of our sun, is the remnant of a star which originally was well over Chandrasekhar's limit, if we count in the mass of the ejected gas around it.

So we now have to explain how the original over-the-limit star could have become a white dwarf. The reason for Chandrasekhar's limit is that, the more massive the star, the more it has to shrink (i.e., the denser it has to become) to provide the energy necessary to reconvert its iron to helium, and there is a limit to the possible shrinkage, so to speak. However, a very massive star could obtain an additional boost of energy from another process. When such a star starts to collapse, its iron core is still surrounded with a voluminous outer mantle of unburned fuel. As the outer regions collapse and their temperature rises, these still combinable substances "take fire" all at once. The result is an explosion which blasts the outer material away from the body of the star. The white dwarf left at the conclusion of such an explosion would be below Chandrasekhar's limit.

This may be the explanation not only of the Crab Nebula but also of all supernovae. Our sun, by the way, being below Chandrasekhar's limit, may become a white dwarf some day but apparently will never become a supernova.

Hoyle suggests that the matter blasted into space by a supernova may spread through the galaxies and serve as raw material for the formation of new, "second-generation" stars, rich in iron and other metallic elements.

As for white dwarfs, though they are dying, it seems that their death will be indefinitely prolonged. Their only source of energy is their gravitational contraction, but this force is so immense that it can supply the charily-radiating white dwarfs with enough energy to last tens of billions of years before they dim out altogether and become "black dwarfs." In the five-billion-year lifetime of the Universe (assuming this is its correct age) perhaps no white dwarf formed has yet come to its end.

THE WINDOWS TO THE UNIVERSE

MAN'S GREATEST WEAPONS in his conquest of knowledge are his understanding mind and the inexorable curiosity that drives it on. And his resourceful mind has continually invented new instruments which have opened up horizons beyond the reach of his unaided sense organs.

The best-known example is the vast surge of new knowledge that followed the invention of the telescope in 1609. The telescope, es-

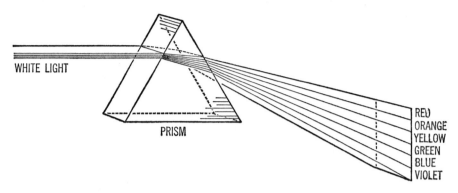

WHITE LIGHT

PRISM

RED
ORANGE
YELLOW
GREEN
BLUE
VIOLET

NEWTON'S EXPERIMENT *splitting the spectrum of white light.*

sentially, is simply an oversized eye. In contrast to the quarter-inch pupil of the human eye, the 200-inch telescope on Palomar Mountain has more than 31,000 square inches of light-gathering area. Its light-collecting power intensifies the brightness of a star some hundreds of thousands of times, as compared with what the naked eye can see.

But this is not the full measure of the telescope's gifts to man. The first step toward making it something more than a mere light-collector came in 1666 when Isaac Newton discovered that light could be separated into a spectrum of colors. He passed a beam of sunlight through a triangularly shaped "prism" of glass and found that the beam spread out into a band made up of red, orange, yellow, green, blue, and violet light, each color fading gently into the next. (The phenomenon itself, of course, has always been familiar in the form of the rainbow, the result of sunlight passing through water droplets, which act like tiny prisms.)

What Newton showed was that sunlight, or "white light," is a mixture of many specific radiations (we now call them wavelengths) which impress the eye as so many different colors. A prism separates the colors because, on passing from air into glass, and from glass into air, light is bent, or "refracted," and each wavelength undergoes a different amount of refraction — the shorter the wavelength, the greater the refraction. The short wavelengths of violet light are refracted most; the long wavelengths of red, least.

In 1814 a German optician named Joseph von Fraunhofer, while studying the refractive action of glass on sunlight, found that under certain conditions dark lines crossed the bright solar spectrum. Von Fraunhofer mapped the pattern of these lines carefully, and they have been known ever since as "Fraunhofer lines."

In succeeding decades a number of scientists toyed with the notion that the lines were characteristic of the various elements present in the sun. The dark lines would represent absorption of light at the wavelengths in question by certain elements; bright lines would represent characteristic emissions of light by elements. About 1859 the German chemists Robert Wilhelm Bunsen and Gustav Robert Kirchhoff worked out a system, which amounted to an instrument, for identifying elements in this way. They heated various substances to incandescence, spread out their glow into spectra, measured the location of the lines (in this case, bright lines of emission, against a dark background) on a background scale, and matched up each line with a particular element. Their "spectroscope" was quickly applied to discovering new elements by means of new spectral lines not identifiable with known elements. Within a couple of years Bunsen and Kirchhoff discovered cesium and rubidium in this manner.

The spectroscope was also applied to the light of the sun and the stars, and soon turned up an amazing quantity of new information. For one thing, it detected in the sun and the stars a number of the elements known on the earth and gave an idea of the relative quantities of each. In 1868 came a more exciting discovery. During an eclipse of the sun, astronomers found a new line in its light. The English astronomer Sir Norman Lockyer, sure that the line represented a new element, named it "helium," from the Greek word for "sun." Not until nearly 30 years later was helium found on the earth.

The spectroscope eventually became a tool for measuring the radial velocity of stars, as we saw earlier in this chapter, and for exploring many other matters — the magnetic characteristics of a star, its temperature, whether the star is single or double, and so on.

When, in 1839, the French artist Louis J. M. Daguerre produced the first "daguerreotypes" and thus introduced photography, this too

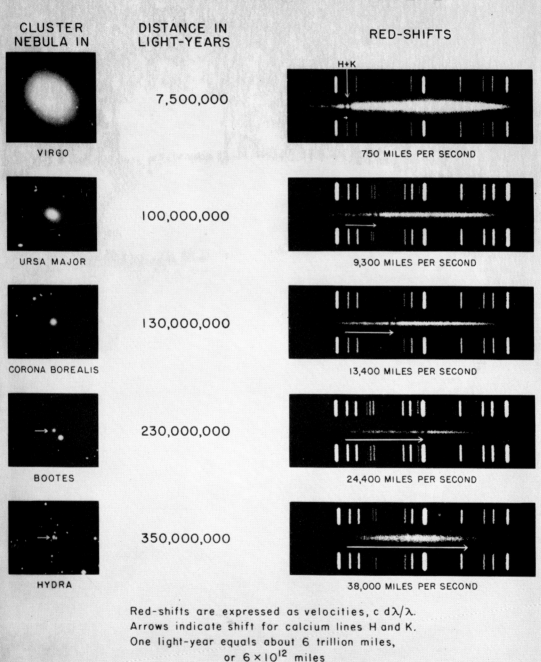

RELATION BETWEEN RED-SHIFT AND DISTANCE FOR EXTRAGALACTIC NEBULAE

CLUSTER NEBULA IN	DISTANCE IN LIGHT-YEARS	RED-SHIFTS
VIRGO	7,500,000	H+K — 750 MILES PER SECOND
URSA MAJOR	100,000,000	9,300 MILES PER SECOND
CORONA BOREALIS	130,000,000	13,400 MILES PER SECOND
BOOTES	230,000,000	24,400 MILES PER SECOND
HYDRA	350,000,000	38,000 MILES PER SECOND

Red-shifts are expressed as velocities, $c\,d\lambda/\lambda$.
Arrows indicate shift for calcium lines H and K.
One light-year equals about 6 trillion miles,
or 6×10^{12} miles

RED-SHIFTS OF DISTANT GALAXIES.

A GLOBULAR CLUSTER *in Canes Venatici.*

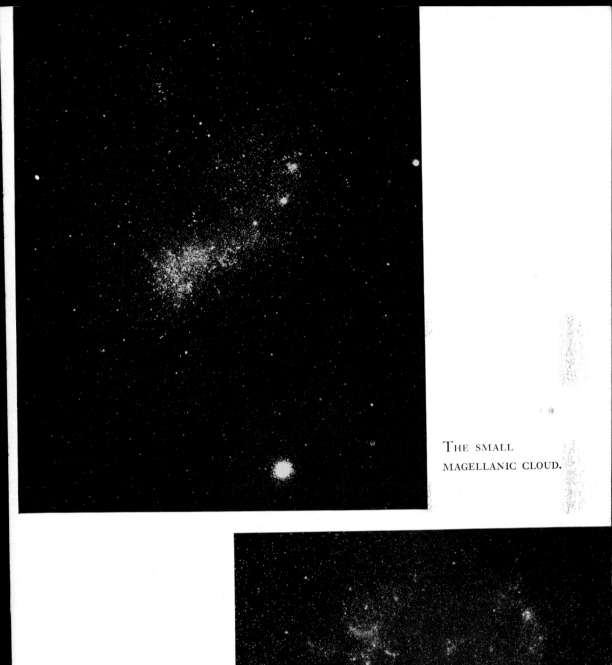

THE SMALL
MAGELLANIC CLOUD.

THE LARGE
MAGELLANIC CLOUD.

THE JODRELL BANK RADIO TELESCOPE. *Its dish is 250 feet in diameter.*

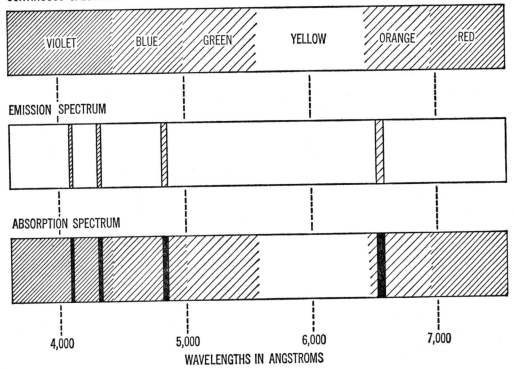

CONTINUOUS SPECTRUM

VIOLET BLUE GREEN YELLOW ORANGE RED

EMISSION SPECTRUM

ABSORPTION SPECTRUM

4,000   5,000   6,000   7,000

WAVELENGTHS IN ANGSTROMS

THE VISIBLE SPECTRUM, *indicating emission and absorption lines.*

at once became an invaluable instrument for astronomy. Through the 1840's various American astronomers photographed the moon, and one picture, by George P. Bond, was a sensation at the Great Exhibition of 1851 in London. They also photographed the sun. In 1860 the Italian astronomer Pietro Angelo Secchi made the first photograph of a total eclipse of the sun. By 1870, photographs of such eclipses had proved that the corona and prominences were part of the sun and not of the moon.

Meanwhile, beginning in the 1850's, astronomers were also making pictures of the distant stars. Photography was well on its way to becoming more important than the human eye in observing the Universe.

The technique of photography with telescopes steadily improved. A major stumbling block was the fact that a large telescope can cover only a very small field, but in the 1930's a German optician, Bernard Schmidt, invented one which could photograph wide swaths of the sky. "Schmidt telescopes" (several versions have been developed) cannot be used for direct viewing with the eye; they are sometimes called "Schmidt cameras." The largest is a 48-inch Schmidt used in conjunction with the 200-inch giant on Palomar. In some respects the Schmidt is the more useful of the two.

ABOUT 1800 William Herschel (the astronomer who first guessed the shape of our galaxy) performed a very simple but interesting experiment. In a beam of light transmitted through a prism, he held a thermometer beyond the red end of the spectrum. The mercury climbed! Plainly some form of invisible radiation existed at wavelengths below the visible spectrum. The radiation Herschel had discovered became known as "infrared" — below the red.

At about the same time a German physicist, Johann Wilhelm Ritter,was exploring the other end of the spectrum. He found that silver nitrate, which breaks down to metallic silver and darkens when it is exposed to blue or violet light, would break down even more rapidly if it was placed beyond the point in the spectrum where violet faded out. Thus Ritter discovered the "light" now called "ultraviolet" (beyond the violet). Between them, Herschel and Ritter had widened the time-honored spectrum and crossed into new realms of radiation.

In 1860 the Scottish physicist James Clerk Maxwell worked out a theory which predicted a whole family of radiation associated with electric and magnetic phenomena ("electromagnetic radiation") — a family of which ordinary light was only one small portion. The first definite evidence bearing out his prediction came a quarter of a century later. In 1887 the German physicist Heinrich Rudolf Hertz, generating an oscillating current from the spark of an induction coil, produced and detected radiation of extremely long wavelengths — much longer than those of ordinary infrared. These were, of course, "radio waves."

The wavelengths of visible light are measured in microns (millionths of a meter). They range from 0.39 micron (extreme violet) to 0.78 micron (extreme red). Next come the "near infrared" (0.78 to 20 microns) and then the far "infrared" (20 to 1,000 microns). It is here that radio waves begin: the so-called "microwaves" run from 1,000 to 160,000 microns and long-wave radio goes as high as many billions of microns.

Within a decade after Hertz's discovery, the other end of the spectrum opened up similarly. In 1895 the German physicist Wilhelm Konrad Roentgen accidentally discovered a mysterious radiation which he called "X-rays." Their wavelengths turned out to be shorter than ultraviolet. Later, "gamma rays," associated with radioactivity, were shown by the British physicist Ernest Rutherford to have wavelengths even smaller than those of X-rays.

The short-wave half of the spectrum is now divided roughly as follows: The wavelengths from 0.39 down to 0.17 micron belong to the "near ultraviolet," from 0.17 down to 0.01 micron to the "far ultraviolet," from 0.01 to 0.00001 micron to X-rays, and gamma rays range from this down to less than a billionth of a micron.

Newton's original spectrum was thus expanded enormously. If we consider each doubling of wavelength as equivalent to one octave (as is the case in sound), the full electromagnetic spectrum amounts to almost 60 octaves. Visible light occupies just one octave near the center of the spectrum.

With a wider spectrum, of course, we can get a fuller view of the stars. We know that sunshine is rich in ultraviolet and in infrared. Our atmosphere cuts off most of these radiations. But in 1931, quite by accident, a radio window to the Universe was discovered.

KARL G. JANSKY, a young radio engineer at the Bell Telephone Laboratories, was studying the static that always accompanies radio reception. He came across a very faint, very steady noise which could not be coming from any of the usual sources. He finally decided that the static was caused by radio waves from outer space.

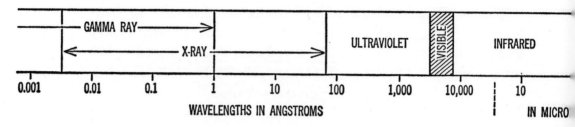

THE SPECTRUM *of electromagnetic radiation.*

At first the radio signals from space seemed strongest in the direction of the sun, but day by day the direction of strongest reception slowly drifted away from the sun and made a circuit of the sky. By 1933 Jansky decided the radio waves were coming from the Milky Way and, in particular, from the direction of Sagittarius, toward the center of the Galaxy.

Thus was born "radio astronomy." Astronomers did not take to it immediately, for it had serious drawbacks. It gave no neat pictures — only wiggles on a chart which were not easy to interpret. More important, radio waves are much too long to resolve a source as small as a star. The radio signals from space had wavelengths hundreds of thousands and even millions of times the wavelength of light, and no ordinary radio receiver could give anything more than a general idea of the direction they were coming from.

These difficulties obscured the importance of the new discovery, but a young radio ham named Grote Reber carried on, for no reason other than personal curiosity. He spent time and money building a small "radio telescope" with a "dish" antenna in his back yard. Beginning in 1938, he found a number of sources of radio waves other than the one in Sagittarius — one in the constellation Cygnus, for instance, and another in Cassiopeia. (Such sources of radiation are now called "radio stars," whether the sources are actually stars or not.)

During World War II, while British scientists were developing radar, they discovered that the sun was interfering by sending out signals in the microwave region. This aroused their interest in radio

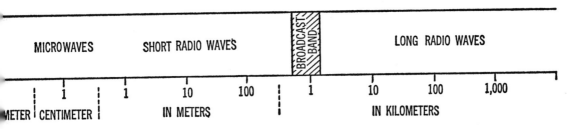

astronomy, and after the war the British pursued their tuning-in on the sun. They found that the sun's radio signals were associated with sunspots. (Jansky had conducted his experiments during a period of minimal sunspot activity, which is why he detected the Galactic radiation rather than that of the sun.)

The British pioneered in building large antennas and arrays of widely separated receivers (a technique first used in Australia) to sharpen reception and pinpoint radio stars. Their 250-foot dish at Jodrell Bank in England was the first really large radio telescope.

In 1947 the Australian astronomer John C. Bolton narrowed down the third strongest radio source in the sky, and it proved to be none other than the Crab Nebula. It seemed unlikely that the star itself was sending the signals; other white dwarfs emit no radio waves to speak of. Therefore it appeared that the source must be the Nebula's cloud of expanding gas. This strengthened other evidence that the cosmic radio signals arise primarily from turbulent gas. Sunspots are associated with turbulences in the solar atmosphere. The radio signals from the Galactic center may originate in the clouds of gas in that direction. Jupiter and Venus, with turbulent atmospheres, have been found to emit radio waves. Still other evidence along the same line comes from the strongest known radio star, called "Cass" because it is located in Cassiopeia. Walter Baade and Rudolph Minkowski at Palomar trained the 200-inch telescope on the spot where this source was pinpointed by British radio telescopes, and they found streaks of turbulent gas. It is possible that these may be remnants of the supernova of 1604, which Kepler observed in Cassiopeia.

The most remarkable discovery so far was made in 1951. The second strongest radio star lies in the constellation Cygnus. Reber first reported it in 1944. As radio telescopes later narrowed down its location, it began to appear that this radio star was outside our galaxy — the first found beyond the Milky Way. Then in 1951 Baade, studying the indicated portion of the sky with the 200-inch telescope, found an odd galaxy in the center of the field. It had a double center and seemed to be distorted. Baade at once suspected that this odd, distorted, double-centered galaxy was not one galaxy but two, joined broadside-to like a pair of clashing cymbals. Baade thought they were two colliding galaxies — a possibility which he had already discussed with other astronomers.

It took another year to settle the matter. The spectroscope showed absorption lines which could only be explained by supposing the dust and gas of the two galaxies to be coming into collision. The collision is now accepted to be a fact. Moreover, it seems likely that galactic collisions are fairly common, especially in dense clusters, where galaxies may be separated by distances not much more than their own diameters.

When two galaxies collide, the stars themselves are not likely to encounter one another: they are so widely spaced that one galaxy could pass through the other without any stars coming even close. But dust and gas clouds are stirred into vast turbulence, and thereby generate very powerful radio radiation. The colliding galaxies in Cygnus are 260 million light-years away, yet their radio signals reaching us are stronger than those of the Crab Nebula, only 4,000 light-years away. By this token, we should be able to detect colliding galaxies at far greater distances than we can see with the optical telescope. The 250-foot Jodrell Bank radio telescope, for instance, should outrange the 200-inch Hale telescope. The Soviet Union is now reported to have a 350-foot dish in operation; the United States announced in 1959 that it was building a 600-foot radio telescope in Sugar Grove, W. Va. In charge of this giant dish will be Otto Struve, great-grandson of the Struve who, in 1840, was one of the first to determine the parallax of a star.

IN A SENSE, the galaxy hardest for us to see is our own. For one thing, we are imprisoned within it, while the others can be viewed as a whole from outside. It is like the difference between trying to view a city from the roof of a low building and seeing it from an airplane. Furthermore, we are far out from the center, and to make matters worse, we lie in a spiral arm clogged with dust. In other words, we are on a low roof on the outskirts of the city on a foggy day.

We can actually "see" the dust clouds, in a negative way, as dark areas in the Milky Way. Examples are the dark Horsehead Nebula, outlined starkly against the surrounding brilliance of millions of stars, and the even more dramatically named Coalsack in the Southern Cross.

Although the gas and dust clouds hide the spiral arms of the Galaxy from direct vision, they do not hide the structure of the arms from the spectroscope. Hydrogen atoms in the clouds are ionized (broken up into positively charged protons and negatively charged electrons) by the energetic radiation from the bright Population I stars in the arms. Beginning in 1951, streaks of ionized hydrogen were found, marking out the lines of the blue giants, *i.e.*, the spiral arms. Their spectra were similar to the spectra shown by the spiral arms of the Andromeda galaxy.

The nearest such streak of ionized hydrogen includes the blue giants in the constellation of Orion, and this streak is therefore called the "Orion Arm." Our solar system is in that arm. Two other arms were located in the same way. One lies farther out from the Galactic center than our own and includes giant stars in the constellation Perseus (the "Perseus Arm"). The other lies closer to the Galactic center and contains bright clouds in the constellation Sagittarius (the "Sagittarius Arm"). Each arm seems to be about 10,000 light-years long.

Then radio came along as a still more powerful tool. Not only could it pierce through the obscuring clouds, but it made the clouds themselves tell their story — through their own voice. This came about as the result of a brilliant inspiration of the Dutch astronomer H. C. Van de Hulst. Most of the hydrogen in space consists of ordinary atoms — that is, not ionized. In 1944 Van de Hulst suggested that these atoms, on colliding, might change their energy state and in so doing emit a weak radiation in the radio part of the spectrum. He calculated that the wavelength of the radiation should be 21 centimeters. Sure enough, with the development of new radio techniques after the war, this "song of hydrogen" was detected in 1951.

By tuning in on the 21-centimeter radiation of collections of hydrogen, astronomers were able to trace out the spiral arms and follow them for long distances — in most cases nearly all the way around the Galaxy. More arms were found, and maps of the concentration of hydrogen show half a dozen or more streaks.

What is more, the song of hydrogen told something about its movements. Like all waves, this radiation is subject to the Doppler-Fizeau effect. It allows astronomers to measure the velocity of the moving hydrogen clouds, and thereby to explore, among other things, the rotation of our galaxy. This new technique confirmed that the Galaxy rotates in a period of 200 million years.

In science, each new discovery unlocks doors leading to new mysteries. And the greatest progress comes from the unexpected — the discovery that overthrows previous notions. An interesting example at the moment is a puzzling phenomenon brought to light by radio study of a concentration of hydrogen at the center of our galaxy. The hydrogen seems to be expanding, yet is confined to the equatorial plane of the Galaxy. The expansion itself is suprising, because there is no theory to account for it. And if the hydrogen is expanding, why has it not all dissipated away during the long lifetime of the Galaxy? The observation may or may not be significant, but it raises questions which might lead to the discovery of an important new fact or principle.

ASTRONOMERS now look forward not only to bigger and better instruments but to a day when they may break clean through the obscuring effect of the earth's atmosphere and the Galaxy's clouds. It will then not be any longer a question of one or two windows opened to the Universe, but of the whole wall knocked down. The entire electromagnetic spectrum will lie open to us.

One step toward that end is to get beyond the atmosphere. If, for instance, an astronomical observatory could be established on the airless moon, it would represent a star-gazer's heaven. Pending that happy day, observations can be, and have been, made by instruments carried to the top of the atmosphere by balloons and rockets. There, instruments can pick up short-wave radiation in the ultraviolet and beyond, and studies have been made of the sun's ultraviolet and X-ray radiation.

The discovery of X-rays coming from the sun is something of a surprise. The temperature of the sun's surface is only 6,000 degrees — high enough to vaporize any earthly substance but not to produce X-rays. The answer lies in the sun's corona, the tenuous halo of gases stretching outward millions of miles, which is much "hotter" than the sun's atmosphere. X-ray radiation increases sharply when a solar flare erupts into the corona. The X-ray intensity at that time implies a temperature as high as 100 million degrees in the corona above the flare. (Temperature here has to be distinguished from heat. The temperature is a measure of the kinetic energy of the atoms or particles in the gas, but since the particles are few, the actual heat content per unit of volume is low. The X-rays are produced by collisions between the extremely energetic particles.)

Ultraviolet investigations of the stars and interstellar space began in 1957 and have produced some puzzles. It was expected that some blue-white giants would increase in brilliance in the ultraviolet, for they radiate strongly in that part of the spectrum. But certain regions of the sky registered as "ultraviolet stars" without such an obvious explanation. Among them is the region of the Orion nebula in our galaxy. Astronomers have not yet worked up a reasonable explanation to account for the nebula's emitting ultraviolet light.

The first-magnitude star Spica is the center of another bright ultraviolet region. Now Spica is a hot star with a surface temperature of 28,000 degrees, and if there were nebulosity around it which would shine in the ultraviolet, as does the Orion nebula, then the nebulosity should radiate visible light, as the Orion nebula does. But there is no visible nebula around Spica, although the ultraviolet radiation of its surroundings is so strong that it drowns out that of the star itself — a very surprising fact on its own account.

With the installation of permanent observatories above our atmosphere — in a space-station or on the moon — astronomy will begin a new age in which our progress of recent years, amazing and glorious though it has been, will seem no more than a prelude to the real adventure that will then open up before us.

CHAPTER

3

THE EARTH

BIRTH OF THE SOLAR SYSTEM

HOWEVER GLORIOUS the unimaginable depths of the Universe and however puny the earth in comparison, it is on the earth that we live and to the earth that we must return.

By the time of Newton, it had become possible to speculate intelligently about the creation of the earth and the solar system as a separate problem from the creation of the Universe as a whole. The picture of the solar system showed it to be a structure with certain unifying characteristics.

1) All the major planets circle the sun in approximately the plane of the sun's equator. In other words, if you were to prepare a three-dimensional model of the sun and its planets, you would find it could be made to fit into a very shallow cakepan.

2) All the major planets circle the sun in the same direction—

counter-clockwise if you were to look down upon the solar system from the direction of the North Star.

3) Each major planet (except Uranus) rotates around its axis in the same counter-clockwise sense as its revolution around the sun, and the sun itself also rotates counter-clockwise.

4) The planets are spaced at smoothly increasing distances from the sun and have nearly circular orbits.

5) All the satellites, with minor exceptions, circle their respective planets in the plane of the planetary equator and in a counter-clockwise direction.

The general regularity of this picture naturally suggested that some single process had created the whole system. Of course, the irregularities have always been hard to explain away, but there are only a few of them and they may be accounted for as results of accidents. For instance, the minor planets called "asteroids" have irregular orbits, some of them considerably tilted to the general plane, but it seems possible that these bodies are remnants of an exploded planet, in which case their irregular orbits would not be surprising. Again, the fact that Pluto's orbit is tilted well out of the general plane and is somewhat elongated may be explainable on the theory that Pluto was originally a satellite of Neptune and was thrown away from that planet by some cosmic collision or other accident. A similar accident might account for Neptune's satellite Triton orbiting around Neptune in the "wrong" direction — that is, clockwise.

WHAT, THEN, is the process that produced the solar system? All the theories so far proposed fall into two classes: catastrophic and evolutionary. The catastrophic view is that the sun was created in single blessedness and gained a family as the result of some violent event. The evolutionary ideas hold that the whole system came into being in an orderly way.

In the eighteenth century, when scientists were still under the spell of the Biblical stories of great events such as the Flood, it was

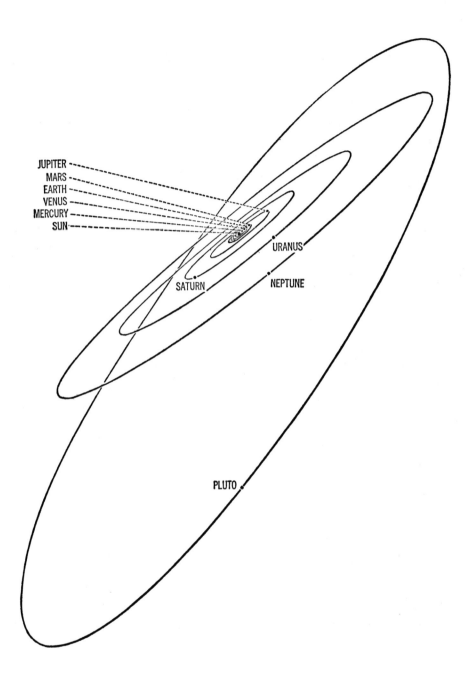

THE SOLAR SYSTEM, *drawn schematically.*

fashionable to assume that the history of the earth was full of violent catastrophes. Why not one super-catastrophe to start the whole thing going? One popular theory was the proposal of the French naturalist Georges Louis Leclerc de Buffon that the solar system had been created out of the debris resulting from a collision between the sun and a comet. Buffon's theory collapsed, however, when it was discovered that comets were only wisps of extremely thin dust.

In the nineteenth century, as concepts of long-drawn-out natural processes such as Hutton's uniformitarian principle (see page 42) won favor, catastrophes went out of fashion. Instead, scientists turned more and more to theories involving evolutionary processes, following Newton rather than the Bible.

Newton himself had suggested that the solar system might have been formed from a thin cloud of gas and dust which slowly condensed under gravitational attraction. As the particles came together, the gravitational field would become more intense, the condensation would be hastened, and finally the whole mass would collapse into a dense body (the sun), made incandescent by the energy of the contraction.

In essence, this is the basis of the most popular theories of the origin of the solar system today. But a great many thorny problems had to be solved to answer specific questions. How, for instance, could a highly dispersed gas be brought together by the extremely weak force of gravitation? In recent years scientists have proposed another plausible mechanism — the pressure of light. That light exerts pressure is illustrated by the comets, whose tails always point away from the sun because they are pushed in that direction by the pressure of the sunlight. Now particles in space are bombarded by radiation from all sides, but if two particles come close enough together to shade each other, they will be under less radiation pressure on the shaded than on the unshaded sides. The difference in pressure will tend to push them toward each other. As they come closer, gravitational attraction will accelerate their meeting.

If this is the way the sun was created, what about the planets? Where did they come from? The first attempts to answer this were put forward by the German philosopher Immanuel Kant in 1755 and independently by the French astronomer and mathematician Pierre Simon de Laplace in 1796. Laplace's picture was the more detailed.

As Laplace described it, the vast, contracting cloud of matter was rotating to start with. As it contracted, the speed of its rotation increased, just as a skater spins faster when he pulls in his arms. (This is due to the "conservation of angular momentum." Since angular momentum is equal to the speed of motion times the distance from the center of rotation, when the distance from the center decreases the speed of motion increases in compensation.) And as the rotating cloud speeded up, according to Laplace, it began to throw off a ring of material from its rapidly rotating equator. This removed some of the angular momentum, so that the remaining cloud slowed down, but as it contracted further, it again reached a speed at which it threw off another ring of matter. So the coalescing sun left behind a series of rings — doughnut-shaped clouds of matter. These rings, Laplace suggested, slowly condensed to form the planets, and along the way they themselves threw off small rings which formed their satellites.

Laplace's "nebular hypothesis" seemed to fit the main features of the solar system very well — and even some of its details. For instance, the rings of Saturn might be satellite-rings which had failed to coagulate. Similarly, the asteroids, circling around the sun in a belt between Mars and Jupiter, might be products of sections of a ring which had not united to form a planet. And when Helmholtz and Kelvin worked up theories attributing the sun's energy to its slow contraction (see Chapter 2), that, too, seemed to fit right in with Laplace's picture.

THE NEBULAR HYPOTHESIS held the field through most of the nineteenth century. But fatal flaws began to appear well before its end. In 1859 James Clerk Maxwell, analyzing Saturn's rings mathematically, showed that a ring of gaseous matter thrown off by any body could only condense to a collection of small particles like the rings of Saturn; it would never form a solid body, because gravitational forces would pull the ring apart before such a condensation materialized.

The problem of angular momentum also arose. It turned out that the planets, making up only a little more than 0.1 per cent of the mass of the whole solar system, carried 98 per cent of its total angular momentum! The sun, in other words, retained only a tiny fraction of the angular momentum of the orginal cloud. How did almost all of the angular momentum get shoved into the small rings split off the nebula?

By 1900 the nebular hypothesis was so dead that the idea of any evolutionary process at all seemed discredited. The stage was set for the revival of a catastrophic theory. In 1900 two American scientists, Thomas Chrowder Chamberlin and Forest Ray Moulton, proposed a new one, this time explaining the planets as the result of a near-collision between our sun and another star. The encounter pulled gaseous matter out of both suns, and the clouds of material left in the vicinity of our sun afterward condensed into "planetesimals" and these into planets. As for the problem of angular momentum, the British scientists James Hopwood Jeans and Harold Jeffreys soon suggested that the passing sun's gravitational attraction had given the dragged-out masses of gas a kind of sidewise yank (put "English" on them, so to speak), and thus imparted angular momentum to them.

But these ideas also failed when put to the test of mathematical analysis. Attempts to patch up the theory by imagining various kinds of solar collisions had little success. And so, after the planetesimal theory had come to a dead end, astronomers returned to the evolutionary idea and took another look at Laplace's nebular hypothesis.

By that time, their view of the Universe had expanded enormously. They now had to account for the formation of galaxies. This called, of course, for much bigger clouds of gas and dust than Laplace had envisaged as the parent of the solar system. And it now

C. F. von Weizsäcker's model of the origin of the solar system. *His theory holds that the great cloud from which it was
formed broke up into eddies and sub-eddies which then coalesced
into the sun, the planets, and their satellites.*

appeared that such vast collections of matter would break up into
eddies, each of which could condense into a separate system.

In 1944 the German astronomer C. F. von Weizsäcker made a

8 3

thorough analysis of this idea. He calculated that the largest eddies would contain enough matter to form galaxies. During the turbulent contraction of such an eddy, sub-eddies would develop. Each sub-eddy would be large enough to give birth to a solar system (with one or more suns). On the outskirts of the solar eddy itself, sub-sub-eddies might give rise to planets. This would take place at junctions where sub-sub-eddies met, moving against each other like meshing gears; at such places dust particles would collide and coalesce. As a result of these collisions, first planetesimals and then planets would form.

Weizsäcker's "eddy hypothesis" does not entirely satisfy his fellow astronomers, but it seems to make better sense than any other idea so far and has put the evolutionary concept firmly in the saddle again.

This is quite important with regard to the question whether there is life elsewhere in the Universe. Catastrophic events, especially collisions or near-collisions among the stars so widely dispersed in space, must be extremely rare. But if solar systems are formed by an evolutionary process, it seems likely that almost every star has a family of planets. In that case, the Universe must certainly contain many groups of intelligent beings besides man.

OF SHAPE AND SIZE

ONE OF THE MAJOR INSPIRATIONS of the ancient Greeks was their decision that the earth has the shape of a sphere. They conceived this idea originally (tradition credits Pythagoras of Samos with being the first to suggest it about 525 B.C.) on philosophical grounds — *e.g.*, that a sphere was the perfect shape. But the Greeks also verified it with observations. Around 350 B.C. Aristotle marshaled conclusive evidence that the earth was not flat but round. His most telling argument was that as one traveled north or south, new stars appeared over the horizon ahead and visible ones disap-

peared below the horizon behind. At about the same time, Hera-
clides of Pontus suggested that it was far easier to suppose that the
round earth rotated than that the entire vault of the heavens revolved
around the earth.

The idea of the earth as a perfect sphere held sway for nearly
2,000 years — until Isaac Newton changed the picture after taking
a careful look at what would happen to a rotating ball. He noted
that the earth's surface material has to move much more rapidly at
the equator than near the poles, because during the 24-hour period
of the earth's rotation a point on the equator travels 25,000 miles
while one near a pole moves only a few hundred miles or less. Now,
the faster the rotation, the stronger the centrifugal force — that is,
the force pushing material away from the center of rotation. It follows, therefore, that the centrifugal force increases steadily from
zero at the stationary poles to a maximum at the rapidly whirling
equatorial belt. This means that the earth should be pushed out
somewhat around its middle. In other words, it should be an "oblate
spheroid," with an equatorial "bulge" and flattened poles. It must
have roughly the shape of a tangerine rather than that of a golf ball.

The earth rotates so slowly that the flattening and bulging are
too slight to be readily detected. But at least two astronomical observations supported Newton's reasoning. First, Jupiter (and Saturn,
too) can clearly be seen to be markedly flattened at the poles. (Jupiter is much larger than the earth and rotates much faster — at 27,000
miles per hour at its equator.) Secondly, if the earth really bulges
at the equator, the varying gravitational pull on the bulge by the
moon, which most of the time is either north or south of the equator
in its circuit around the earth, should cause the earth to wobble a
little in its rotation. And in fact, Hipparchus of Nicaea had noted
such a wobble thousands of years before (without, of course, knowing the reason). The wobble has the effect of causing the sun to
reach the point of equinox about 50 seconds of arc eastward each
year (that is, in the direction of morning). Since the equinox thus
comes to a preceding (*i.e.*, earlier) point each year, Hipparchus

named this shift the "precession of the equinoxes," and it is still known by that name.

Naturally scientists set out in search of more direct proof of the earth's distortion. They resorted to a standard device for solving geometrical problems — trigonometry. On a curved surface, the angles of a triangle add up to more than 180 degrees. The greater the curvature, the greater the excess over 180 degrees. Now if the earth was an oblate spheroid, as Newton had said, the excess should be greater on the more sharply curved surface of the equatorial bulge than on the less curved surface toward the poles. In the 1730's French scientists made the first test by doing some large-scale surveying at separate sites in the north and the south of France. On the basis of these measurements, the French astronomer Jacques Cassini decided that the earth bulged at the poles, not at the Equator! To use an exaggerated analogy, its shape was more like that of a cucumber than of a tangerine.

But the difference in curvature between the north and the south of France obviously was too small to give conclusive results. Consequently, in 1735 and 1736 a pair of French expeditions went forth to more widely separated regions — one to Peru, near the Equator, and the other to Lapland, approaching the Arctic. By 1744 their surveys had given a clear answer: the earth was distinctly more curved in Peru than in Lapland.

Today the best measurements show that the diameter of the earth is 26.7 miles longer through the Equator than along the axis through the poles (*i.e.*, 7,926.68 miles against 7,899.98 miles).

Perhaps the most important scientific result of the eighteenth-century inquiry into the shape of the earth was that it made the scientific community dissatisfied with the state of the art of measurement. No decent standards for precise measurement existed. This dissatisfaction was partly responsible for the adoption, during the French Revolution half a century later, of the logical and scientifically worked out "metric" system based on the meter. The metric system now is used by scientists all over the world, to their great satisfaction, and it is the system in general public use in every civilized country except the English-speaking nations, chiefly Great Britain and the United States.

THE SMOOTHED-OUT, sea-level shape of the earth is called the "geoid." But of course the earth's surface is pocked with irregularities — mountains, ravines, and so on. Even before Newton raised the question of the planet's over-all shape, scientists had tried to measure the magnitude of these minor deviations from a perfect sphere (as they thought). They resorted to the device of a swinging pendulum. Galileo, as a 17-year-old boy, had discovered that a pendulum of a given length always completed its swing in the same time, whether the swing was short or long; he is supposed to have made the discovery while watching the swinging chandeliers in the Cathedral of Pisa during services. A pendulum with a length of 39.1 inches makes a complete swing in just one second. (The Dutch astronomer Christian Huyghens used this fact to devise the first modern clock, known as the "grandfather clock.") The investigators of the earth's irregularities made use of the fact that the period of a pendulum's swing depends on the strength of gravity at any given point. A pendulum that swings perfect seconds at sea-level, for instance, will take slightly longer than a second to complete a swing on a mountain top, where gravity is slightly weaker because the mountain top is farther from the center of the earth.

In 1673 a French expedition to the north coast of South America (near the Equator) found that at that location the pendulum was slowed even at sea-level. Newton later took this as evidence for the existence of the equatorial bulge. After the expedition to Peru and Lapland had proved his theory, a member of the Lapland expedition, the French mathematician Alexis Claude Clairault, worked out methods of calculating the oblateness of the earth from pendulum swings. Thus the geoid, or sea-level shape of the earth, can be determined.

A knowledge of the exact shape of the geoid is essential for accurate map-making. As late as the 1950's the distance between New

York and London, for instance, was not known to better than a mile or so, and the locations of some islands in the Pacific on maps had a possible error of several miles. In these days of air travel and (alas!) potential missile-aiming, this is inconvenient. But truly accurate mapping has now been made possible — oddly enough, not by surveys of the earth's surface but by astronomical measurements of a new kind. The chief instrument of these measurements is the man-made satellite called Vanguard I, launched by the United States on March 17, 1958. Vanguard I makes a revolution around the earth in two and a half hours, and in the first couple of years of its lifetime it had already made more revolutions than the moon had in all the centuries it has been observed with the telescope. By observations of Vanguard I's position at specific times from specific points on the earth, the distances between these observing points can be calculated precisely. In this way, positions and distances not known to within a matter of miles were, in 1959, determined to within a hundred yards or so. (Another satellite named Transit I-B, launched by the United States on April 13, 1960, is the first of a series intended to extend this into a system for the accurate location of position on the earth's surface, something which could greatly improve and simplify air and sea navigation.)

Like the moon, Vanguard I circles the earth in an ellipse which is not in the earth's equatorial plane. As in the case of the moon, the perigee (closest approach) of Vanguard I shifts because of the attraction of the equatorial bulge. Because Vanguard I is far closer to the bulge and far smaller than the moon, it is affected to a greater extent, and because of its many revolutions, the effect of the bulge can be well studied. It was found, for instance, that the perigee-shift of Vanguard I was not the same in the Northern Hemisphere as in the Southern. This showed that the bulge was not quite symmetrical with respect to the Equator. The bulge seemed to be 25 feet higher (that is, 25 feet more distant from the earth's center) at spots south of the Equator than at spots north of it. Further calculations showed that the South Pole was 50 feet closer to the center of the earth (counting from sea-level) than was the North Pole.

The newspaper stories therefore described the earth as "pear-shaped." Actually, the deviation is perceptible only by the most refined measurements; no one looking at the earth from space would see anything resembling a pear in its shape.

A KNOWLEDGE of the exact size and shape of the earth makes it possible to calculate its volume. This comes out to about 260 billion cubic miles. Calculating the earth's mass, however, is a more complex matter. We have no direct means of knowing exactly what materials make up its interior or what its average density is. But Newton's law of gravitation gives us a formula for working out the mass. According to Newton, the gravitational force (f) between any two objects in the Universe can be expressed as follows:

$$f = \frac{g m_1 m_2}{d^2}$$

where m_1 and m_2 are the masses of the two bodies concerned and d is the distance between them, center to center. As for g, that represents the "gravitational constant."

What the value of the constant was, Newton could not say. If we can learn the values of the other factors in the equation, however, we can find g, for by transposing the terms we get:

$$g = \frac{f d^2}{m_1 m_2}$$

To find the value of g, therefore, all we need to do is to measure the gravitational force between two bodies of known mass at the separation of a known distance. The trouble is that gravitational force is the weakest force we know, and the gravitational attraction between two masses of any ordinary size that we can handle is almost impossible to measure.

Nevertheless, in 1798 the English physicist Henry Cavendish, a

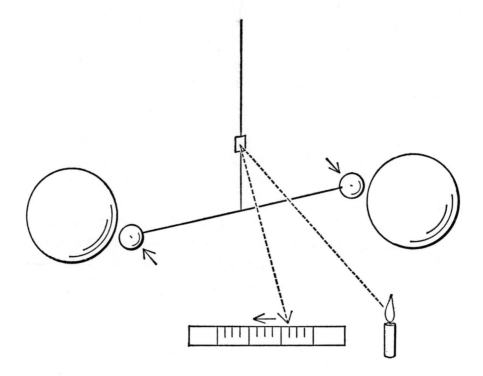

HENRY CAVENDISH'S APPARATUS FOR MEASURING GRAVITY. *The two small balls are attracted by the larger ones, causing the thread on which they are suspended to twist. The mirror shows the amount of this slight twist by the deflection of reflected light on the scale.*

wealthy, neurotic genius who lived in almost complete seclusion but performed some of the most astute experiments in the history of science, managed to make the measurement. Cavendish attached a ball of known mass to each end of a long rod and suspended this dumbbell-like contraption on a fine thread. Then he placed a larger ball, also of known mass, close to each ball on the rod — on opposite sides, so that gravitational attraction between the fixed large balls and the suspended small balls would cause the horizontally hung dumbbell to turn, thus twisting the thread. The dumbbell did indeed turn slightly. Cavendish now measured how much force was needed to produce this amount of twist of the thread. This told him the value of *f*. He also knew m_1 and m_2, the masses of the balls, and *d*, the distance between the attracted balls. So he was able to compute the value of *g*. Once he had that, he could calculate the mass of the earth, because the earth's gravitational pull (*f*) on any given body can be measured. Thus Cavendish "weighed" the earth for the first time.

The measurements have since been greatly refined. In 1928 P. R. Heyl at the United States Bureau of Standards determined the value of *g* to be 0.00000006673 dyne centimeter squared per gram squared. You needn't be concerned about those units, but note the smallness of the figure. It is a measure of the weakness of gravitational force. Two one-pound weights placed a foot apart attract each other with a force of only one-half of one billionth of an ounce.

The fact that the earth itself attracts such a weight with the force of one pound even at a distance of 4,000 miles from its center emphasizes how massive the earth is. In fact, the mass of the earth turns out to be 6,595,000,000,000,000,000,000,000 tons or, in metric units, 5,983,000,000,000,000,000,000,000 kilograms.

From the mass and volume of the earth, its average density is easily calculated. In metric units, the answer comes out to 5.522 grams per cubic centimeter (5.522 times the density of water). The density of the earth's surface rocks averages only about 2.8 grams per cubic centimeter, so the density of the interior must be much greater. Does it increase smoothly all the way down to the center? The first proof that it does not — that the earth is made up of a series of different layers — came from the study of earthquakes.

THE LAYERS OF THE PLANET

O N NOVEMBER 1, 1755, a great earthquake struck the city of Lisbon, demolishing every house in the lower part of the city. Then a tidal wave swept in from the ocean. Sixty thousand people were killed and the city was left a scene of devastation.

The shock was felt over an area of a million square miles. Because it was All Souls' Day, people were in church, and it is said that all over southern Europe those in the cathedrals saw the chandeliers dance and sway.

The Lisbon disaster made a great impression on the scholars of the day. It was an optimistic time when many thinkers felt that the new science of Galileo and Newton would place in man's hands the means of making the earth a human paradise. This blow showed that there were still giant, unpredictable, and apparently malicious forces beyond man's control. The earthquake inspired Voltaire, the great literary figure of the time, to write his famous pessimistic satire *Candide*, with its ironical refrain that all was for the best in this best of all possible worlds.

Scientists began turning their thoughts earnestly to what the causes of earthquakes might be. The English geologist John Michell (who had studied the forces involved in "torsion," or twisting, later used by Cavendish to measure the mass of the earth) suggested in 1760 that earthquakes were waves set up by the shifting of masses of rock miles below the surface. To study earthquakes properly, an instrument for detecting and measuring these waves had to be developed, and this did not come to pass until 100 years after the Lisbon quake. In 1855 the Italian physicist Luigi Palmieri devised the first "seismograph" (from Greek words meaning "earthquake-writing").

In its simplest form, the seismograph consists of a massive block suspended by a comparatively weak spring from a support firmly fixed in bedrock. When the earth moves, the suspended block remains still, because of its inertia. However, the spring attached to the bedrock stretches or contracts a little with the earth's motion. This motion is recorded on a slowly rotating drum by means of a pen attached to the stationary block, writing on smoked paper. Actually, two blocks are used, one oriented to record the earthquake waves traveling north and south, the other, east and west. Nowadays the most delicate seismographs, such as one at Fordham University, use a ray of light in place of a pen, to avoid the frictional drag of the pen on the paper. This ray shines on sensitized paper, making tracings which are developed as a photograph.

The English engineer John Milne, using seismographs of his own design, showed conclusively in the 1890's that Michell's description of earthquakes as waves propagated through the body of the earth was correct. Milne was instrumental in setting up stations for the study of earthquakes and related phenomena in various parts of the world, particularly in Japan.

The earth is now known to have at least ten major earthquakes per year. The largest ones are estimated to release a total energy equal to 100,000 ordinary atomic bombs, or, if you prefer, 100 large H-bombs. It is only because their energies are dissipated over a large area that they are not more destructive than they are.

Once seismographs allowed the detailed study of earthquake-waves, it was found that there were two general varieties: "surface waves" and "bodily waves." The surface waves follow the curve of the earth; the bodily waves go through the interior — and by virtue of this short-cut usually are the first to arrive at the seismograph. These bodily waves in turn are of two types: primary ("P waves") and secondary ("S waves"). The primary waves, like sound waves, travel by alternate compression and expansion of the medium (to visualize them, think of the pushing together and pulling apart of an accordion). Such waves can pass through any medium — solid or fluid. The secondary waves, on the other hand, have the familiar form of snakelike wiggles at right angles to the direction of travel, and they cannot travel through liquids or gases.

The primary waves move faster than secondary waves and consequently reach a seismograph station sooner. From the time lag of the secondaries, it is possible to estimate the distance of the earthquake. And its location or "epicenter" (the spot on the earth's surface directly above the rock disturbance) can be pinpointed by getting distance bearings at three or more stations: the three radii trace out three circles which will intersect at a single point.

The speed of both the P and S types of waves is affected by the kind of rock, the temperature, and the pressure, as laboratory studies

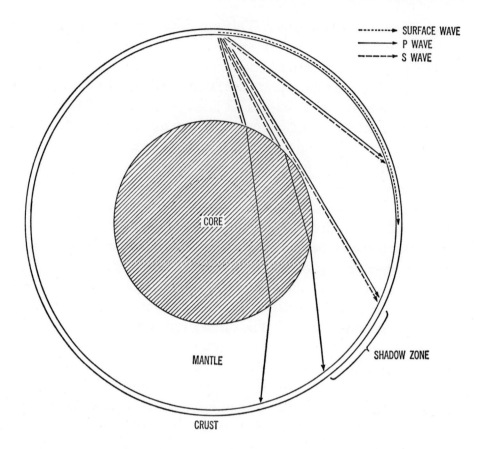

EARTHQUAKE WAVES' ROUTES IN THE EARTH. *Surface waves travel along the crust. The earth's liquid core refracts the P-type bodily waves. S-waves cannot travel through the core.*

have shown. Therefore earthquake waves can be used as probes to investigate conditions deep under the earth's surface.

A primary wave near the surface travels at five miles per second; a thousand miles below the surface, judging from the arrival times, its velocity must be nearly eight miles per second. Similarly, a secondary wave has a velocity of less than three miles per second near the surface and four miles per second at a depth of a thousand miles.

Since increase in velocity is a measure of increase in density, we can estimate the density of the rock beneath the surface. At the surface of the earth, as I've mentioned, the average density is 2.8 grams per cubic centimeter; 1,000 miles down it amounts to five grams per cubic centimeter; 1,800 miles down, nearly six grams per cubic centimeter.

At the depth of 1,800 miles there is an abrupt change. Secondary waves are stopped cold. This must mean that the region below is liquid: the waves have reached the boundary of the earth's "liquid core." And primary waves on reaching this level change direction sharply; apparently they are refracted by entering the liquid core.

The boundary of the liquid core is called the "Gutenberg discontinuity," after the American geologist Beno Gutenberg, who in 1914 defined the boundary and showed that the core extended to 2,160 miles from the earth's center. At the boundary, the density of the material jumps from six to nine and thereafter it increases smoothly to 11½ grams per cubic centimeter at the center.

WHAT IS THE NATURE of the liquid core? It must be composed of a substance which has a density of from 9 to 11½ grams per cubic centimeter under the conditions of temperature and pressure in the core. The pressure is estimated to range from 10,000 tons per square inch at the top of the liquid core to 25,000 tons per square inch at the center of the earth. The temperature is less certain. On the basis of the rate at which temperature is known to increase with depth in deep mines, and of the rate at which rocks can conduct heat, geologists estimate (rather roughly) that temperatures in the liquid core must be somewhere between 1,000 and 3,000 degrees C.

The substance of the core must be some common element — common enough to be able to make up a sphere half the diameter of the earth and one-third its mass. The only heavy element that is at all common in the Universe is iron. At the earth's surface its density is only 7.86 grams per cubic centimeter, but under the enormous

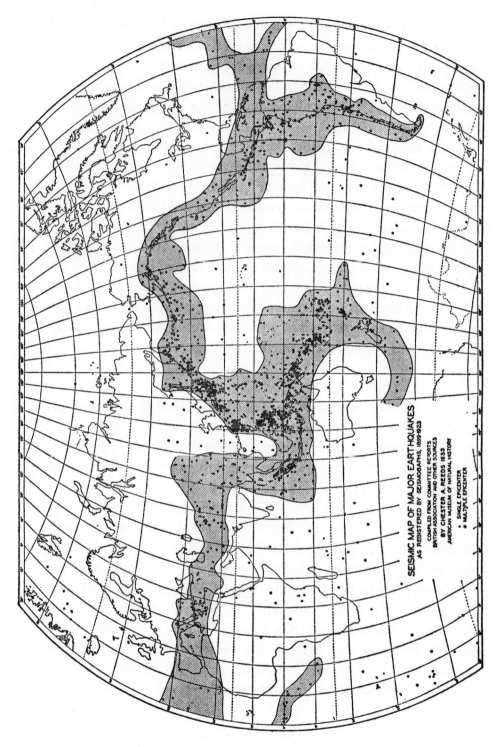

SEISMIC MAP OF MAJOR EARTHQUAKES
AS REGISTERED BY SEISMOGRAPHS, 1899-1923

COMPILED FROM COMMITTEE REPORTS,
BRITISH ASSOCIATION AND OTHER SOURCES
BY CHESTER A. REEDS 1933
AMERICAN MUSEUM OF NATURAL HISTORY

• SINGLE EPICENTER
: MULTIPLE EPICENTER

pressures of the core, it would have a density in the correct range —9 to 12 grams per cubic centimeter. What is more, under center-of-the-earth conditions it would be liquid.

If more evidence is needed, meteorites supply it. These fall into two broad classes: "stony" meteorites, composed chiefly of silicates, and "iron" meteorites, made up about 90 per cent of iron, 9 per cent nickel, and 1 per cent other elements. Many scientists believe that the meteorites are remnants of a shattered planet; if so, the iron meteorites may be pieces from the liquid core of that planet and the stony meteorites fragments of its mantle. (Indeed, in 1866, long before seismologists had probed the earth's core, the composition of the iron meteorites suggested to the French geologist Gabriel Auguste Daubrie that the core of our planet was made of iron.)

Today most geologists accept the liquid nickel-iron core as one of the facts of life as far as the earth's structure is concerned. One major refinement, however, has been introduced. In 1936 the Danish geologist I. Lehmann, seeking to explain the puzzling fact that some primary waves show up in a "shadow zone" on the surface from which most such waves are excluded, proposed that a discontinuity within the core about 800 miles from the center introduced another bend in the waves and sent a few careening into the shadow zone. Gutenberg supported this view, and now many geologists differentiate between an "outer core" which is liquid nickel-iron and an "inner core" which differs from the outer core in some way, perhaps in being solid or slightly different chemically.

THE PORTION of the earth surrounding the nickel-iron core is called the "mantle." It seems to be composed of silicates, but judging from the velocity of earthquake waves passing through them, these silicates are different from the typical rocks of the earth's surface. Their properties suggest that they are rocks of the so-called "olivine" type (olive-green in color), which are comparatively rich in magnesium and iron and poor in aluminum.

The mantle does not quite extend to the surface of the earth. A

Serbian geologist named Andrija Mohorovičić, while studying the waves produced by a Balkan earthquake in 1909, decided that there was a sharp increase in wave velocity at a point about 20 miles beneath the surface. This "Mohorovičić discontinuity" (known as "Moho" for short) is now accepted to be the boundary of the earth's "crust."

The nature of the crust and of the upper mantle is best explored by means of the "surface waves" I mentioned earlier. Like the "bodily waves," the surface waves come in two varieties. One kind are called "Love waves" (after their discoverer A. E. H. Love). The Love waves are horizontal ripples, like the shape of a snake moving over the ground. The other variety is the "Rayleigh waves" (named after the English physicist John W. S. Rayleigh); these ripples are vertical, like the path of a sea-serpent moving through the water.

Analysis of these surface waves (notably by Maurice Ewing of Columbia University) shows that the crust is of varying thickness. It is thinnest under the ocean basins, where the Moho discontinuity in some places is only eight to ten miles below sea-level. Since the oceans themselves are five to seven miles deep in spots, the solid crust may be as thin as three miles under the ocean deeps. Under the continents, on the other hand, the Moho discontinuity lies at an average depth of about 20 miles below sea-level, and it plunges to a depth of nearly 40 miles beneath mountain ranges. This fact, combined with evidence from gravity measurements, shows that the rock in mountain ranges is less dense than the average.

The general picture of the crust is that of a structure composed of two main types of rocks — basalt and granite — with the less dense granite riding buoyantly on the basalt, forming continents and, in places where the granite is particularly thick, mountains (just as a large iceberg rises higher out of the water than a small one). Young mountains thrust their granite roots deep into the basalt, but as the mountains are worn down by erosion, they adjust by floating slowly upward (to maintain the equilibrium of mass called "isostasy"). In the Appalachians, a very ancient mountain chain, the root is about gone.

SATURN AND ITS RINGS, *photographed with the 100-inch telescope on Mt. Wilson.*

THE MOON *photographed with the 100-inch telescope.*

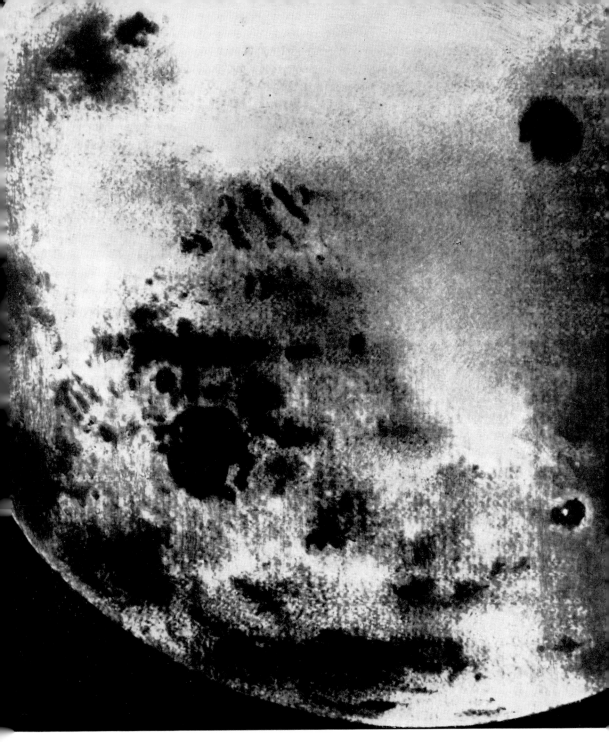

THE FAR SIDE OF THE MOON, *photographed by the Soviet Union's Lunik III in October 1959.*

FOUCAULT'S FAMOUS EXPERIMENT *in Paris in 1851 which showed
the rotation of the earth on its axis by means of the swing of a pendulum; the plane of its swings turned clockwise.*

GLACIAL STRATA *exposed in the Franz Josef Fiord of northeastern Greenland.*

GLACIAL FORMATION *atop Mt. Kilimanjaro in central Africa.*

Sᴇᴅɪᴍᴇɴᴛᴀʀʏ ғᴏʀᴍᴀᴛɪᴏɴ *under water in Moriches Inlet off Long Island, photographed from an airplane.*

GRAND CANYON *from the air, clearly showing the erosion of the rock by the Colorado River.*

THE HEART OF ANTARCTICA: *an aerial photograph of the Sentinel Mountains made during the IGY.*

The basalt beneath the oceans is covered with a quarter to a half mile of sedimentary rock, but little or no granite — the Pacific basin is completely free of granite. The thinness of the crust under the oceans has suggested a dramatic project: why not drill a hole through the crust down to the Moho discontinuity and tap the mantle to see what it is made of? It will not be an easy task, for it will mean anchoring a ship over an abyssal section of the ocean, lowering drilling gear through miles of water, and then drilling through a greater thickness of rock than anyone has yet drilled. Nevertheless, the United States has already decided to drill a "Mohole" in the Puerto Rican trench in the Atlantic, and the Soviet Union is reported to be making preparations for a Mohole of its own.

THE "floating" of the granite in the basalt inevitably suggests the possibility of "continental drift." In 1912 the German geologist Alfred Lothar Wegener suggested that the continents were originally a single piece of granite; at some early stage of the earth's history this fractured and the continents drifted apart. He argued that they were still drifting — Greenland, for instance, moving away from Europe at the rate of a yard a year. What gave him (and others) the idea was mainly the fact that the eastern coastline of South America seemed to fit like a jigsaw piece into the shape of the western coast of Africa.

The theory eventually foundered on hard facts. The continental movement has not been confirmed, and the underlying basalt seems far too stiff to allow the continental granite to drift sideways. Slow motions up and down to establish isostasy, yes; motions sideways, no.

An even more dramatic notion was the suggestion in the 1890's by the British astronomer George Howard Darwin (a son of Charles Darwin) that the moon is a piece of the earth that was wrenched out of the Pacific Ocean, which might account for the absence of any granite there. Unfortunately, this story, too, comes up against some hard facts. It doesn't seem likely that the earth could ever have been spinning so rapidly as to lose a chunk the size of the moon through centrifugal action. Besides, with the going out of fashion of the catastrophic theories of solar-system origin, the subsidiary catastrophe involved in the birth of the moon has also gone out of fashion. The new evolutionary theories argue that the moon, like the earth, was formed out of the slow accretion of planetesimals, and at the same time.

We are left, however, with a number of puzzling questions. Why is there little or no iron in the moon, if it was formed from the same cloud of material as the earth? Then, too, why is the moon so large compared to the earth? No other satellite in the solar system is anything like 1/80th as massive as the planet it circles. Again, why is the moon circling the earth outside the equatorial plane, being tilted to it by about 18 degrees, whereas most of the other planctary satellites in the solar system follow orbits in the equatorial plane? And why is the Pacific so barren of granite?

THE FACT that the earth consists of two chief portions — the silicate mantle and the nickel-iron core (in about the same proportions as the white and yolk of an egg) — has persuaded most geologists that the earth must have been liquid at some time in its early history. It might then have consisted of two mutually insoluble liquids. The silicate liquid, being the lighter, would float to the top and cool by radiating its heat into space. The underlying iron liquid, insulated from direct exposure to space, would give up its heat far more slowly and would thus remain liquid to the present day.

There are at least three ways in which the earth could have become hot enough to melt, even from a completely cold start as a collection of planetesimals. These bodies, on colliding and coalescing, would give up their energy of motion ("kinetic energy") in the form of heat. Then, as the growing planet was compressed by gravitational force, still more energy would be liberated as heat. And thirdly, the radioactive substances of the earth — uranium, thorium, and potassium — have delivered large quantities of heat over the ages as they have broken down; in the early stages, when there was a

great deal more radioactive material than now, radioactivity itself
might have supplied enough heat to liquefy the earth.

Not all scientists are willing to accept a liquid stage as an absolute
necessity. The American chemist Harold Clayton Urey, in particular, believes that most of the earth was always solid. He argues that
in a largely solid earth an iron core could still be formed by a slow
separation of iron; even now, he suggests, iron may be migrating
from the mantle into the core at the rate of 50,000 tons a second.

Cooling of the earth from an original molten or near-molten state
would help to explain its wrinkled exterior. As the cooling earth
shrank, its crust would occasionally buckle. Minor buckling would
give rise to earthquakes. Larger buckling, or a steady accumulation
of smaller adjustments, would eventually produce mountain ranges.
The mountain-building eras, however, would be relatively brief.
After mountains were formed, they would be worn down by erosion
in fairly short order (on the geological time scale), and then would
come a long period of stability before compressional forces built up
great enough strains to start a new crust-buckling stage. Thus during
most of its lifetime the earth would be a rather drab and featureless
planet, with low continents and shallow seas.

The trouble with this view is that the earth does not seem really
to be cooling off. It appears that over the last several hundred million years radioactivity has been generating enough heat in the crust
and mantle at least to keep the earth's internal temperature from
falling; if anything, the earth may be very slowly heating up. Yet,
despite that, we are now living at the tag end of a mountain-building
era (fortunately for those of us who are fond of rugged scenery).
If the earth has not been cooling and shrinking during that period,
how were our present mountains built?

A couple of decades ago a new theory was put forward by the
Israeli physicist C. L. Perkeris and elaborated by the American geologist D. T. Briggs. It begins by supposing that heat coming from
the core periodically sets up a series of vertical eddies in the mantle.
The eddies of heated material rise toward the crust and sink again
after they cool there. Since the mantle is not liquid, merely plastic,

this motion is very slow — perhaps not more than two inches a year.

Now, where two neighboring eddies move downward, a portion of crust is sucked downward too, forming a root of light crustal material in the heavier mantle. This root is converted by the mantle's heat into granite. Afterward, isostasy causes the root and its over-lay of light material to rise and form a mountain chain. The period of mountain building, lasting perhaps 60 million years, is fol-lowed by a quiescent period of 500 million years during which enough heat accumulates in the mantle to start a new cycle.

But this theory also has come up against a serious objection: Van-guard I's revelation of the asymmetry in the equatorial bulge, giving the earth a "pear" shape (see pages 88–89). John O'Keefe of the Na-tional Aeronautics and Space Administration pointed out in 1959 that the persistence of this asymmetry means the mantle must be more rigid than had been thought. He suggested that the mantle has the rigidity of brick, all the way down to the boundary of the core. If this is so, then the existence of slowly churning vertical eddies of mantle material would seem to be out of the question.

THE OCEAN

THE EARTH is unusual among the planets of the solar system in possessing a surface temperature which permits water to exist in all three states: liquid, solid, and vaporized. The earth is also the only body in the solar system, as far as we know, to have oceans. Actually I should say "ocean," because the Pacific, Atlantic, Indian, Arctic, and Antarctic oceans all comprise one connected body of salt water in which the Europe-Asia-Africa mass, the American con-tinents and smaller bodies such as Antarctica and Australia can be considered islands.

The statistics of this ocean are impressive. It has a total area of 140 million square miles and covers more than 70 per cent of the earth's surface. Its volume, reckoning the average depth of the oceans as

2 1/3 miles, is about 330 million cubic miles — 0.15 per cent of the total volume of our planet. And it contains 98 per cent of all the H_2O on the earth.

The ocean is of peculiar importance to life. Almost certainly the first forms of life originated there, and from the standpoint of sheer quantity the oceans still contain most of our planet's life. On land, life is confined to within a few feet of the surface (though birds and airplanes do make temporary sorties from this base); in the oceans, life permanently occupies the whole of a realm as deep as seven miles or more in some places.

And yet, until recent years mankind has been as ignorant of the oceans, and particularly of the ocean floor, as of another planet. Even today astronomers know more about the surface of the moon than geologists know about the surface of the earth under the oceans.

The founder of modern oceanography was an American naval officer named Matthew Fontaine Maury. In his early thirties he was lamed in an accident which, however unfortunate for himself, brought benefits to humanity. Placed in charge of the depot of charts and instruments (undoubtedly intended as a sinecure), he threw himself into the task of charting ocean currents. In particular, he studied the course of the Gulf Stream, and gave it a description which has become a classic remark in oceanography: "There is a river in the ocean." Maury also initiated international cooperation in studying the ocean; he was the moving figure behind a historic international conference held in Brussels in 1853. In 1855 he published the first textbook in oceanography, entitled *Physical Geography of the Sea.* The Naval Academy at Annapolis honored his achievements by naming Maury Hall after him.

Since Maury's time, the ocean currents have been thoroughly mapped. What's more, oceanographers have even begun to explore the more sluggish circulation of the ocean depths. That the deeps cannot maintain a dead calm is clear from several indirect forms of evidence. For one thing, the life at the top of the sea is continually consuming its mineral nutrients — phosphate and nitrate — and carrying this material down to the deeps with itself after death; if there were no circulation to bring it up again, the surface would become depleted of these minerals. For another thing, the oxygen supplied to the oceans by absorption from the air would not percolate down to the depths at a sufficient rate to support life there if there were no conveying circulation. Actually oxygen is found in adequate concentration down to the very floor of the abyss. This can be explained only by supposing that there are regions in the ocean where oxygen-rich surface waters sink.

The engine that drives this vertical circulation is temperature difference. The ocean's surface water is cooled in arctic regions, and it therefore sinks. This continual flow of sinking water spreads out all along the ocean floor, so that even in the tropics the bottom water is very cold — near the freezing point. Eventually the cold water of the depths wells up toward the surface, for it has no other place to go. After rising to the surface, the water warms and drifts off toward the Arctic or the Antarctic, there to sink again.

The continental barriers complicate this general picture. To follow the actual circulations, oceanographers have resorted to oxygen as a tracer. Cold water absorbs more oxygen than warm water can. The arctic surface water, therefore, is particularly rich in oxygen. After it sinks, it steadily loses oxygen to organisms feeding in it. So by sampling the oxygen concentration in deep water at various locations, it is possible to plot the direction of the deep-sea currents.

Such mapping has shown that one major current flows from the Arctic Ocean down the Atlantic, another from the Antarctic up the South Atlantic. The Pacific Ocean gets no direct flow from the Arctic to speak of because the only outlet into it is the narrow and shallow Bering Strait. This is why it is the end of the line for the deep-sea flow. That the north Pacific is the dead-end of the global flow is shown by the fact that its deep waters are poor in oxygen.

More direct evidence for this picture of the deep-sea currents was obtained in 1957 during a joint British-American oceanographic expedition. The investigators used a special float, invented by the British oceanographer John C. Swallow, which is designed to keep its level at a depth of a mile or more and is equipped with a device for sending out short-wave sound waves. By means of these signals the float can be tracked as it moves with the deep-sea current. The expedition thus traced the deep-sea current down the Atlantic along its western edge.

All this information will acquire practical importance when the world's expanding population turns to the ocean for more food. Scientific "farming of the sea" will require knowledge of these fertilizing currents, just as land farming requires knowledge of river courses, ground water, and rainfall.

IT IS only within the last century that man has plumbed the great deeps of the ocean. The sea bottom became a matter of practical interest when it was decided to lay a telegraph cable across the Atlantic. In 1850 Maury worked up a chart of the Atlantic sea-bottom for purposes of cable-laying. It took 15 years, punctuated by many breaks and failures, before the Atlantic cable was finally laid — under the incredibly persevering drive of the United States financier Cyrus West Field, who lost a fortune in the process.

Systematic exploration of the sea-bottom began with the famous around-the-world expedition of the British *Challenger* in the 1870's. To measure the depth of the oceans the *Challenger* had no better device than the time-honored method of paying out a cable with a weight on the end until it reached the bottom. This procedure is not only fantastically laborious (for deep sounding) but also of low accuracy. Ocean-bottom exploration was revolutionized in 1924 with the introduction of echo-sounding by means of ultrasonic (short-wave) sound waves — in principle the same as radar. The time interval from the sending of the signal (a sharp pulse) and the return of its echo measures the distance to the bottom. The only thing the operator has to worry about is whether the reading signals a false echo from a school of fish or some other obstruction. (Obviously the instrument may be useful to fishing fleets.)

The echo-sounding method not only is swift and convenient but also makes it possible to trace a continuous profile of the bottom over which the vessel moves, so that oceanographers are obtaining a picture of the topography of the ocean bottom. It turns out to be more rugged than the land surface, and its features have a grander scale. There are plains of continental size and mountain ranges longer and higher than any on land. The island of Hawaii is the top of an underwater mountain 33,000 feet high — higher than anything in the Himalayas — so that Hawaii may fairly be called the tallest mountain on the earth. Moreover, there are deep abysses (trenches) in which the Grand Canyon would be lost. The trenches, all located alongside island archipelagoes, have a total area amounting to nearly 1 per cent of the ocean bottom. This may not seem much, but it is actually equal to one-half the area of the United States, and the trenches contain 15 times as much water as all the rivers and lakes in the world. The deepest of them are in the Pacific; they are found there alongside the Philippines, the Marianas, the Kuriles, the Solomons, and the Aleutians. There are other great abysses in the Atlantic off the West Indies and the South Sandwich Islands, and there is one in the Indian Ocean off the East Indies.

Besides the trenches, oceanographers have traced on the ocean bottom canyons, sometimes thousands of miles long, which look like river channels. Some of them actually seem to be extensions of rivers on land, notably a canyon extending from the Hudson River into the Atlantic. It is tempting to suppose that these were once river beds on land, when the ocean was lower than now. But some of the undersea channels are so far below the present sea-level that it seems altogether unlikely they could ever have been above the ocean. In recent years various oceanographers, notably Maurice Ewing and Bruce C. Heezen, have developed another theory: that the undersea canyons were gouged out by turbulent flows of soil-laden water, avalanching down the off-shore continental slopes.

For some time scientists have been trying to learn what lies under the sea bottom by punching into it and bringing up long cores — something like the proposed Mohole but on a comparatively tiny scale. Cores taken from the deepest part of the Atlantic have contained fossils of sea organisms which tell a good deal about ancient life on the earth.

THE DEEP SEA, surprisingly enough, teems with life. Until nearly a century ago life in the ocean was thought to be confined to the surface region. The Mediterranean, long the principal center of civilization, is indeed rather barren of life in its lower levels. But this sea is a semi-desert — warm and low in oxygen. When, in 1872, the *Challenger* made the first systematic attempt to dredge up life-forms from the ocean bottoms, it found plenty. Off the Azores in the Atlantic it brought up sea-lilies (a type of animal related to the starfish) from a depth of a mile.

Since World War II at least five expeditions have succeeded in dredging up life from great depths. These were the voyages of the Swedish ship *Albatross*, the Soviet ship *Vitiaz*, the Danish ship *Galathea*, the American ship *Vema*, and a second *Challenger* built by Great Britain. The new *Challenger* reached 6¾ miles down into the Marianas Trench in the western Pacific and brought up bacteria from the floor of the abyss. They look much like bacteria of the surface, but cannot live at a pressure of less than a thousand atmospheres!

The creatures of the trenches are so adapted to the great pressures of these bottoms that they are unable to rise out of their trench; in effect, they are imprisoned in an island. They have experienced a segregated evolution. Yet they are in many respects related to other organisms closely enough so that it seems their evolution in the abyss has not gone on for a very long time. One can visualize some groups of ocean creatures being forced into lower and lower depths by the pressure of competition, just as other groups were forced higher and higher up the continental shelf until they emerged onto the land. The first group had to become adjusted to higher pressures, the second to the absence of water. On the whole, the latter adjustment was probably the more difficult, so we should not be amazed that life exists in the abyss.

From earliest times, man has enjoyed being terrorized by legends

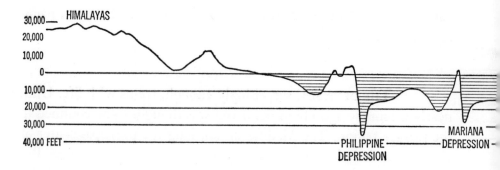

PROFILE OF THE PACIFIC BOTTOM. *The great trenches in the sea floor go deeper below sea level than the height of the Himalayas, and the Hawaiian peak stands higher from the bottom than the tallest land mountain.*

of sea monsters. There is, in fact, good reason to suppose that giant squids, which might pass for sea monsters, may exist, though they have not yet been caught. Possibly such creatures are responsible for some of the sea-serpent tales of excited sailors.

Biologists, scarcely less romantic than other men, have long dreamed of finding creatures so ancient that they could be studied as "living fossils." In the late 1930's their dream, incredibly, came true. On December 25, 1938, a trawler fishing off South Africa brought up an odd fish about five feet long. What was odd about it was that its fins were attached to fleshy lobes rather than directly to the body. A British zoologist, J. L. B. Smith, who had the chance of examining it, recognized it as a matchless Christmas present. It was a coelacanth, a primitive fish which zoologists had thought extinct for lo! these 70 million years. Here was a living specimen of an animal which was supposed to have disappeared from the earth before the dinosaurs reached their prime.

World War II halted the hunt for more coelacanths, but in 1952 another was fished up off Madagascar. By now about a dozen have been found. Because it is adapted to fairly deep waters, the coelacanth dies soon after being brought to the surface.

Evolutionists have been particularly interested in studying the

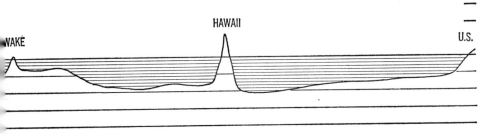

coelacanth specimens because it was from this fish that the first amphibians developed; in other words, the coelacanth is a rather direct descendant of our fishy ancestors.

Just as the ideal way to study outer space is to send men out there, so the ideal way to study the ocean deeps is to send men down there. A diver in a diving suit can go down about 300 feet. In the 1930's Charles William Beebe managed to get down to about 3,000 feet in his "bathysphere," a small, thick-walled craft equipped with oxygen and with chemicals to absorb carbon dioxide. Today we have a ship that can descend to the deepest deeps of the ocean. It is the "bathyscaphe," invented in 1947 by the Swiss physicist Auguste Piccard. Built to withstand great pressures, it uses a heavy ballast of iron pellets (which can be jettisoned) to take it down, and a "balloon" containing gasoline (which is lighter than water) to provide buoyancy and stability. In 1953 Piccard went down more than two miles in his first bathyscaphe. Later he and his son Jacques built an improved version. This craft, named the *Trieste*, was bought by the United States Navy for research. On January 14, 1960, Jacques Piccard and a Navy man, Don Walsh, took it to what may have been the bottom of the Marianas trench: the depth they reached was nearly seven miles. There, at the ultimate ocean depth, they found water currents and living creatures.

The voyages of the *Trieste* have already contributed some curious and interesting information to man's knowledge of the dark undersea world: glimpses of luminescent animals, abrupt transitions from one layer of water to another, shifts in currents, strange animals burrowing into the loose sea floor or raising clouds of mud as they skitter about.

THE ICE CAPS

THE EXTREMITIES of our planet have always fascinated mankind, and one of the most adventurous chapters in the history of science has been the exploration of the poles. They are charged with romance, spectacular phenomena, and elements of man's destiny — the strange auroras in the sky, the extreme cold, and especially the immense ice caps, or glaciers, which hold the key to the world climate and man's way of life.

The actual push to the poles came rather late in human history. It began during the great age of exploration that followed the discovery of the Americas by Christopher Columbus. The first Arctic explorers went chiefly to find a sea-route around the top of North America. Following this will-o'-the-wisp, the English navigator Henry Hudson (in the employ of Holland) found Hudson Bay and his death in 1610. Six years later another English navigator, William Baffin, discovered what came to be called Baffin Bay and penetrated to within 800 miles of the North Pole. Eventually, in the years 1846 to 1848, the British explorer John Franklin worked his way over the northern coast of Canada and discovered the "Northwest Passage" (and a most impractical passage for ships it is). He died on the voyage.

There followed a half-century of efforts to reach the North Pole, motivated in large part by sheer adventure and the desire to be the first to get there. In 1873 the Austrian explorers Julius Payer and Carl Weyprecht reached within 600 miles of the Pole and named a group of islands they found Franz Josef Land, after the Austrian emperor. In 1896 the Norwegian explorer Fridtjof Nansen drifted on the Arctic ice to within 300 miles of the Pole. At length, on April

6, 1909, the American explorer Robert Edwin Peary arrived at the Pole itself.

By now, the North Pole has lost much of its mystery. It has been explored on the ice, from the air, and under water. Richard Evelyn Byrd and Floyd Bennett were the first to fly over it, in 1926, and submarines have traversed its waters.

Meanwhile, the largest northern ice cap, which is centered in Greenland, has drawn a number of scientific expeditions. The Greenland glacier has been found to cover about 640,000 of that island's 840,-000 square miles, and its ice is known to reach a thickness of a mile in some places.

FAR LARGER is the South Pole's great continental glacier. The Antarctic ice cap covers seven times the area of the Greenland glacier and may be as thick as two miles. This is due to the great size of the Antarctic continent — some five million square miles, though how much of this is land and how much ice-covered sea is still uncertain. Some explorers believe that Antarctica is a group of large islands bound together by ice, but at the moment the continent theory seems to have the upper hand.

The famous English explorer James Cook (better known as Captain Cook) was the first European to cross the Antarctic Circle. In 1773 he circumnavigated the Antarctic regions. (It was perhaps this voyage that inspired Samuel Taylor Coleridge's *The Rime of the Ancient Mariner*, published in 1798, which described a voyage from the Atlantic to the Pacific by way of the icy regions of Antarctica.)

In 1819 the British explorer Williams Smith discovered the South Shetland Islands, just 50 miles off the coast of Antarctica; in 1821 a Russian expedition sighted a small island ("Peter I Island") within the Antarctic Circle and in the same year the Englishman George Powell and the American Nathaniel B. Palmer first laid eyes on a peninsula of the Antarctic continent itself — now called Palmer Peninsula.

In the following decades explorers inched toward the South Pole.

The Englishman James Weddell penetrated an ocean inlet east of Palmer Peninsula (now called Weddell Sea) to within 900 miles of the Pole. Another British explorer, James Clark Ross, discovered the other major ocean inlet into Antarctica (now called the Ross Sea) and got within 710 miles of the Pole. In 1902–04 a third Briton, Robert Falcon Scott, traveled over the Ross ice shelf to within 500 miles of it. And in 1909 still another Englishman, Ernest Shackleton, crossed the ice to within about 100 miles of the Pole.

On December 16, 1911, the goal was finally reached by the Norwegian explorer Roald Amundsen. Scott, making a second dash of his own, got to the South Pole just three weeks later, only to find Amundsen's flag already planted there. Scott and his men perished on the ice on their way back.

In the late 1920's the airplane helped to make good the conquest of Antarctica. The Australian explorer George Hubert Wilkins flew over 1,200 miles of its coastline, and Richard Evelyn Byrd in 1929 flew over the South Pole. By that time the first base, Little America I, had been established in the Antarctic.

THE North and South polar regions became focal points of the greatest international project in science of modern times. This had its origin in 1882–83, when a number of nations joined in an "International Polar Year" of exploration and scientific investigation of phenomena such as the aurorae, the earth's magnetism, etc. The project was so successful that in 1932–33 it was repeated with a second International Polar Year. In 1950 the United States geophysicist Lloyd Berkner (who had been a member of the first Byrd Antarctic Expedition) proposed a third such year. The proposal was enthusiastically adopted by the International Council of Scientific Unions. This time scientists were prepared with powerful new research instruments and bristling with new questions — about cosmic rays, about the upper atmosphere, about the ocean depths, even about the possibility of the exploration of space. An ambitious "International Geophysical Year" (IGY) was arranged, and the time selected was July 1, 1957, to December 31, 1958 (a period of maximum sunspot activity). The enterprise enlisted heart-warming international cooperation; even the "cold-war" antagonists, the Soviet Union and the United States, managed to bury the hatchet for the sake of science.

Although the most spectacular achievement of the IGY, from the standpoint of public interest, was the successful launching of man-made satellites by the Soviet Union and the United States, science reaped many other fruits which were no less important. Outstanding among these was a vast international exploration of Antarctica. The United States alone set up seven stations, probing the depth of the ice and bringing up from miles down samples of the air trapped in it (which must date back millions of years) and of bacterial remnants. Meteorological observations yielded invaluable data which should improve our understanding of climate and weather. The Soviet group established a base at the "Pole of Inaccessibility" — the spot in Antarctica farthest inland. Temperatures lower than 100 degrees below zero were recorded for the first time. In the most dramatic feat, a British exploring team crossed the continent for the first time (with half-tracks and the resources of modern science at its disposal).

The success of the IGY and the warmth generated by this demonstration of cooperation in the midst of the cold war led to an agreement in 1959 among 12 nations to bar all military activities (including nuclear explosions and the dumping of radioactive wastes) from the Antarctic. Thus Antarctica will be reserved for scientific activities.

THE EARTH'S LOAD of ice, amounting to six million cubic miles, covers about 10 per cent of its land area. About 86 per cent of the ice is piled up in the Antarctic continental glacier and 10 per cent in the Greenland glacier. The remaining 4 per cent makes up the small glaciers in Iceland, Alaska, the Himalayas, the Alps and a few other locations.

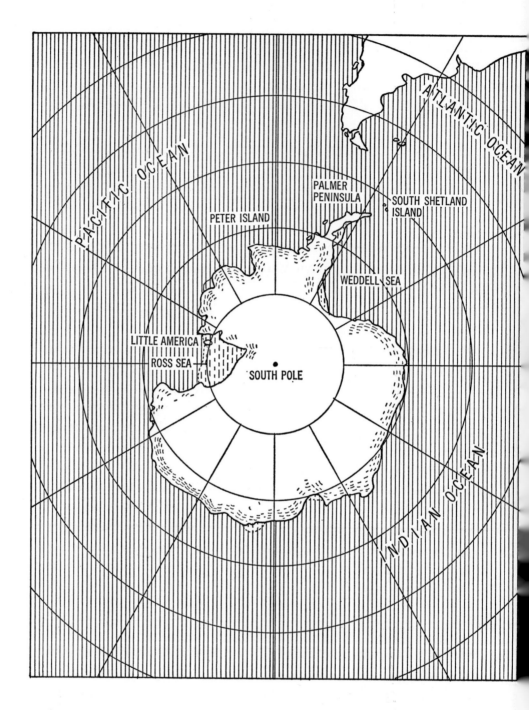

THE MAJOR CONTINENTAL GLACIERS *are today largely restricted to Greenland and Antarctica. At the height of the last ice age the*

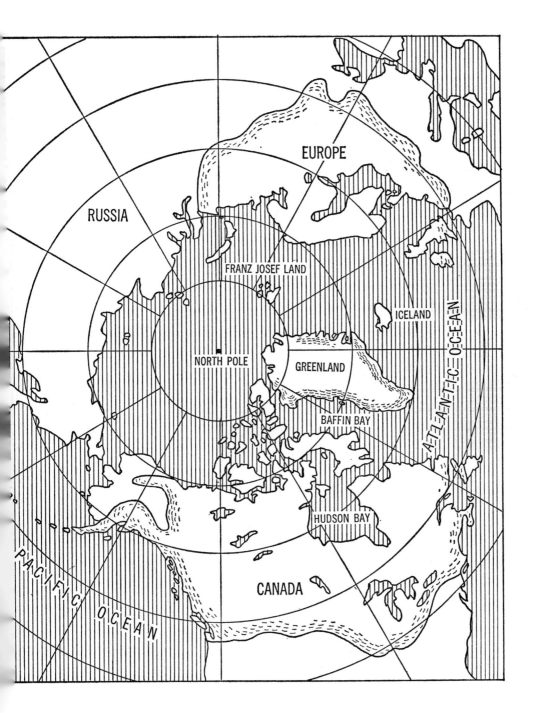

glaciers extended over most of northern and western Europe, and south of the Great Lakes on the North American continent.

The Alpine glaciers have been under study for a long time. In the 1820's two Swiss geologists, J. Venetz and Jean de Charpentier, noticed that rocks characteristic of the central Alps were scattered all over the plains to the north. How had they got there? The geologists speculated that the mountain glaciers had once covered a much larger area and had left boulders and piles of debris behind when they retreated.

A Swiss zoologist, Jean Louis Rodolphe Agassiz, looked into this notion. He drove lines of stakes into the glaciers and waited to see whether they moved. By 1840 he had proved beyond doubt that glaciers flowed like very slow rivers. Meanwhile he had traveled over Europe and found marks of glaciers in France and England. He found boulders foreign to their surroundings in other areas and scoured marks on rock which could only have been made by the grinding of glaciers, carrying pebbles encrusted along their bottoms.

Agassiz went to the United States in 1846 and became a Harvard professor. He found signs of glaciation in New England and the Midwest. By 1850 it seemed quite obvious that there must have been a time when a large part of the Northern Hemisphere was under a large continental glacier. The deposits left by the glacier have been studied in detail since Agassiz's time. These studies have shown that the ice advanced and retreated four times. When they advanced, the climate to the south was wetter and colder; when they retreated (leaving lakes behind, of which the largest still in existence are the Canadian-American "Great Lakes"), the climate to the south grew warmer and drier.

The last retreat of the ice took place between 8,000 and 12,000 years ago. Before the ice ages, there was a period of mild climate on the earth lasting at least 100 million years. There were no continental glaciers, even at the poles. Coal beds in Spitzbergen and signs of coal even in Antarctica testify to this, because coal marks the site of ancient lush forests.

The coming and going of glaciers leaves its mark not only on the climate of the rest of the earth but upon the very shape of the continents. For instance, if the now-shrinking glaciers of Greenland and

Antarctica were to melt completely, the ocean level would rise nearly 200 feet. It would drown the coastal areas of all the continents, including many of the world's largest cities. On the other hand, Alaska, Canada, Siberia, Greenland, and even Antarctica would become more habitable.

There is evidence that during the height of the glaciation, the sea-level mark may have been as much as 440 feet lower than it is now. Not only were the continents larger, but the present desert areas, such as the Sahara, the Arabian, and the Gobi deserts, probably had ample rainfall.

The major question regarding the ice ages involves their cause. What makes the ice advance and retreat, and why is it that the glaciations have been relatively brief, the present one having occupied only one million of the last 100 million years?

It takes only a small change in temperature to bring on or to terminate an ice age — just enough fall in temperature to accumulate a little more snow in the winter than melts in the summer or enough rise to melt a little more snow in the summer than falls in the winter. It is estimated that a drop in the earth's average annual temperature of only 3 ½ degrees C. is sufficient to make glaciers grow, while a rise of the same amount would melt Antarctica and Greenland to bare rock in a matter of centuries.

Such changes in the temperature of the earth have indeed taken place in the past. A method has now been evolved by which primeval temperatures can be measured with amazing accuracy. The chemist Harold Urey calculated in 1947 that the ratio of the common variety of oxygen (oxygen 16) to its rarer isotopes (*e.g.*, oxygen 18) would vary with temperature. Consequently if one measured the ratio of oxygen 16 to oxygen 18 in an ancient fossil of a sea animal, one could tell the temperature of the ocean water at the time the animal lived. By 1950 Urey and his group had developed the technique to so fine a point that by analyzing the shell layers of a millions-of-years-old fossil (an extinct form of squid), they could determine that the creature was born during a summer, lived four years, and died in the spring.

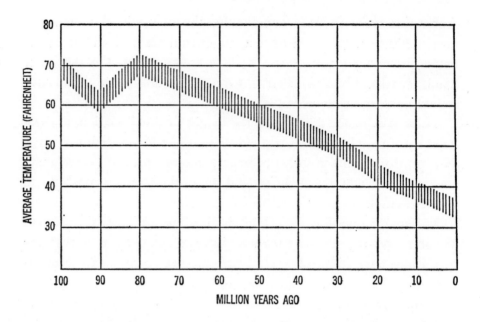

THE RECORD OF THE OCEAN TEMPERATURES *during the last hundred million years.*

This "thermometer" has established that 100 million years ago the average world-wide ocean temperature was about 70 degrees F. It cooled slowly to 61 degrees ten million years later and then rose to 70 degrees again ten million years after that. Since then the ocean temperature has declined steadily. This decline may be what killed off the dinosaurs (which were probably adapted to mild and equable climates) and put a premium on the warm-blooded birds and mammals, which can maintain a constant internal temperature.

Cesare Emiliani, using the Urey technique, studied the shells of foraminifera brought up in cores from the ocean floor. He found that the over-all ocean temperature was about 50 degrees F. 30 million years ago, 43 degrees 20 million years ago, and is now 35 degrees.

What caused these long-term changes in temperature? One possible explanation is the so-called "greenhouse effect" of carbon dioxide. Carbon dioxide absorbs infrared radiation rather strongly. This means that when there are appreciable amounts of it in the atmosphere, it tends to block the escape of heat at night from the sun-warmed earth. The result is that heat accumulates. On the other hand, when the carbon dioxide content of the atmosphere falls, the earth steadily cools.

If the current concentration of carbon dioxide in the air should double (from 0.03 per cent of the air to 0.06 per cent) that small change would suffice to raise the earth's over-all temperature by three degrees and would bring about the complete and quick melting of the continental glaciers. If the carbon dioxide dropped to half the present amount, the temperature would drop sufficiently to bring the glaciers down to New York City again.

Volcanoes discharge large amounts of carbon dioxide into the air; the weathering of rocks absorbs carbon dioxide (thus forming limestone). Here, then, is a possible pair of mechanisms for long-term climatic changes. A period of greater than normal volcanic action might release a large amount of carbon dioxide into the air and initiate a warming of the earth. Contrariwise, an era of mountain-building, exposing large areas of new and unweathered rock to the air, could lower the carbon dioxide concentration in the atmosphere. This is what may have happened at the close of the Mesozoic (the age of reptiles) some 80 million years ago, when the long decline in the earth's temperature began.

BUT WHAT ABOUT the comings and goings of the four ice ages within the last million years? Why was there this rapid alternation of glaciation and melting in comparatively short spells of tens of thousands of years?

In 1920 a Serbian physicist named Milutin Milankovich suggested that slight variations in the earth's relation to the sun might explain the situation. Sometimes the earth's tilt changes a little; sometimes its perihelion (closest approach to the sun in its orbit) is slightly closer than at other times. A combination of these factors, Milankovich argued, could so affect the amount of heat received from the sun by, say, the Northern Hemisphere as to cause a cyclic rise and fall of its average temperature. He thought that such a cycle might last 40,000 years, giving the earth a "Great Spring," "Great Summer," "Great Fall," and "Great Winter," each some 10,000 years in length.

The difference between Great Summer and Great Winter is small, and the theory implies that only after a long period of over-all temperature decline, did the additional small temperature fall of the Great Winter suffice to reduce the Northern Hemisphere's temperature to the point where the ice ages began a million years ago. According to the Milankovich theory, we are now in a Great Summer and in 10,000 years or so will begin to enter another Great Winter.

The Milankovich theory has never satisfied geologists, mainly because it implies that the ice ages of the Northern and Southern Hemispheres have come at different times, which has not been demonstrated. In recent years several other theories have been proposed: that the sun has cycles of slight fluctuation in its output of heat, that dust from volcanic eruptions, rather than carbon dioxide, has produced the "greenhouse" warming, and so on. At the moment, the most interesting hypothesis is a new one advanced by Maurice Ewing of the Lamont Geological Observatory and a colleague, William Donn.

Ewing and Donn ascribe the succession of ice ages in the Northern Hemisphere to the geographical conditions around the North Pole. The Arctic Ocean is nearly surrounded by land. In the mild eons before the recent ice ages began, when this ocean was open water, winds sweeping across it picked up water vapor and dropped snow on Canada and Siberia. As glaciers grew on the land, according to the Ewing-Donn theory, the earth absorbed less heat from the sun, because the cover of ice, as well as clouds resulting from stormier weather, reflected away part of the sunlight. Consequently the general temperature of the earth dropped. But as it did so, the Arctic Ocean froze over, and now the winds picked up less moisture from it. Less moisture in the air meant less snow each winter. So the trend was reversed: with less snowy winters, summer melting took the upper hand over winter snowfall. The glaciers retreated until the earth warmed sufficiently to melt the Arctic Ocean to open water again — at which point the cycle started anew with a rebuilding of the glaciers.

It seems a paradox that the melting of the Arctic Ocean, rather than its freezing, should bring on an ice age. Geophysicists, however, find the theory plausible and capable of explaining many things. The main problem about the theory is that it makes the absence of ice ages up to a million years ago more mysterious than ever. But Ewing and Donn have an answer for that. They suggest that during the long period of mildness before the ice ages the North Pole may have been located in the Pacific Ocean. In that case, most of the snow would have fallen in the ocean instead of on land, and no important glaciers could have got started.

There is actually a good deal of evidence that the North Pole has moved around considerably in the past, possibly by a rolling over of the earth that changed its axis of rotation. The English geophysicist S. K. Runcorn has found indications of such wandering in the alignment of bits of magnetized iron in ancient rocks; these natural "compass needles" show that the earth's magnetic pole was in different places at different times.

Whatever the cause of the ice ages may have been, it seems now that man himself may be changing the climate in store for the future. The American physicist Gilbert N. Plass has suggested that we may be seeing the last of the ice ages, because the furnaces of civilization are loading the atmosphere with carbon dioxide. A hundred million chimneys are ceaselessly pouring carbon dioxide into the air; the total amount is about six billion tons a year — 200 times the quantity coming from volcanoes. Plass pointed out that since 1900 the carbon dioxide content of our atmosphere has increased about 10 per cent. This addition to the earth's "greenhouse" shield against the escape of heat, he calculated, should raise the average temperature by about 1.1 degrees C. per century. During the first half of the twentieth century the average temperature has indeed risen at this rate, according to the available records (mostly in North America and Europe). If the warming continues at the same rate, the continental glaciers may disappear in a century or two.

Investigations during the IGY seemed to show that the glaciers are indeed receding almost everywhere. One of the large glaciers in the Himalayas was reported in 1959 to have receded 700 feet since 1935. Others had retreated 1,000 or even 2,000 feet. Fish adapted to frigid waters are migrating northward, and warm-climate trees are advancing in the same direction. The sea level is rising slightly each year, as would be expected if the glaciers are melting. The sea level is already so high that at times of violent storms at high tide, the ocean is not far from threatening to flood the New York subway system.

CHAPTER

4

THE ATMOSPHERE

THE SHELLS OF AIR

ARISTOTLE supposed the world to be made up of four shells, constituting the four elements of matter: earth (the solid ball), water (the ocean), air (the atmosphere), and fire (an invisible outer shell which occasionally became visible in the flashes of lightning). The universe beyond these shells, he said, was composed of an unearthly, perfect fifth element which he called "ether" (in Latin the name became "quintessence").

There was no room in this scheme for nothingness: where earth ended, water began; where both ended, air began; where air ended, fire began; and where fire ended, ether began and continued to the end of the Universe. "Nature," said the ancients, "abhors a vacuum" (Latin for "nothingness").

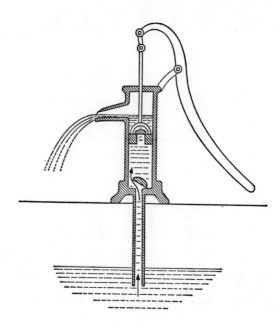

PRINCIPLE OF THE WATER PUMP. *When the handle raises the piston, a partial vacuum is created in the cylinder and water rises into it through a one-way valve. After repeated pumping the water level is high enough for the water to flow out of the spout.*

The suction pump, an early invention to lift water out of wells, seemed to illustrate this abhorrence of a vacuum admirably. A piston is fitted tightly within a cylinder. When the pump-handle is pushed down, the piston is pulled upward, leaving a vacuum in the lower part of the cylinder. But since Nature abhors a vacuum, the surrounding water opens a one-way valve at the bottom of the cylinder and rushes into the vacuum. Repeated pumping lifts the water higher and higher in the cylinder until it pours out of the pump spout.

According to Aristotelian theory, it should have been possible in this way to raise water to any height. But miners who had to pump water out of the bottoms of mines found that no matter how hard and long they pumped, they could never lift the water higher than 33 feet above its natural level.

Galileo got interested in this puzzle toward the end of his long and inquisitive life. He could come to no conclusion except that apparently Nature abhorred a vacuum only up to certain limits. He wondered whether the limit would be lower if he used a liquid denser than water, but he died before he could try this experiment.

Galileo's students Evangelista Torricelli and Vincenzo Viviani did perform it. Selecting mercury (which is 13.5 times as dense as water), they filled a yard-long glass tube with mercury, stoppered the open end, upended the tube in a dish of mercury, and removed the stopper. The mercury began to run out of the tube into the dish, but when its level had dropped to 30 inches above the level in the dish, it stopped pouring out of the tube and held at that level.

What was holding the mercury up? Viviani suggested that it was the weight of the atmosphere, pressing down on the liquid in the dish. This was a revolutionary thought, for the Aristotelian notion had been that air had no weight, being drawn only to its proper sphere above the earth. Now it became plain that a 33-foot column of water, or a 30-inch column of mercury, measured the weight of the atmosphere — that is, the weight of a column of air of the same cross-section from sea-level up to as far as the air went.

The experiment also showed that Nature did not necessarily abhor a vacuum under all circumstances. The space left in the closed end of the tube after the mercury fell was a vacuum, containing nothing but a very small quantity of mercury vapor. This "Torricellian vacuum" was the first decent vacuum produced by man.

If AIR had a finite weight, it must have some finite height. The weight of the atmosphere turned out to be 14.7 pounds per square inch; on this basis the atmosphere was just about five miles high — if it was evenly dense all the way up. But in 1662 the English chemist Robert Boyle showed that it could not be, because pressure increased air's density. He stood up a tube shaped like the letter J, and poured some mercury into the mouth of the tube, on the tall side of the J. The mercury trapped a little air in the closed end on the short side. As he poured in more mercury, the air pocket shrank. At the same time its pressure increased, Boyle discovered, for it shrank less and less as the mercury column grew weightier. By actual measurement, Boyle showed that reducing the volume of gas to one-half doubled its pressure; in other words, the volume varied in inverse ratio to the pressure. This historic discovery, known as "Boyle's Law," was the first step in the long series of discoveries about matter that eventually led to the atomic theory.

Since air contracted under pressure, it must be densest at sea-level

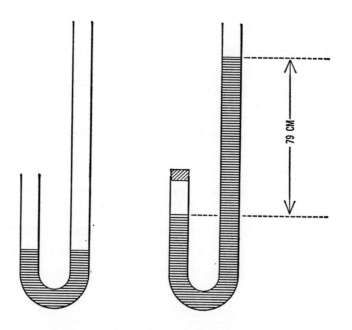

DIAGRAM OF BOYLE'S EXPERIMENT. *When the left arm of the tube is stoppered and more mercury is poured into the right arm, the trapped air is compressed. Boyle showed that the volume of the trapped air varied inversely with the pressure. That is "Boyle's Law."*

and steadily become thinner as the weight of the overlying air declined toward the top of the atmosphere. Theoretical calculations showed that, if the temperature was the same all the way up, the air pressure would decrease tenfold with every 12 miles of rise in altitude. In other words, at 12 miles the column of mercury it could support would have dropped from 30 inches to three inches; at 24 miles it would be three tenths of an inch; at 36 miles, three hundredths of an inch, and so on. At 108 miles, the air pressure would amount to only 0.000000003 of an inch of mercury. This doesn't sound like much, but over the whole earth the weight of the air above 108 miles would still total six million tons.

Actually all these figures are only approximations, because the air temperature changes with height. Nevertheless, they do clarify the picture, and we can see that the atmosphere has no definite boundary: it simply fades off gradually into the near-emptiness of space. Meteor trails have been detected as high as 100 miles, which means that there is still enough air to burn these tiny bits of matter to incandescence by friction. And the aurora borealis (Northern Lights), formed of glowing wisps of gas bombarded by particles from outer space, has been located as high as 500 to 600 miles above sea level.

UNTIL the late eighteenth century it seemed that man would never be able to get any closer to the upper atmosphere than the top of the Alps or the Himalayas. In 1782 two French brothers, Joseph Michel and Jacques Etienne Montgolfier, abruptly raised these sights. They lit a fire under a large bag with an opening underneath and thus filled the bag with hot air. The bag slowly rose, and the Montgolfiers had successfully launched man's first balloon. Within a few months balloons were being made with hydrogen, a gas 14 times lighter than air, so that each pound of hydrogen can carry aloft a payload of 13 pounds. Now gondolas went up carrying animals, and soon men.

Within a year of the launching of the first balloon, an American named John Jeffries made a balloon flight over London with a barometer and other instruments, plus an arrangement to collect air at various heights. By 1804 the French scientist Joseph Louis Gay-Lussac had ascended nearly four and a half miles, and brought down samples of the rarefied air.

This was nearly the limit for men in an open gondola; three men had flown earlier to six miles, but only one had survived the lack of sufficient oxygen there. Unmanned balloons carrying instruments could, however, be sent higher, and they brought back information about the temperatures and pressures up to 13 and a half miles.

In the first few miles of altitude rise, the temperature dropped, as was expected. At seven miles or so, it was 55 degrees below zero Centigrade. But then came a surprise. Above this level, the temperature did not decrease.

The French meteorologist Leon Phillippe Teisserenc de Bort suggested that the atmosphere might have two layers: (1) a turbulent lower layer containing clouds, winds, storms, and all the familiar weather changes (he called this layer the "troposphere," from the Greek for "sphere of change"), and (2) a quiet upper layer containing sub-layers of lighter gases, helium and hydrogen (he named this the "stratosphere," meaning sphere of layers). Teisserenc de Bort called the level at which the temperature ceased to decline the "tropopause" — "end of change," or the boundary between the troposphere and the stratosphere. The tropopause has since been found to vary from an altitude of about ten miles above sea level at the Equator to only five miles above at the poles.

During World War II, high-flying United States bombers discovered a dramatic phenomenon just below the tropopause: the "jet-stream," consisting of very strong, steady, west-to-east winds blowing at speeds up to 500 miles per hour. Actually there are two jet-streams, one in the Northern Hemisphere at the general latitude of the United States, the Mediterranean and north China, and one in the Southern at the latitude of New Zealand and Argentina. The streams meander, often debouching into eddies far north or south of their usual course. Airplanes now take advantage of the opportunity to ride on these swift winds. But far more important is the discovery that the jet-streams have a powerful influence on the movement of air masses at lower levels. This knowledge has already helped to advance the art of weather forecasting.

Now the satellites that man can send above the atmosphere have begun to help further, for they make it possible to get a view of the troposphere — a global view — which we have never had before. On April 1, 1960, the United States launched the first "weather-eye" satellite, Tiros I, which promptly began to send down pictures of vast stretches of the earth's surface and its cloud cover. This sort of information, provided for the whole earth by a network of weather satellites, may change weather forecasting from a guessing game to something more like a science.

In the 1930's, thanks to sealed cabins, man reached the stratosphere. First the Piccard brothers (Auguste and Jean Felix), Swiss physicists, rose to eleven miles in a balloon carrying a sealed gondola. Then new balloons of plastic material, lighter and less porous than silk, made it possible to go higher and remain up longer. In 1938 a balloon named Explorer II went to 13 miles, and since World War II manned balloons have gone as high as 19 miles and unmanned balloons almost to 27 miles.

These higher flights showed that the zone of constant temperature did not extend indefinitely upward. The stratosphere came to an end at a height of about 20 miles, and above that the temperature started to rise!

This "upper atmosphere," containing only 2 per cent of the earth's total air mass, was in turn penetrated in the 1940's. This time man needed a new type of vehicle altogether — the rocket.

THE CHINESE in ancient times invented and used small rockets for psychological warfare — to frighten the enemy. Modern Western civilization adapted rockets to a bloodier purpose. In 1801 a British artillery expert, William Congreve, having learned about rockets in the Orient, devised a number of deadly missiles. Some were used against the United States in the War of 1812, notably at the bombardment of Fort McHenry in 1814, which inspired Francis Scott Key to write the "Star-Spangled Banner," singing of "the rockets' red glare."

Around the beginning of the twentieth century, two men independently conceived a new and finer use of rockets — exploring the upper atmosphere and space. They were a Russian, Konstantin Eduardovich Tsiolkovsky, and an American, Robert Hutchings Goddard. (It is odd indeed, in view of later developments, that a Russian and an American were the first heralds of the age of rocketry. Tsiolkovsky is now honored by having his name attached to a crater on the other side of the moon — a crater first seen as a result of the photograph sent down by the Soviet moon-circling satellite, Lunik III, in October, 1959.)

The Russian was the first in print; he published his speculations and calculations in 1911 to 1913, while Goddard did not publish until 1919. But Goddard was the first to put speculation into practice. On March 16, 1926, from a snow-covered farm in Auburn, Mass., he fired a rocket 200 feet into the air. The remarkable thing about his rocket was that it was powered by a liquid fuel, instead of gunpowder.

Unfortunately, Goddard's accomplishment got almost no recognition except from his outraged neighbors, who managed to have him ordered to take his experiments elsewhere. Goddard went off to shoot his rockets in greater privacy, and between 1930 and 1935 his vehicles attained speeds of as much as 550 miles an hour and heights of a mile and a half. He developed systems for steering a rocket in flight and gyroscopes to keep a rocket headed in the proper direction. Goddard also patented the idea of multistage rockets. Because each successive stage sheds part of the original weight and starts at a high velocity imparted by the preceding stage, a rocket divided into a series of stages can attain much higher speeds and greater heights than could a rocket with the same quantity of fuel all crammed into a single stage.

During World War II, the United States Navy halfheartedly

THE MONTGOLFIER BROTHERS' HOT-AIR BALLOON, *launched at Versailles September 19, 1783.*

DMITRI MENDELEEV, *the Russian chemist, ascending in a balloon in 1887 to study the atmosphere.*

Astronaut *entering a rocket capsule in 1960 in training for space flight.*

Aurora *photographed in Alaska during the IGY.*

supported further experiments by Goddard. Meanwhile, the German government threw a major effort into rocket research, an effort which culminated in the development of the V-2 under the guidance of the rocket expert Wernher von Braun, who, since the war, has placed his talents at the disposal of the United States.

On August 10, 1945, almost on the very day of the war's end, the "father of rocketry" died — just too soon to see his spark blaze into flame at last. The United States and the Soviet Union, stimulated by the successes of the V-2, plunged into rocket research, each carrying off as many German experts in rocketry as could be lured to its side.

By 1949 the United States had fired a captured German V-2 to a height of 128 miles, and in the same year its rocket experts sent a WAC-Corporal, the second stage of a two-stage rocket, to 250 miles. The exploration of the upper atmosphere had begun.

Rockets alone would have accomplished little in that exploration had it not been for a companion invention — "telemetering." Telemetering was first applied to atmospheric research, in a balloon, in 1925 by a Russian scientist named Pyotr A. Molchanoff. (The Russians apparently had a number of "firsts" even before Sputnik.)

Essentially, this technique of "measuring at a distance" entails translating the conditions to be measured (*e.g.,* temperature) into electrical impulses which are transmitted back to earth by radio. The observations take the form of changes in the intensity or spacing of the pulses. For instance, a temperature change affects the electrical resistance of a wire, and so changes the nature of the pulse; a change in air pressure similarly is translated into a certain kind of pulse by the fact that air cools the wire, the extent of the cooling depending upon the pressure; radiation sets off pulses in a detector, and so on. Nowadays telemetering has become so elaborate that the rockets seem to do everything but talk, and their intricate messages have to be interpreted by rapid computers.

Rockets and telemetering, then, showed that above the stratosphere there was a new region, called the "mesosphere," marked by a rise in temperature. After rising from its stratospheric level of minus 55 degrees C. to minus 45 degrees, the temperature began to drop again and fell to a minimum of minus 70 degrees at a height of about 50 miles.

This seems to be the top of the mesosphere. Beyond it the thin air amounts to only a few thousandths of 1 per cent of the total mass of the atmosphere. But this scattering of air atoms steadily increases in temperature to an estimated 1,000 degrees at 300 miles and probably to still higher levels above that height. It is therefore called the "thermosphere" ("sphere of heat") — an odd echo of Aristotle's original sphere of fire. Of course, temperature here does not signify heat in the usual sense: it is merely a measure of the speed of the particles.

Above 300 miles we come to the "exosphere," which may extend to as high as 1,000 miles and gradually merges into interplanetary space.

A NEW ERA began when, on October 4, 1957 (within a month of the hundredth anniversary of Tsiolkovsky's birth), the Soviet Union put the first man-made satellite in orbit. Sputnik I traveled around the earth in an elliptical orbit — 156 miles above the surface (or 4,100 miles from the earth's center) at perigee and 560 miles away at apogee. An elliptical orbit is something like the course of a roller coaster. In going from apogee (the highest point) to perigee, the satellite slides downhill, so to speak, and loses gravitational potential. This brings an increase in velocity, so that at perigee the satellite starts uphill again at top speed, as a roller coaster does. The satellite loses velocity as it climbs (as does the roller coaster) and is moving at its slowest speed at apogee, before it turns downhill again.

Sputnik I at perigee was in the mesosphere, where the air resistance, though slight, was sufficient to slow the satellite a bit on each trip. On each successive revolution, it failed to attain its previous apogee height. Slowly, it spiralled inward. Eventually it lost so much energy that it yielded to the earth's pull sufficiently to dive into the

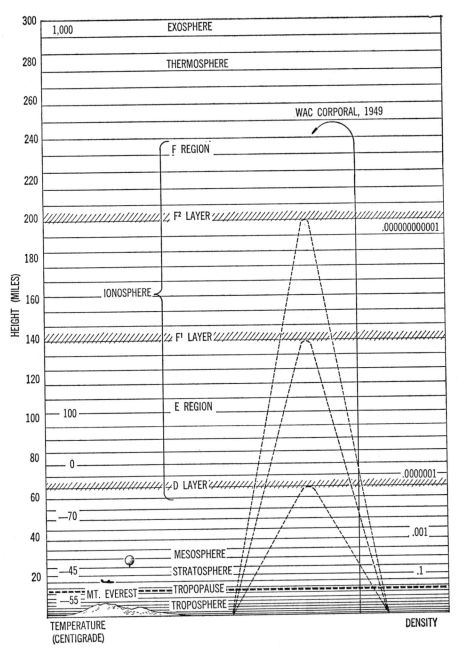

PROFILE OF THE ATMOSPHERE. *The dotted lines indicate the reflection of radio signals from the Kennelly-Heaviside and Appleton layers of the ionosphere.*

denser atmosphere, there to be burned up by friction with the air.

The rate at which a satellite's orbit decays in this way depends partly on the mass of the satellite, partly on its shape, and partly on the density of the air through which it passes. Thus the density of the atmosphere at that level can be calculated. The satellites have given man the first direct measurements of the density of the upper atmosphere. The density proved to be higher than had been thought, but at the altitude of 150 miles, for instance, it is still only one ten-millionth of that at sea level, and at 225 miles, only one trillionth.

THE GASES IN AIR

UP TO THE TIME of the Scientific Revolution, air was considered a simple, homogeneous substance. In the early seventeenth century, the Flemish chemist Jan Baptista van Helmont began to suspect that there were a number of chemically different gases. He studied the vapor given off by fermenting fruit juice (carbon dioxide) and recognized it as a new substance. Van Helmont was, in fact, the first to use the term "gas" — a word he is supposed to have coined from "chaos," the ancients' word for the original substance out of which the Universe was made (not a bad stroke of intuition for van Helmont).

The first to realize that air was a mixture of gases was the great eighteenth century French chemist Antoine-Laurent Lavoisier. In experiments in which he heated mercury in a closed vessel, he found that the mercury combined with part of the air, forming a red powder (mercuric oxide), but four-fifths of the air remained a gas. No amount of heating would consume any of this remaining gas. A candle would not burn in it, nor could mice live in it.

Lavoisier decided that air was made up of two gases. The one-fifth that combined with mercury in his experiment was the portion of the air that supported life and combustion. This he called "oxygen."

The remainder he called "azote," from Greek words meaning "no life." Later it became known as "nitrogen," because the substance was present in sodium nitrate, commonly called "niter."

Nitrogen is a comparatively inert gas; that is, it does not readily combine with other substances. It can, however, be forced into combination, for instance, by heating it with magnesium metal, forming the solid magnesium nitride. Some years after Lavoisier's discovery, the brilliant English chemist Henry Cavendish removed the oxygen and carbon dioxide from a sample of air (an easy task) and tried to exhaust the remaining nitrogen by combining it with another substance. He failed. No matter what he did, he could not get rid of a small bubble of remaining gas, amounting to less than 1 per cent of the original quantity. Cavendish thought this might be an unknown gas, even more inert than nitrogen. But not all chemists are Cavendishes, and the puzzle was not followed up, so the nature of this residue of air was not discovered for another century.

In 1882 the British physicist Robert John Strutt, Lord Rayleigh, compared the density of nitrogen obtained from air with the density of nitrogen obtained from certain chemicals and found, to his surprise, that the air nitrogen was definitely denser. Could it be that nitrogen obtained from air was not pure but contained small quantities of another, heavier gas? A Scottish chemist, Sir William Ramsay, and Lord Rayleigh looked into the matter further. By this time they had spectroscopy available to help. When they heated the small residue of gas left after exhaustion of nitrogen from air and examined its spectrum, they found a new set of bright lines — lines that belonged to no known element. To their newly discovered, very inert element they gave the name "argon" (from a Greek word meaning "inert").

Argon accounted for nearly all of the approximately 1 per cent of unknown gas in air — but not quite all. There were still several "trace constituents" in the atmosphere, each constituting only a few parts per million. During the 1890's Ramsay went on to discover four more inert gases in air: "neon" (new), "krypton" (hidden), "xenon" (stranger), and helium, which had been discovered more than 30 years before in the sun. In recent decades the infrared spectroscope has turned up three others: nitrous oxide ("laughing gas"), whose origin is unknown; methane, a product of the decay of organic matter; and carbon monoxide. Methane is released by bogs, and some 45,000,000 tons of the same gas, it has been calculated, are added to the atmosphere each year by the venting of intestinal gases by cattle and other large animals. The carbon monoxide is probably man-made, resulting from the incomplete combustion of wood, coal, gasoline, etc.

ALL THIS, of course, refers to the composition of the lowest reaches of the atmosphere. What about the stratosphere? Teisserenc de Bort believed that helium and hydrogen might exist in some quantity up there, floating on the heavier gases underneath. He was mistaken. In the middle 1930's Russian balloonists brought down samples of air from the upper stratosphere, and it proved to be made up of oxygen and nitrogen in the same one-to-four mixture as the air of the troposphere.

But there were reasons to believe some unusual gases existed in the upper atmosphere, and one of the reasons was the phenomenon called the "airglow." This is the very feeble general illumination of all parts of the night sky even in the absence of the moon. The total light of the airglow is considerably greater than that of the stars, but it is so diffuse that it is not noticeable except to the delicate light-gathering instruments of the astronomer.

The source of the light had been a mystery for many years. In 1928 the astronomer V. M. Slipher succeeded in detecting in the airglow some mysterious spectral lines which had been found earlier in nebulae and were thought to represent an unfamiliar element, named "nebulium." Eventually, through experiments in the laboratory, physicists learned that the lines came from "atomic oxygen;" that is, oxygen not combined in the normal form of the two-atom molecule. Similarly, other strange spectral lines from the aurora turned out to represent atomic nitrogen. Both atomic oxygen and atomic nitrogen in the upper atmosphere are produced by energetic radiation from the sun, which breaks down the molecules into single atoms. Fortunately this high-energy radiation is absorbed or weakened before it reaches the lower atmosphere.

The airglow, then, comes from the recombination at night of the atoms that are split apart by solar energy during the day. In recombining, the atoms give up some of the energy they absorbed in splitting, so that the airglow is a kind of delayed and very feeble return of sunlight in a new and specialized form. The rocket experiments of the 1950's supplied direct evidence of this. Spectroscopes carried by the rockets recorded the green lines of atomic oxygen most strongly at a height of 60 miles. A smaller proportion of the nitrogen was in the atomic form, because nitrogen molecules hold together more strongly than do oxygen molecules; nevertheless, the red light of atomic nitrogen was strong at a height of 95 miles.

Slipher had also found lines in the airglow which were suspiciously like well-known lines emitted by sodium. The presence of sodium seemed so unlikely that the matter was dropped in embarrassment. What would sodium, of all things, be doing in the upper atmosphere? It is not a gas, after all, but a very reactive metal which does not occur alone anywhere on the earth. It is always combined with other elements, most commonly in sodium chloride (table salt). But in 1938 French scientists established that the lines were indeed identical with the sodium lines. Unlikely or not, sodium had to be in the upper atmosphere. Again rocket experiments clinched the matter: their spectroscopes recorded the yellow light of sodium unmistakably, and most strongly at a height of 55 miles. Where the sodium comes from is still a mystery: it may come from ocean salt spray, or perhaps from vaporized meteors.

In 1956 a team of United States scientists produced an artificial airglow. They fired a rocket which at 60 miles released a cloud of nitric oxide gas. This accelerated the recombination of oxygen atoms in the upper atmosphere. Observers on the ground easily sighted the bright glow that resulted. A similar experiment with sodium vapor also was successful: it created a clearly visible yellow glow. When Soviet scientists sent "Lunik III" in the direction of the moon in October, 1959, they arranged for it to expel a cloud of sodium vapor as a visible signal that it had gone into orbit.

At lower levels in the atmosphere, atomic oxygen disappears, but the solar radiation is still energetic enough to bring about the formation of the three-atom variety of oxygen called "ozone." The ozone concentration is greatest at a height of 15 miles. Even there, in what is called the "ozonosphere," it makes up only one part in four million of the air, but that is enough to absorb ultraviolet light sufficiently to protect life on the earth.

HIGH TEMPERATURES and energetic radiation can do more than force atoms apart or into new combinations. They can chip electrons away from atoms and so "ionize" the atoms. What remains of the atom is called an "ion" and differs from ordinary atoms in carrying an electric charge. The word "ion" comes from a Greek word meaning "traveler." Its origin lies in the fact that when an electric current passes through a solution containing ions, the positively charged ions travel in one direction and the negatively charged ions in the other.

A young Swedish student of chemistry named Svante August Arrhenius coined the term and was the first to suggest this idea, as the only means of explaining the behavior of certain solutions that conducted an electric current. His notions, advanced in the thesis he presented for his degree of Doctor of Philosophy in 1884, were so revolutionary that his examiners could scarcely bring themselves to pass him. The charged particles within the atom had not yet been discovered, and the concept of an electrically charged atom seemed ridiculous. Arrhenius got his degree, but with only a minimum passing grade.

When the electron was discovered in the late 1890's, Arrhenius's theory suddenly made startling sense. He was awarded the Nobel Prize in chemistry in 1903 for the same thesis which 19 years earlier had nearly lost him his doctor's degree. (This sounds like an improbable movie scenario, I admit, but the history of science contains many episodes which make Hollywood seem unimaginative.)

The discovery of ions in the atmosphere did not emerge until after Guglielmo Marconi started his experiments with wireless. When, on December 12, 1901, he sent signals from Cornwall to Newfoundland, across 2,100 miles of the Atlantic Ocean, scientists were startled. Radio waves travel only in a straight line; how had they managed to go around the curvature of the earth and get to Newfoundland?

A British physicist, Oliver Heaviside, and an American electrical engineer, Arthur Edwin Kennelly, soon suggested that the radio signals might have been reflected back from the sky by a layer of charged particles high in the atmosphere. The "Kennelly-Heaviside layer," as it has been called ever since, was finally located in the 1920's. The British physicist Edward Victor Appleton discovered it by paying attention to a curious fading phenomenon in radio transmission. He decided that the fading was the result of interference between two versions of the same signal, one coming directly from the transmitter to his receiver, the other by a roundabout route via reflection from the upper atmosphere. The delayed wave was out of phase with the first, so the two waves partly cancelled each other; hence the fading.

It was a simple matter then to find the height of the reflecting layer. All he had to do was to send signals at such a wavelength that the direct signal completely cancelled the reflected one — that is, the two signals arrived at directly opposite phases. From the wavelength of the signal used, and the known velocity of radio waves, he could calculate the difference in the distances the two trains of waves had travelled. In this way he determined that the Kennelly-Heaviside layer was some 65 miles up.

The fading of radio signals generally occurred at night. Appleton found that shortly before dawn radio waves were not reflected back by the Kennelly-Heaviside layer but were reflected from still higher layers (now sometimes called the "Appleton layers") which began at a height of 140 miles.

For all these discoveries Appleton received the Nobel Prize in physics in 1947. He had defined the important region of the atmosphere called the "ionosphere." It is now divided into a number of layers. From the stratopause up to 65 miles or so is the "D region." Above that is the Kennelly-Heaviside layer, called the "D layer." Above the D layer, to a height of 140 miles, is the "E region" — an intermediate area relatively poor in ions. This is followed by the Appleton layers: the "F_1 layer" at 140 miles and "F_2 layer" at 200 miles. The F_2 layer is the richest in ions, the F_1 layer being significantly strong only in the daytime. Above these layers is the "F region."

These layers reflect and absorb only the long radio waves used in ordinary radio broadcasts. The shorter waves, such as those used in television, pass through, for the most part. That is why TV broadcasting is limited in range — a limitation which will eventually be remedied by satellite relay stations in the sky. The radio waves from space (*e.g.,* from radio stars) also pass through the ionosphere, fortunately; if they did not, there would be no radio astronomy.

The ionosphere is strongest at the end of the day, after the day-long effect of the sun's radiation, and weakens by dawn because many ions and electrons have recombined. Storms on the sun, intensifying the streams of particles and high-energy radiation sent to the earth, cause the ionized layers to strengthen and thicken. The regions above the ionosphere also flare up into auroral displays. During these electric storms long-distance transmission of radio waves on the earth is disrupted and sometimes blacked out altogether.

It has turned out that the ionosphere is only one of the belts of radiation surrounding the earth. Outside the atmosphere, in what used to be considered "empty" space, man's satellites in 1958 disclosed a shocking surprise. To understand it we must make an excursion into the subject of magnetism.

MAGNETS

MAGNETS got their name from the ancient Greek town of Magnesia, near which the first "lodestones" were discovered. The lodestone is an iron oxide with natural magnetic properties. Tradition has it that Thales of Miletus, about 550 B.C., was the first philosopher to describe it.

Magnets became something more than a curiosity when it was discovered that a steel needle stroked by a lodestone was magnetized, and that if the needle was allowed to pivot freely in a horizontal plane, it would end up lying along a north-south line. Such a needle was, of course, of tremendous use to mariners; in fact, it became indispensable to ocean navigation, though the Polynesians did manage to cross the Pacific without a compass.

It is not known who first put such a magnetized needle on a pivot and enclosed it in a box to make a compass. The Chinese are supposed to have done it first and passed it on to the Arabs, who, in turn, passed it on to the Europeans. This is all very doubtful and may be only legend. At any rate, in the thirteenth century the compass came into use in Europe and was described in 1269 by a French scholar best known by his Latinized name of Peter Peregrinus. Peregrinus named the end of the magnet that pointed north the "north pole" and the other the "south pole."

Naturally, people speculated as to why a magnetized needle should point north. Because magnets were known to attract other magnets, some thought there was a gigantic lodestone mountain in the far north toward which the needle strained. Others were even more romantic and gave magnets a "soul" and a kind of life.

The scientific study of magnets began with William Gilbert, the court physician of Queen Elizabeth I. It was Gilbert who discovered that the earth itself was a giant magnet. He mounted a magnetized needle so that it could pivot freely in a vertical direction, and its north pole then dipped toward the ground. Using a spherical lodestone as a model of the earth, he found that the needle behaved in the same way when it was placed over the "northern hemisphere" of his sphere. Gilbert published these findings in 1600 in a classic book entitled *De Magnete*.

In the three and a half centuries that have elapsed since Gilbert's work, no one has ever explained the earth's magnetism to everyone's satisfaction. For a long time scientists speculated that the earth might have a gigantic iron magnet as its core. Although the earth was indeed found to have an iron core, it is now certain that this core cannot be a magnet, because iron, when heated, loses its magnetic properties at 760 degrees C., and the temperature of the earth's core must be at least 1,000 degrees.

The most plausible present theory grew out of the work of the nineteenth-century English genius Michael Faraday, who discovered the connection between magnetism and electricity.

In the 1820's Faraday started with an experiment which had been first described by Peter Peregrinus (and which still amuses young students of physics). The experiment consists in sprinkling fine iron filings on a piece of paper above a magnet and gently tapping the paper. The shaken filings tend to line up along arcs from the north pole to the south pole of the magnet. Faraday decided that these marked actual "magnetic lines of force," forming a magnetic "field."

Faraday, who had been attracted to the subject of magnetism by the Danish physicist Hans Christian Oersted's observation that an electric current flowing in a wire deflected a nearby compass needle, came to the conclusion that the current must set up magnetic lines of force around the wire.

Well, then, thought Faraday (who had one of the most efficient intuitions in the history of science), if electricity could set up a magnetic field, should not the reverse be true? Ought not a magnet produce a current of electricity?

In 1831 Faraday performed the experiment that was to change human history. He wound a coil of wire around one segment of an iron ring and a second coil of wire around another segment of the ring. Then he connected the first coil to a battery. His reasoning was that if he sent a current through the first coil, it would create magnetic lines of force which would be concentrated in the iron ring, and this induced magnetism in turn would produce a current in the second coil. To detect that current, he connected the second coil to a galvanometer — an instrument for measuring electrical currents which had been devised by the German physicist Johann Salomo Christoph Schweigger in 1820.

The experiment did not work as Faraday had expected. The flow of current in the first coil generated nothing in the second coil. But Faraday noticed that at the moment when he turned on the current, the galvanometer needle kicked over briefly, and it did the same thing, but in the opposite direction, when he turned the current off. He guessed at once that it was the movement of magnetic lines of force across a wire, not the magnetism itself, that set up the current. When a current began to flow in the first coil, it initiated a magnetic field which, as it spread, cut across the second coil, setting up a momentary electric current there. Conversely, when the current from the battery was cut off, the collapsing lines of magnetic force again

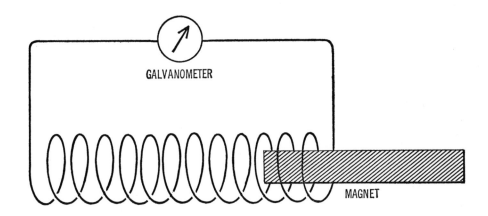

GALVANOMETER

MAGNET

A FARADAY EXPERIMENT ON THE INDUCTION OF ELECTRICITY. *When the magnet is moved in or out of the coil of wire, the cutting of its lines of force by the wire produces an electrical current in the coil.*

cut across the wire of the second coil, causing a momentary surge of electricity in the direction opposite that of the first flow.

Thus Faraday discovered the principle of electrical induction and created the first "transformer." He proceeded to demonstrate the phenomenon more plainly by using a permanent magnet and moving it in and out of a coil of wire; although no source of electricity was involved, a current flowed in the coil whenever the magnet's lines of force cut across the wire.

Faraday's discoveries not only led directly to the creation of the dynamo for generating electricity but also laid the foundation for James Clerk Maxwell's "electromagnetic" theory, which linked together light and other forms of radiation (such as radio) in a single family of "electromagnetic radiations."

Now THE CLOSE CONNECTION between magnetism and electricity points to a possible explanation of the earth's magnetism. The compass needle has traced out its magnetic lines of force, which run from the "north magnetic pole," located off northern Canada, to the "south magnetic pole," located at the rim of Antarctica. (The earth's magnetic field has been detected at great heights by rockets carrying "magnetometers.") The new suggestion is that the earth's magnetism may originate in the flow of electric currents deep in its interior.

The physicist Walter M. Elsasser has proposed that the rotation of the earth sets up slow eddies in the molten iron core, circling west to east. These eddies have the effect of producing an electric current, likewise circling west to east. Just as Faraday's coil of wire produced magnetic lines of force within the coil, so the circling electric current does in the earth's core. It therefore creates the equivalent of an internal magnet extending north and south. This magnet in turn accounts for the earth's general magnetic field, oriented roughly along the axis of rotation, so that the magnetic poles are near the north and south geographic poles.

The sun also has a general magnetic field and local fields appar-

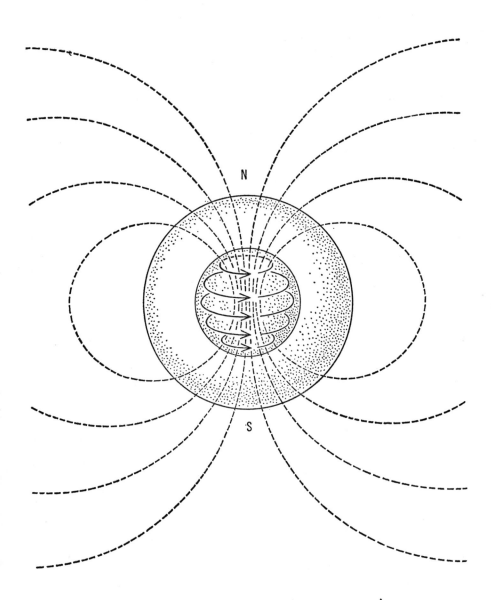

ELSASSER'S THEORY OF THE GENERATION OF THE EARTH'S MAGNETIC
FIELD. *Movements of material in the molten nickel-iron core set up
electric currents which in turn generate magnetic lines of force.
The dotted lines show the earth's magnetic field.*

ently associated with the sunspots. Studies of these fields (made possible by the fact that intense magnetism affects the wavelength of the light emitted) suggest that there are circular flows of electric charge within the sun.

Even if circling electric currents in the iron core are accepted as the source of the earth's magnetic field, there remain a number of puzzling details that await explanation. For instance, why don't the magnetic poles coincide with the geographic poles? The north magnetic pole is off the coast of northern Canada about a thousand miles from the North Pole. Similarly, the south magnetic pole is near the Antarctica shore line west of Ross Sea, about a thousand miles from the South Pole. Furthermore, the magnetic poles are not directly opposite each other on the globe. A line through the earth connecting them (the "magnetic axis") does not pass through the center of the earth.

Again, the deviation of the compass needle from "true north" (*i.e.*, the direction of the North Pole) varies irregularly as one travels east or west. (In fact, the compass needle shifted on Columbus's first voyage, and Columbus hid this from his crew lest it excite terror which would force him to turn back. Nowadays a "gyroscopic compass," first introduced by the American inventor Elmer Ambrose Sperry in 1911, maintains a fixed direction reference to guide ships — or rockets.)

More mysteriously, even at the same spot the magnetic compass's deviation from true north (called "declination") changes with time. For instance, the declination at London shifted 32 degrees of arc in two centuries; it was eight degrees east of north in 1600 and steadily swung around counterclockwise until it was 24 degrees west of north in 1800. Since then it has shifted back and in 1950 was only eight degrees west of north.

It looks very much as if the magnetic poles slowly drift about, sometimes to one side of the geographic pole, sometimes to the other. Evidence that the poles have shifted in really radical fashion was found, as I have already mentioned, by the physicist S. K. Runcorn (see Chapter 3). He discovered "fossil magnets" — iron minerals

LAUNCHING OF THE FIRST U.S. SATELLITE, *Explorer I, on January 31, 1958.*

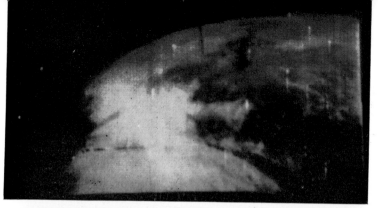

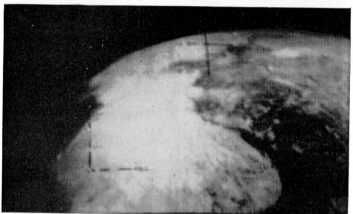

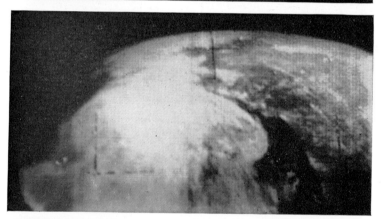

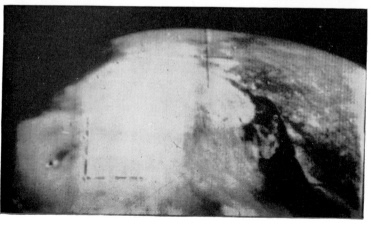

THE EARTH FROM A ROCKET
This series of photographs
made by the U.S. meteoro-
logical rocket Tiros I, shows
the eastern part of the U.S.
and Canada; the dark area in
the lower right corner is the
St. Lawrence. The pictures
were made at one-minute intervals from an altitude of
about 450 miles several hundred miles east of the Atlantic Coast. The white areas
are cloud cover.

A Tiros I *photograph showing a typhoon (whirlpool at right) 1,000 miles east of Australia.*

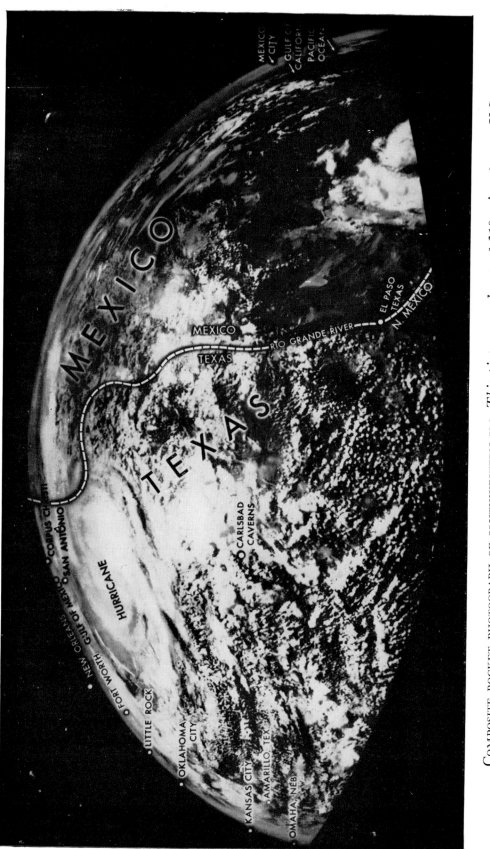

COMPOSITE ROCKET PHOTOGRAPH OF SOUTHWESTERN U.S. *This picture, made up of 310 prints from a U.S. Navy Aerobee film, shows about 1.25 million square miles, or two-fifths of the continental U.S.*

once free to move in the plastic earth but later frozen in place — which pointed in directions very different from the present direction of the north magnetic pole. Some even pointed toward the south magnetic pole! Just how the poles could have wandered so extensively, and even switched places, is so hard to explain that many geologists are not yet ready to accept the idea that they have actually migrated.

In addition to long-term drifts of the magnetic field, there are small changes during the course of the day. These suggest some connection with the sun. Furthermore, there are "disturbed days" when the compass needle jumps about with unusual liveliness. The earth is then said to be experiencing a "magnetic storm." Magnetic storms are identical with electric storms and are usually accompanied by an increase in the intensity of auroral displays.

The Aurora Borealis (Latin for "northern dawn") is a beautiful display of moving, colored streamers or folds of light, giving an effect of unearthly splendor. Its counterpart in the Antarctic is called the Aurora Australis ("southern dawn"). The auroral streamers seem to follow the earth's magnetic lines of force and to concentrate, and become visible, at those points where the lines crowd most closely together — that is, at the magnetic poles. During magnetic storms the northern aurora can be seen as far south as Boston and New York.

In 1882 the Scottish physicist Balfour Stewart suggested that the daily variations of the magnetic field might be caused by electric currents flowing through the upper atmosphere. At the time this seemed a fanciful notion, but the discovery of the ionosphere later proved that his idea was basically correct. It is easy to see why there should be daily variations. During the day solar energy increases the number of charged particles in the upper atmosphere, so we should expect a daily ebb and flow of magnetic fields with day and night. But what about the disturbed days and the magnetic storms? Again the finger of suspicion points to the sun.

Sunspot activity seems to generate magnetic storms. How such a disturbance 93 million miles away could affect the earth was a complete mystery until the spectrohelioscope, invented by the astronomer George Ellery Hale, brought forth a possible answer. This instrument allows the sun to be photographed in light of a particular color — for instance, the red light of hydrogen. Furthermore, it shows the motions or changes taking place on the sun's surface. It gives good pictures of the "solar flares" — great bursts of flaming hydrogen. Now the spectrohelioscope is able to show not only the flares shooting out from the limb of the sun but also those coming out in our direction from the center of the sun's disk: in hydrogen light these hydrogen-rich bursts appear as light blotches against the darker background of the rest of the disk. It turned out that solar flares were followed by magnetic storms on the earth only when the flare was pointed toward the earth.

Apparently, then, magnetic storms were the result of bursts of charged particles, chiefly electrons, shot from the flares to the earth across 93 million miles of space.

As a matter of fact, there was plenty of evidence that, wherever the electrons might come from, the earth was bathed in an aura of electrons extending pretty far out in space. Radio waves generated by lightning had been found to travel along the earth's magnetic lines of force at great heights. (These waves, called "whistlers" because they were picked up by receivers as odd whistling noises, had been discovered accidentally by the German physicist Heinrich Barkhausen during World War I.) The radio waves could not follow the lines of force unless electrons were present.

The British astronomer Sydney Chapman, who played a prominent part in the IGY, has observed that there are measurable concentrations of electrons all the way out to the moon, so that, in a manner of speaking, the moon can be considered to be within the earth's "atmosphere." And in fact, both the earth and the moon are in effect within the sun's "corona" of electrons.

Very possibly the clouds of electrons occasionally shot to the earth by the sun have an effect on the earth's weather. Their presence or absence may control the quantity of rainfall. If so, a better understanding of the ebb and flow of solar electrons may lead to better weather prediction.

ALL THIS brings us back to the big surprise that startled the scientific world in 1958.

One of the prime jobs given to the man-made satellites was to measure the radiation in the upper atmosphere and nearby space, especially the intensity of the cosmic rays. How intense was this radiation up beyond the atmospheric shield? The satellites carried "Geiger counters," which measure particle radiation in the following way. The counter has a box containing gas under a voltage not quite strong enough to send a current through the gas. When a high-energy particle of radiation penetrates into the box, it converts an atom of the gas into an ion. This ion, hurtled forward by the energy of the blow, smashes neighboring atoms to form more ions, which in turn smash their neighbors to form still more. The resulting shower of ions can carry an electric current, and for a fraction of a second a current pulses through the counter. The pulse is telemetered back to earth. Thus the instrument counts the particles, or flux of radiation, at the location where it happens to be.

When the first successful American satellite, "Explorer I," went into orbit on January 31, 1958, its counter detected about the expected concentrations of particles at heights up to several hundred miles. But at higher altitudes (and Explorer I went as high as 1,575 miles) the count fell off; in fact, at times it dropped to zero! This might have been dismissed as due to some peculiar kind of accident to the counter, but Explorer III, launched on March 26, 1958, and reaching an apogee of 2,100 miles, had just the same experience. So did the Soviet Sputnik III, launched on May 15, 1958.

James A. Van Allen of the State University of Iowa, who was in charge of the radiation program, and his aides came up with a possible explanation. The count fell virtually to zero, they decided, not because there was little or no radiation, but because there was too much. The instrument could not keep up with the particles entering it, and it blanked out in consequence. (This would be analogous to the blinding of our eyes by a flash of too-bright light.)

When Explorer IV went up on July 26, 1958, it carried special counters designed to handle heavy loads. One of them, for instance, was shielded with a thin layer of lead (analogous to dark sun-glasses) which would keep out most of the radiation. And this time the counters did tell another story. They showed that the "too-much-radiation" theory was correct. Explorer IV, reaching a height of 1,368 miles, sent down counts which, allowing for the shielding, disclosed that the radiation intensity up there was far higher than scientists had imagined. In fact, it was so intense that it raised a deadly danger to space flight by man.

It turned out that the Explorer satellites had only penetrated the lower regions of this intense field of radiation. In the fall of 1958 the two satellites shot by the United States in the direction of the moon — Pioneer I, which went out 70,000 miles, and Pioneer III, which reached 65,000 miles — showed two main bands of radiation encircling the earth. They were named the "Van Allen radiation belts." The inner belt extends from about 1,000 to 3,000 miles above the earth's surface. Actually it has been found to be a double band, consisting of two intense layers separated by a relatively clear area. The outer belt occupies the region between 8,000 and 12,000 miles. Both bands curve to follow the magnetic lines of force and are thickest and most dangerous above the equatorial region. The inner band is almost confined there, but the outer band curves in a crescent-shaped cross-section, converging upon the magnetic poles. There seems to be a cone of relative freedom from radiation above each polar region. The first fears about the hazard of the Van Allen radiation for space travel seem to have been exaggerated. It will be troublesome to have to launch ships from northern Canada, but it can be done. (To be sure, data sent back by Explorer VII, launched on October 13, 1959, showed that even in relatively clear space there are sporadic bursts of radiation, for which solar flare activity undoubtedly is responsible.)

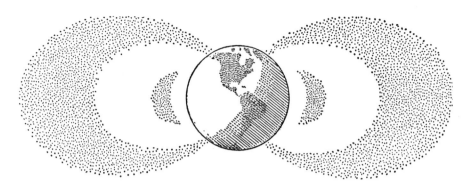

THE VAN ALLEN RADIATION BELTS, AS TRACED BY SATELLITES. *They appear to be made up of charged particles trapped in the earth's magnetic field.*

At first it was thought that all of the Van Allen radiation consisted of particles from the sun. The outer band certainly seems to stem directly from solar electrons, which are trapped by the earth's magnetic field and then follow its lines of force. But the inner band, according to a theory suggested by the University of Maryland physicist S. Fred Singer, originates in a different way. The theory is that cosmic rays bombarding atoms in the earth's upper atmosphere knock out neutrons (uncharged nuclear particles) when they shatter the atoms; that some of these neutrons (called cosmic-ray "albedo") bounce out of the atmosphere into space; that they then decay into protons, as free neutrons always do within a short time; and that the charged protons are trapped by magnetic lines of force of the earth, at the height where they form the inner band.

The entrapment of charged particles along the magnetic lines of force had been predicted in the 1950's by a Greek amateur in science named Nicholas Christofilos. He had sent his calculations to scientists engaged in such research, but no one had paid much attention to them. (In science, as in other fields, professionals tend to disregard amateurs.) It was only when the professionals independently came up with the same results that Christofilos achieved recognition and was welcomed into American laboratories. His idea about particle entrapment is now called the "Christofilos effect."

To test whether the effect really occurs in space, the United States in August and September of 1958 fired three rockets carrying nuclear bombs 300 miles up and there exploded the bombs — an experiment which was named "Project Argus." The flood of charged particles resulting from the nuclear explosions spread out along the lines of force and were indeed trapped there. The resulting band persisted for a considerable time; Explorer IV detected it during several hundred of its trips around the earth. The cloud of particles also gave rise to feeble auroral displays and disrupted radar for a while.

Naturally scientists were curious to find out whether there were radiation belts beyond the Van Allen ones. Two lunar probes, one by the Soviet Union and the other by the United States, settled this question. The Soviet Union's Lunik I, sent into a permanent orbit around the sun (as man's first artificial planet) on January 2, 1959, transmitted back its observations up to a distance of 373,000 miles before the signals were lost. The United States moon probe Pioneer IV, launched two months later, sent back information from as far as 407,000 miles. Both showed definitely that no high-energy radiation belts existed outside the two already discovered. However, on March 11, 1960, Pioneer V was placed in a solar orbit that will carry it close to the orbit of Venus (it is a so-called "Venus-probe"). Its strong transmitters, capable of being heard from millions of miles distance, recorded the existence of a ring of low-energy, charged particles circling the earth about 30,000 to 50,000 miles above the surface.

The Soviet Union's Lunik II, which actually hit the moon, in September 1959, found no radiation belts around the moon. This was not surprising, for scientists had already surmised that the moon had no magnetic field of any consequence. The over-all density of the moon has long been known to be but 3.3 grams per cubic centimeter (about three-fifths that of the earth) and it couldn't have so low a density unless it were almost entirely silicate, with no iron core to

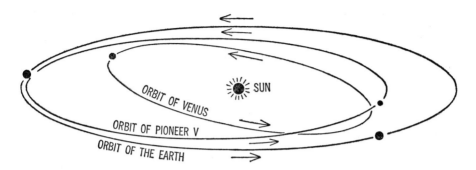

ORBIT OF THE UNITED STATES' "ARTIFICIAL PLANET" PIONEER V,
*launched March 11, 1960, is shown in relation to the sun and the
orbits of the earth and Venus. The dot on the rocket's orbit indicates roughly its position on August 9, 1960, when it was closest to
the sun.*

speak of. The lack of a magnetic field would seem to follow, if present theories are correct.

If space travelers need have no fears about radiation around the
moon, the same is probably not true about the planets. Jupiter and
Saturn, for instance, appear to have radiation belts which are both
more intense and more extensive than those of the earth.

METEORS

EVEN THE GREEKS knew that "shooting stars" were not really
stars, because no matter how many fell, the celestial population
of stars remained the same. Aristotle reasoned that a shooting star,
being a temporary phenomenon, had to be something within the atmosphere (and this time he was right). These objects were therefore
called "meteors," meaning "things in the air." Meteors that actually
reach the earth's surface are called "meteorites."

The ancients even witnessed some falls of meteorites to the earth, and found them to be lumps of iron. Hipparchus of Nicaea is said to have reported such a fall. The Kaaba, the sacred black stone in Mecca, is supposed to be a meteorite and to have gained its sanctity through its heavenly origin. The *Iliad* mentions a lump of rough iron being awarded as one of the prizes in the funeral games for Patroclus; this must have been meteoric in origin, because the time was the Bronze Age, before the metallurgy of iron ore had been developed. In fact, meteoric iron was probably in use as early as 3,000 B.C.

During the eighteenth century, with the Age of Reason in full sway, science made a backward step in this particular respect. The scorners of superstition laughed at stories of "stones from the sky." Farmers who came to the Académie Française with samples of meteorites were politely but impatiently shown the door. When two Connecticut scholars reported having witnessed a fall, President Thomas Jefferson (in one of his more unfortunate remarks) said that he would sooner believe that two Yankee professors would lie than that stones would fall from heaven.

However, on November 13, 1833, the United States was treated to a meteor shower which for some hours turned the sky into a Roman-candle display more brilliant than any ever seen before or since. No meteorites reached the ground, as far as is known, but the spectacle stimulated the study of meteors, and astronomers turned to it for the first time in all seriousness.

By noting the times of year when meteors came thickest, and the positions in the sky from which they seemed to come, the meteor-watchers were able to work out orbits of various clouds of meteors. In this way they learned that a meteor shower occurred when the earth's orbit intersected the orbit of a meteor cloud.

The orbits of the meteor clouds were very elongated, like those of comets rather than those of ordinary planets. In fact, some meteor-cloud orbits seemed to be associated with specific comets, a point first made in 1866 by the Italian astronomer Giovanni Virginio Schiaparelli.

Most of the meteorites found on the ground were iron, and it seemed that iron meteorites must far outnumber the stony type. This proved to be wrong, however. A lump of iron lying half-buried in a stony field is very noticeable, whereas a stone among other stones is not. When astronomers made counts of meteorites found after they were actually seen to fall, they discovered that the stony meteorites outnumbered iron ones nine to one. (For a time, most stony meteorites were discovered in Kansas, which may seem odd until one realizes that in the stoneless, sedimentary soil of Kansas a stone is as noticeable as a lump of iron would be elsewhere.)

Meteorites have seldom done any damage, nor has one ever made a direct hit on a human being, as far as is known, though a woman in Alabama reported being bruised by a glancing blow from a meteorite in 1954. Nevertheless, there have been a few tremendous meteoric strikes. In 1908, for instance, a strike in northern Siberia gouged out craters up to 150 feet in diameter and knocked down trees for 20 miles around. Fortunately, the meteorite fell in a wilderness; had it fallen from the same part of the sky five hours later in the earth's rotation, it might have hit St. Petersburg, then the capital of Russia. If it had, the city would have been wiped out as thoroughly as by an H-bomb. One estimate is that the total weight of the meteorite was 40,000 tons.

There are signs of even heavier strikes in prehistoric times. In Coconino County in Arizona there is a round crater about four-fifths of a mile across and 600 feet deep, surrounded by a lip of earth 100 to 150 feet high. It looks like a miniature crater of the moon. It was long assumed to be an extinct volcano, but a mining engineer named D. M. Barringer insisted it was the result of a meteoric collision, and the hole now bears the name of "Barringer Crater." The crater is surrounded by lumps of meteoric iron — thousands (perhaps millions) of tons of it altogether. More meteoric iron has been extracted from it and its surroundings than in all the rest of the world.

Barringer Crater, formed in the desert an estimated 50,000 years ago, has been preserved fairly well. In most parts of the world similar craters would have been obliterated by water and plant overgrowth.

Observations from airplanes, for instance, have sighted previously unnoticed circular formations, partly water-filled and partly overgrown, which are almost certainly meteoritic. Several have been discovered in Canada, including Brent Crater in Central Ontario and Chubb Crater in northern Quebec, each of which is two miles or more in diameter and perhaps hundreds of millions of years old.

The craters of the moon visible to us with telescopes range from holes no larger than Barringer Crater to giants 150 miles across. The moon, lacking air, water, or life, is a nearly perfect museum for craters, since they are subject to no wear except from the very slow action of temperature change resulting from the two-week alternation of lunar day and lunar night. Perhaps the earth would be pockmarked like the moon if it were not for the healing action of wind, water, and growing things.

Anyone who is inclined to be complacent about meteors or to think that colossal strikes were just a phenomenon of the solar system's early history might give some thought to the asteroids, or planetoids. Whatever their origin — whether they are surviving planetesimals or remnants of an exploded planet — there are some pretty big ones around and about. Most of them orbit the sun in a belt between Mars and Jupiter. But in 1898 a German astronomer, G. Witt, discovered one whose orbit, upon calculation, turned out to lie between Mars and the earth. He named it Eros, and ever since planetoids with unusual orbits have been given masculine names. (Those with ordinary orbits, between Mars and Jupiter, are given feminine names even when named after men, *e.g.*, Rockefellia, Carnegia, Hooveria.)

The orbits of Eros and the earth approach to within 13 million miles of each other, which is half the minimum distance between the earth and Venus, our closest neighbor among the full-sized planets. In 1931 Eros reached a point only 17 million miles from the earth. Several other "earth-grazers" have since been found. In 1932 two planetoids named Amor and Apollo were discovered with orbits approaching within ten million and seven million miles, respectively, of the earth's orbit. In 1936 there turned up a still closer planetoid, named Adonis, which could approach to as close as 1.5 million miles from the earth. And in 1937 a planetoid given the name Hermes swam into sight in an orbit which might bring it within 200,000 miles of the earth, or actually closer than the moon. (The calculations of Hermes' orbit may not be entirely reliable, because the object did not stay in sight long.)

Eros, the largest of the "earth-grazers," is a brick-shaped object perhaps 15 miles long and five miles broad. Others, like Hermes, are only about one mile in diameter. Still, even Hermes would gouge out a crater about 100 miles across if it hit the earth. Fortunately the odds against an encounter are enormous.

METEORITES, as the only pieces of extra-terrestrial matter we can examine, are exciting not only to astronomers, geologists, chemists, and metallurgists, but also to cosmologists, who are concerned with the origins of the Universe and the solar system. The meteorites may be samples of primitive matter formed in the early history of our system. As such, they give us an independent clock for measuring the age of our system. Their ages can be estimated in various ways, including measurement of products of radioactive decay. In 1959 John H. Reynolds of the University of California determined the age of a meteorite that had fallen in North Dakota to be five billion years, which would therefore be the minimum age of the solar system.

Meteorites make up only a tiny fraction of the matter falling into the earth's atmosphere from space. The small meteors that burn up in the air without ever reaching the ground amount to a far greater aggregate mass. Individually these bits of matter are extremely small; a shooting star as bright as Venus comes into the atmosphere as a speck weighing only one gram (1/28 of an ounce). Some visible meteors are only one 10,000th as massive as that!

The total number of meteors hitting the earth's atmosphere can be computed, and it turns out to be incredibly large. Each day there are more than 20,000 weighing at least one gram, nearly 200 million others large enough to make a glow visible to the naked eye, and many billions more of still smaller sizes.

We know about these very small "micrometeors" because the air has been found to contain dust particles with unusual shapes and a high nickel content, quite unlike ordinary terrestrial dust. Another evidence of the presence of micrometeors in vast quantities is the faint glow in the heavens called "zodiacal light" — so called because it is most noticeable in the neighborhood of the plane of the earth's orbit, where the constellations of the zodiac occur. The zodiacal light is very dim and cannot be seen even on a moonless night unless conditions are favorable. It is brightest near the horizon where the sun has set or is about to rise, and on the opposite side of the sky there is a secondary brightening called the "Gegenschein" (German for "opposite light"). The zodiacal light differs from the airglow: its spectrum has no lines of atomic oxygen or atomic sodium but is just that of reflected sunlight and nothing more. The reflecting agent, presumably, is dust concentrated in space in the plane of the planets' orbits — in short, micrometeors. Their number and size can be estimated from the intensity of the zodiacal light.

Micrometeors have now been counted with new precision by means of the satellites man has sent up. To detect them, some of the satellites are covered with patches of a sensitive material which signals each meteoric hit through a change in its electrical resistance. Others record the hits by means of a sensitive microphone behind the skin, picking up the "pings." The satellite counts have indicated that 3,000 tons of meteoric matter enter our atmosphere each day, five-sixths of it consisting of micrometeors too small to be detected as shooting stars.

The geophysicist Hans Petterson, who has been particularly interested in this meteoric dust, took some samples of air in 1957 on a mountain-top in Hawaii, which is as far from industrial dust-producing areas as one can get on the earth. His findings led him to believe that about five million tons of meteoric dust fall on the earth each year. Petterson tried to get a line on this fall in the past by analyzing cores brought up from the ocean bottom for high-nickel dust.

He found that, on the whole, there was more in the upper sediments than in the older ones below, which indicates — though the evidence is still scanty — that the rate of meteoric bombardment may have increased in recent ages.

Although the rain of meteors may seem heavy, actually it does not amount to even a drizzle in the vastness of space. Apparently meteors will not be a serious barrier to space flight — nothing like the hazard presented by radiation.

THE ORIGIN OF AIR

PERHAPS we should wonder less about how the earth got its atmosphere than about how it has managed to hang on to it through all the eons the earth has been whirling and wheeling through space. The answer to the latter question involves something called "escape velocity."

If an object is thrown upward from the earth, the pull of gravity gradually slows it until it comes to a momentary halt and then falls back. If the force of gravity were the same all the way up, the height reached by the object would be proportional to its initial upward velocity; that is, it would reach four times as high when launched with a speed of two miles an hour as it would when it started at one mile an hour (energy increases as the square of the velocity).

But of course the force of gravity does not remain constant: it weakens slowly with height. (To be exact, it weakens as the square of the distance from the earth's center.) Let us say we shoot an object upward with a velocity of one mile per second. It will reach a height of 80 miles before turning and falling (if we ignore air resistance). If we were to fire the same object upward at two miles per second, it would climb higher than four times that distance. At the height of 80 miles, the pull of the earth's gravity is appreciably lower than at ground level, so that the object's further flight would be subject to a smaller gravitational drag. In fact, the projectile would rise to 350 miles, not 320.

Given an initial upward velocity of 6.5 miles per second, an object will climb 25,800 miles. At that point the force of gravity is not more than one-fortieth as strong as it is on the earth's surface. If we added just one-tenth of a mile per second to the object's initial speed (*i.e.*, launched it at 6.6 miles per second), it would go up to 34,300 miles.

It can be calculated that an object fired up at an initial speed of 6.98 miles per second will never fall back to the earth. Although the earth's gravity will gradually slow the object's velocity, its effect will steadily decline, so that it will never bring the object to a halt (zero velocity) with respect to the earth. (So much for the cliché that "everything that goes up must come down.") Lunik I and Pioneer IV, fired at better than seven miles per second, will never come down.

The speed of 6.98 miles per second, then, is the earth's "escape velocity." The velocity of escape from any astronomical body can be calculated from its mass and size. From the moon, it is only 1.5 miles per second; from Mars, 3.2 miles per second; from Saturn, 23 miles per second; from Jupiter, the most massive planet in the solar system, it is 38 miles per second.

Now all this has a direct bearing on the earth's retention of its atmosphere. The atoms and molecules of the air are constantly flying about like tiny missiles. Their individual velocities vary a great deal, and the only way they can be described is statistically: for example, what fraction of the molecules are moving faster than a particular velocity, or what the average velocity is under given conditions. The formula for doing this was first worked out in 1860 by James Clerk Maxwell and the Austrian physicist Ludwig Boltzmann, and it is called the "Maxwell-Boltzmann Law."

The mean velocity of oxygen molecules in air at room temperature turns out to be 0.3 mile per second. The hydrogen molecule, being only one-sixteenth as heavy, moves on the average four times as fast, or 1.2 miles per second, because, according to the Maxwell-Boltzmann Law, the velocity of a particular particle at a particular temperature is inversely proportional to the square root of its molecular weight.

It is important to remember that these are only average velocities. Half the molecules go faster than the average; a certain percentage go more than twice as fast as the average; a smaller percentage more than three times as fast, and so on. In fact, a tiny percentage of the oxygen and hydrogen molecules in the atmosphere go faster than 6.98 miles per second, the escape velocity.

In the lower atmosphere these speedsters cannot actually escape, because collisions with their slower neighbors slow them down. But in the upper atmosphere, their chances are much better. First of all, the unimpeded radiation of the sun up there excites a large proportion of them to enormous energy and great speeds. And in the second place, the probability of collisions is greatly reduced in the thinner air. Whereas a molecule at the earth's surface travels only four-millionths of an inch (on the average) before colliding with a neighbor, at a height of 65 miles its average free path before colliding is four inches, and at 140 miles, it is 1,100 yards. There the average number of collisions encountered by an atom or molecule is only one per second, against five billion per second at sea level. Thus a fast particle at a height of 100 miles or more stands a good chance of escaping from the earth. If it happens to be moving upward, it is moving into regions of lesser and lesser density and experiences an ever smaller chance of collision, so that it may in the end depart into interplanetary space, never to return.

In other words, the earth's atmosphere leaks. But the leakage applies mainly to the lightest molecules. Oxygen and nitrogen are heavy enough so that only a tiny fraction of them achieves the escape velocity, and not much oxygen or nitrogen has been lost from the earth since their original formation. On the other hand, hydrogen and helium are easily raised to escape velocity. Consequently it is not surprising that no hydrogen or helium to speak of remains in the atmosphere of the earth today.

The more massive planets, such as Jupiter and Saturn, can hold even hydrogen and helium, so they may have large and deep atmospheres composed mostly of these elements (which, after all, are the most common substances in the universe). On the other hand, a small planet like Mars is less able to hold even the comparatively heavy molecules and has an atmosphere only one-tenth as dense as our own. The moon, with a smaller escape velocity, can't hold any atmosphere to speak of and is airless.

Temperature is just as important a factor as gravity. The Maxwell-Boltzmann equation says that the average speed of particles is proportional to the square root of the absolute temperature. If the earth were at the temperature of the sun's surface, all the atoms and molecules in its atmosphere would be speeded up by four to five times, and the earth could no more hold on to its oxygen and nitrogen than it could to hydrogen or helium.

THE EARTH'S POSSESSION of an atmosphere is a strong point against the theory that it and the other planets of the Solar system originated from some catastrophic accident, such as a near-collision between another sun and ours. It argues, rather, in favor of the dust-cloud and planetesimal theory. As the dust and gas of the cloud condensed into planetesimals, and these in turn collected to form a planetary body, gas might have been trapped within a spongy mass, like air in a snowbank. The subsequent gravity contraction of the mass might then have squeezed out the gases toward the surface. Whether a particular gas would be held in the earth would depend in part on its chemical reactivity. Helium and neon, though they must have been among the most common gases in the original cloud, are so inert chemically that they form no compounds and would have escaped as gases in short order. Therefore the concentrations of helium and neon on the earth are insignificant fractions of their concentrations in the Universe generally. It has been calculated, for instance, that the earth has retained only one out of every 50 billion neon atoms present in the original cloud of gas, and our atmosphere has even fewer, if any, of the original helium atoms. I say "if any"

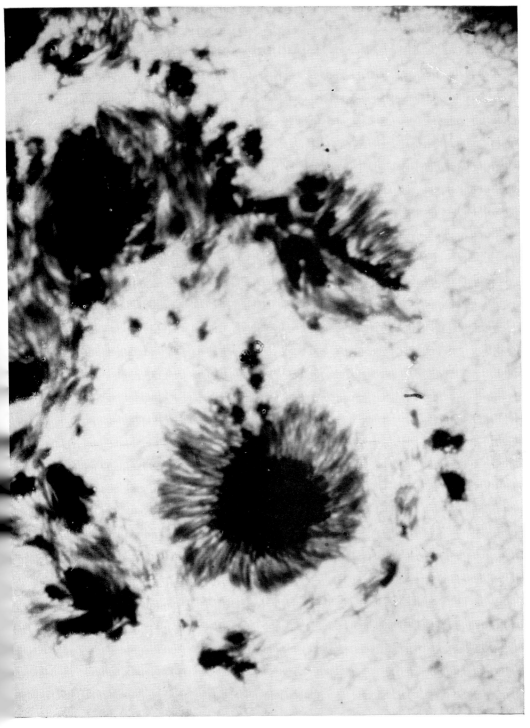

SUN SPOTS *photographed with unprecedented sharpness by the U.S. Stratoscope project from a balloon at 80,000 feet on August 17, 1959. The spots consist of a dark core of relatively cool gases embedded in a strong magnetic field. This group of particularly active spots produced a brilliant aurora and a vigorous magnetic storm on the earth.*

WILLAMETTE
Willamette Oregon
Gift of Mrs. William E. Dodge 2d
Found 1902

A LARGE IRON METEORITE.

THE GREAT METEOR CRATER IN ARIZONA.

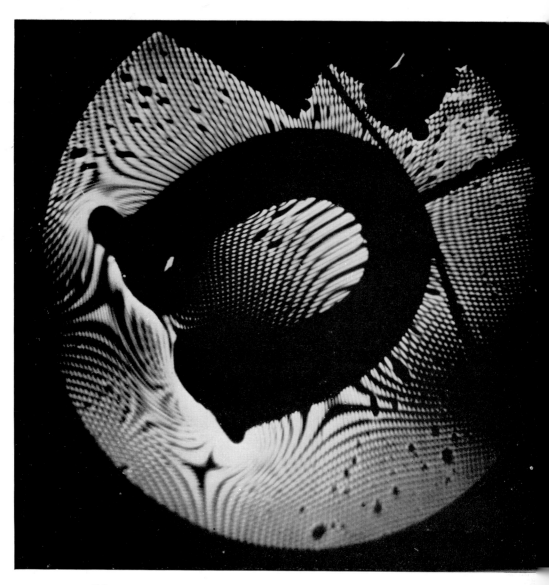

MAGNETIC FIELD, *photographed with an electron microscope by means of a new shadow technique developed by the U.S. National Bureau of Standards. The small horseshoe magnet used here is only about one-fourth of an inch wide.*

because, while there is a little helium in the atmosphere today, all of it may come from the breakdown of radioactive elements and leakage of helium trapped in cavities underground.

On the other hand, hydrogen, though lighter than helium or neon, has been captured with greater efficiency because it has combined with other substances, notably with oxygen to form water. It is estimated that the earth still has one out of every five million hydrogen atoms that were in the original cloud.

Nitrogen and oxygen illustrate the chemical aspect even more neatly. Although the nitrogen molecule and the oxygen molecule are about equal in mass, the earth has held on to one out of six of the original atoms of highly reactive oxygen but only one out of every 800,000 of inert nitrogen.

When we speak of gases of the atmosphere, we have to include water vapor, and here we get into the interesting question of how the oceans originated. In the early stages of the earth's history, even if it was only moderately hot, all the water must have been in the form of vapor. Some geologists believe that the water was then concentrated in the atmosphere as a dense cloud of vapor, and after the earth cooled, it fell in torrents to form the ocean. (The planet Venus has a thick, cloudy mantle which may represent just such an uncondensed ocean, still vaporized because Venus is closer to the sun and hotter. In 1959 observations of Venus from a balloon 20 miles above the earth's surface showed that its atmosphere does contain water vapor.)

On the other hand, some geologists maintain that our oceans have been built up mainly by water seeping up from the earth's interior. Volcanoes show that there is a great deal of water in the crust still, for the gas they discharge is mostly water vapor. According to this theory, the oceans may still be growing very slowly. So the question of the origin of the oceans is far from settled, and there is little definite information to help choose between the alternatives.

The original composition of the earth's atmosphere is another matter of controversy. The geochemist Harold Urey has presented detailed arguments in favor of the idea that the original atmosphere was composed of ammonia and methane. Hydrogen, helium, carbon, nitrogen, and oxygen are the predominant elements in the universe, with hydrogen far and away the most common. In the presence of such a preponderance of hydrogen, carbon would be likely to combine with hydrogen to form methane (CH_4), nitrogen with hydrogen to form ammonia (NH_3), and oxygen with hydrogen to form water (H_2O). Helium and excess hydrogen would, of course, escape; the water would form the oceans; the methane and ammonia, as comparatively heavy gases, would be held by the earth's gravity and so constitute the major portion of the atmosphere.

An interesting point in favor of this theory is that Jupiter, Saturn, Uranus, and Neptune have substantial proportions of ammonia and methane in their atmospheres, though these planets, because of their greater mass, have been able to retain hydrogen and helium too. (In fact, their ammonia and methane were discovered first, because these compounds produce noticeable absorption bands in the spectra, whereas hydrogen and helium do not.)

William W. Rubey of the United States Geological Survey has argued, on the other hand, that the earth's original atmosphere consisted chiefly of carbon dioxide and nitrogen. As evidence, he points to the fact that meteorites (which are probably similar to the planetesimals out of which the earth may have been formed) give off mainly carbon dioxide and nitrogen as gases when they are heated strongly. In 1959 Frank J. Stevenson of the University of Illinois suggested that the earth's rocks still hold trapped 20 times as much nitrogen as the amount in the air, and that they are gradually releasing this as they erode. Again, the atmospheres of Mars and Venus, the planets that most closely resemble the earth, are composed of carbon dioxide and (probably) nitrogen.

Whether the earth's original atmosphere consisted of methane and ammonia or of nitrogen and carbon dioxide, the geochemists agree on one thing: it did not contain free oxygen. Where, then, did the oxygen come from?

The most dramatic suggestion is that it arose through the activity of life. As the result of photosynthesis, the process by which green

plants use the energy of sunlight to convert water and carbon dioxide into the carbon-containing compounds that make up living tissue, the plants liberate oxygen. Thus they steadily increase the atmosphere's oxygen and soak up its carbon dioxide. In this way a
carbon-dioxide-and-nitrogen atmosphere might be converted into
an oxygen-and-nitrogen atmosphere. Photosynthesis could also transform an ammonia-and-methane atmosphere into the one we have
now, but by a more complicated process.

At all events, it seems likely that the earth's oxygen-filled atmosphere (which is unique in the Solar system) is a modern development that has been in existence for only 10 per cent or so of the
earth's lifetime.

CHAPTER

5

THE
ELEMENTS

THE PERIODIC TABLE

T HE GREEKS, whose approach to most problems was theoretical
and speculative, decided that the earth was made of four "elements" — earth, air, water, and fire — and the heavens of a fifth substance, ether. Their successors in the study of matter, the medieval
alchemists, got mired in magic and quackery, but they came to
shrewder and more reasonable conclusions than the Greeks because
they at least handled the materials they speculated about.

Seeking to explain the various properties of substances, the alchemists attached these properties to certain controlling elements
they added to the list. They identified mercury as the element that
imparted metallic properties to substances, and sulfur as the element
that imparted the property of inflammability. One of the last and

best of the alchemists, the sixteenth-century Swiss physician Theo-phrastus Bombastus von Hohenheim, better known as Paracelsus, added salt as the element that imparted resistance to heat.

The alchemists reasoned that one substance could be changed into another by merely adding and subtracting elements in the proper proportions. A metal such as lead, for instance, might be changed into gold by adding the right amount of mercury to the lead. The search for the precise technique of converting "base metal" to gold went on for centuries. In the process the alchemists discovered sub-stances vastly more important than gold — such as the mineral acids and phosphorus. But they never let themselves be diverted from the main quest. Unscrupulous members of the craft indulged in outright fakery, producing gold by sleight-of-hand, to win what we would call today "research grants" from rich patrons. This brought the profession into such disrepute that the very word "alchemist" had to be abandoned. By the seventeenth century "alchemist" had become "chemist" and "alchemy" had graduated to a science called "chem-istry."

In the bright birth of science, one of the first of the new chemists was Robert Boyle, the author of "Boyle's Law" of gases (see Chap-ter 4). In his *The Sceptical Chymist*, published in 1661, Boyle first laid down the specific modern criterion of an element: a basic sub-stance which can be combined with other elements to form "com-pounds" and which, conversely, cannot be broken down to any simpler substance after it is isolated from a compound.

Boyle retained a medieval view about what the actual elements were. For instance, he believed that gold could be formed in some way from other metals. So, in fact, did his contemporary, Isaac New-ton, who devoted a great deal of time to alchemy.

In the century after Boyle, practical chemical work began to make clear which substances could be broken down into simpler substances and which could not. Henry Cavendish showed that hydrogen would combine with oxygen to form water, so water could not be an element. Later Lavoisier resolved the supposed element air into oxygen and nitrogen. It became plain that none of the Greek "elements" was an element by Boyle's criterion.

As for the elements of the alchemists, mercury and sulfur did indeed turn out to be elements "according to Boyle." But so did iron, tin, lead, copper, silver, and gold, and non-metals such as phosphorus, carbon and arsenic. And Paracelsus's "element" salt eventually was broken down into two simpler substances.

Of course, the definition of elements depended on the chemistry of the time. As long as a substance could not be broken down by the chemical techniques of the day, it could still be considered an element. For instance Lavoisier's list of 33 elements included such items as lime and magnesia. But 14 years after Lavoisier's death on the guillotine in the French Revolution the English chemist Humphry Davy, using an electric current to split the substances, divided lime into oxygen and a new element he called "calcium," and similarly split magnesia into oxygen and another new element he named "magnesium."

On the other hand, Davy was able to show that a green gas which the Swedish chemist Carl Wilhelm Scheele had made from hydrochloric acid was not a compound of hydrochloric acid and oxygen, as had been thought, but a true element, and he named it "chlorine" (from the Greek word for "green").

AT THE BEGINNING of the nineteenth century the English chemist John Dalton came up with a radically new way of looking at elements. Oddy enough, this view harked back to some of the Greeks, who had, after all, contributed what has turned out to be perhaps the most important single concept in the understanding of matter.

The Greeks argued about whether matter was continuous or discrete: that is, whether it could be reduced to an ever smaller quantity of material or would be found in the end to consist of indivisible particles. Leucippus of Miletus and his pupil, Democritus of Abdera, insisted that the latter was the case. Democritus, in fact, gave the particles a name: he called them "atoms" (meaning "non-divisible"). He even suggested that different substances were composed of different atoms or combinations of atoms and that one substance could be converted into another by rearranging the atoms. Considering that all this was only an intelligent guess, one is thunderstruck by the correctness of his intuition. Although the idea may seem obvious today, it was so far from obvious at the time that Plato and Aristotle rejected it out of hand.

Dalton's resurrection of the idea of 1803 came at a time when, thanks to the experiments of Boyle and others, gases were surmised to be made up of particles. Dalton showed that the various rules governing the behavior of gases could all be explained on the basis of the atomic nature of matter. (He recognized the priority of Democritus by using the word "atoms.") According to Dalton, each element represented a particular kind of atom, and any quantity of the element was made up of identical atoms of this kind. What distinguished one element from another was the nature of its atoms. And the basic physical difference between atoms was in their weight. Thus sulfur atoms were heavier than oxygen atoms, which in turn were heavier than nitrogen atoms, they in turn heavier than carbon atoms, and these in turn heavier than hydrogen atoms.

Naturally it became important to measure the relative weights of different atoms — to find the "atomic weights" of the elements, so to speak. The tiny atoms themselves were hopelessly beyond the reach of any known weighing technique. But by weighing the quantity of each element separated from a compound, and making deductions from the elements' chemical behavior, it was possible to work out the relative weights of the atoms. The first to go about this systematically was the Swedish chemist Jöns Jacob Berzelius. In 1828 he published a list of atomic weights based on two standards — one giving the atomic weight of oxygen the arbitrary value of 100, the other taking the atomic weight of hydrogen as equal to 1.

Berzelius's system did not catch on at once, but in 1860, at the first International Chemical Congress in Karlsruhe, Germany, the Italian chemist Stanislao Cannizzaro presented new methods for determining atomic weights and described their value so forcefully that the world of chemistry was won over.

The weight of oxygen, rather than hydrogen, was adopted as the standard, because oxygen could more easily be brought into combination with various elements (and combination with other elements was the key step in the usual method of determining atomic weights). Oxygen's atomic weight was arbitrarily taken as exactly 16, so that the atomic weight of hydrogen, the lightest known element, would be just about one — 1.0080, to be exact.

Ever since Cannizzaro's time, chemists have sought to work out atomic weights with greater and greater accuracy. This reached a climax, as far as purely chemical methods were concerned, in the work of the American chemist Theodore William Richards, who in 1904 and thereafter determined the atomic weights with an accuracy previously unapproached. For this he received the Nobel Prize in chemistry in 1914. On the basis of later discoveries about the physical constitution of atoms, Richards's figures have since been corrected to still more refined values.

So atoms have steadily been translated from semi-mystical abstractions into almost tangible objects. Indeed, today we can say that man has at last "seen" the atom. This is accomplished with the so-called "field ion microscope," invented in 1955 by Erwin W. Mueller of Pennsylvania State University. His device strips positively charged ions off an extremely fine needle-tip and shoots them to a fluorescent screen in such a way as to produce a hugely magnified image of the needle-tip. This image actually makes the individual atoms composing the tip visible as bright little dots. Mueller's photographs of atoms bid fair to become classics in the history of science.

AS THE LIST OF ELEMENTS grew in the nineteenth century, chemists began to feel as if they were becoming entangled in a thickening jungle. Every element had different properties, and they could see no underlying order in the list. Since the essence of science is to try to find order in apparent disorder, scientists hunted for some sort of pattern in the properties of the elements.

In 1862, after Cannizarro had established atomic weight as one of the important working tools of chemistry, a French geologist, Alexandre Emile Beguyer de Chancourtois, found that he could arrange the elements in the order of increasing atomic weight in a tabular form, such that elements with similar properties fell in the same vertical column. Two years later a British chemist, John Alexander Reina Newlands, independently arrived at the same arrangement. But both were ignored or ridiculed. Neither could get his suggestions published at the time. Many years later, after the importance of the periodic table had become universally recognized, their papers were published at last. Newlands even got a medal.

It was the Russian chemist Dmitri Ivanovich Mendeleev who got the credit for finally bringing order into the jungle of the elements. In 1869 he and the German chemist, Julius Lothar Meyer, both proposed tables of the elements making essentially the same point that de Chancourtois and Newlands had already made. But Mendeleev received the recognition because he had the courage and confidence to push the idea farther than the others.

In the first place, Mendeleev's "periodic table" (so-called because it showed the periodic recurrence of similar chemical properties) was more complicated than that of Newlands, and nearer what we now believe to be correct. Secondly, where the properties of an element placed it out of order according to its atomic weight, he boldly switched the order, on the ground that the properties were more important than the atomic weight. He was eventually proved correct in this. For instance, tellurium, with an atomic weight of 127.61, should, on the weight basis, come after iodine, whose atomic weight is 126.91. But in the columnar table, putting tellurium ahead of iodine places it under selenium, which it closely resembles, and similarly puts iodine under its cousin bromine.

Finally, and most important, where Mendeleev could find no other way to make his arrangement work, he did not hesitate to leave holes in the table and to announce, with what seemed infinite gall, that elements must be discovered that belonged in those holes. He went farther. For three of the holes, he described the element that would fit each, utilizing as his guide the properties of the elements above and below the hole in the table. And here Mendeleev had a stroke of luck. Each of his three predicted elements was found in his own lifetime, so that he witnessed the triumph of his system. In 1875 the French chemist Lecoq de Boisbaudran discovered the first of these missing elements and named it "gallium" (after the Latin name for France). In 1879 the Swedish chemist Lars Fredrick Nilson found the second and named it "scandium" (after Scandinavia). And in 1886 the German chemist Clemens Alexander Winkler isolated the third and named it "germanium" (after Germany, of course). All three elements had almost precisely the properties predicted by Mendeleev!

WITH THE DISCOVERY of X-rays, a new era opened in the history of the periodic table. In 1911 the British physicist Charles Glover Barkla discovered that when X-rays were scattered by a metal, the scattered rays had a sharply defined penetrating power depending on the metal; in other words, each element produced its own "characteristic X-rays." For this discovery Barkla was awarded the Nobel Prize in physics for 1917. Meanwhile the German physicist Max Theodore Felix von Laue had found that X-rays passing through a crystal were diffracted (bent) and formed a pattern on a photographic plate which showed that they had the properties of waves. Within the same year the English physicist William Lawrence Bragg and his equally distinguished father William Henry Bragg developed an accurate method of calculating the wavelength of a particular type of X-ray from its diffraction pattern. For these discoveries von Laue and the Braggs also won Nobel Prizes. Then in 1914 the young English physicist Henry Gwyn-Jeffreys Moseley determined the wavelengths of the characteristic X-rays produced by various metals and made the important discovery that the wavelength decreased in a very regular manner as one went up the periodic table.

THE PERIODIC TABL

The shaded areas of the table represent the two rare-earth series: The lanthanides and the actinides, named after their respective first members. The number in the lower right hand corner of each box indicates the atomic weight of the element.

1								
Hydrogen								
(H) 1.008								

3	4							
Lithium	Beryllium							
(Li) 6.94	(Be) 9.013							

11	12							
Sodium	Magnesium							
(Na) 22.997	(Mg) 24.32							

19	20	21	22	23	24	25	26	27
Potassium	Calcium	Scandium	Titanium	Vanadium	Chromium	Manganese	Iron	Cobalt
(K) 39.096	(Ca) 40.08	(Sc) 44.96	(Ti) 47.90	(V) 50.95	(Cr) 52.01	(Mn) 54.93	(Fe) 55.85	(Co) 58.

37	38	39	40	41	42	43	44	45
Rubidium	Strontium	Yttrium	Zirconium	Niobium	Molybdenum	Technetium	Ruthenium	Rhodium
(Rb) 85.48	(Sr) 87.63	(Y) 88.92	(Zr) 91.22	(Nb) 92.91	(Mo) 95.95	(Tc) 98.91	(Ru) 101.7	(Rh) 102.

55	56	57	58	59	60	61	62	63
Cesium	Barium	Lanthanum	Cerium	Praseodymium	Neodymium	Promethium	Samarium	Europium
(Cs) 132.91	(Ba) 137.36	(La) 138.92	(Ce) 140.13	(Pr) 140.92	(Nd) 144.27	(Pm) 145	(Sm) 150.43	(Eu) 15

			72	73	74	75	76	77
			Hafnium	Tantalum	Tungsten	Rhenium	Osmium	Iridium
			(Hf) 178.6	(Ta) 180.88	(W) 183.92	(Re) 186.31	(Os) 190.2	(Ir) 19

87	88	89	90	91	92	93	94	95
Francium	Radium	Actinium	Thorium	Protactinium	Uranium	Neptunium	Plutonium	Americiu
(Fr) 223	(Ra) . 226.05	(Ac) 227	(Th) 232.12	(Pa) 231	(U) 238.07	(Np) 237	(Pu) 242	(Am) 2

								2 Helium (He) 4.003
			5 Boron (B) 10.82	6 Carbon (C) 12.01	7 Nitrogen (N) 14.008	8 Oxygen (O) 16.00	9 Fluorine (F) 19.00	10 Neon (Ne) 20.183
			13 Aluminum (Al) 26.97	14 Silicon (Si) 28.09	15 Phosphorus (P) 30.978	16 Sulfur (S) 32.066	17 Chlorine (Cl) 35.457	18 Argon (A) 39.944
28 Nickel) 58.69	29 Copper (Cu) 63.542	30 Zinc (Zn) 65.377	31 Gallium (Ga) 69.72	32 Germanium (Ge) 72.60	33 Arsenic (As) 74.91	34 Selenium (Se) 78.96	35 Bromine (Br) 79.916	36 Krypton (Kr) 83.70
46 Palladium) 106.7	47 Silver (Ag) 107.88	48 Cadmium (Cd) 112.41	49 Indium (In) 114.76	50 Tin (Sn) 118.7	51 Antimony (Sb) 121.76	52 Tellurium (Te) 127.61	53 Iodine (I) 126.91	54 Xenon (Xe) 131.3
64 Gadolinium) 156.9	65 Terbium (Tb) 159.2	66 Dysprosium (Dy) 162.46	67 Holmium (Ho) 164.94	68 Erbium (Er) 167.2	69 Thulium (Tm) 169.4	70 Ytterbium (Yb) 173.04	71 Lutetium (Lu) 174.99	
78 Platinum) 195.23	79 Gold (Au) 197.2	80 Mercury (Hg) 200.61	81 Thallium (Tl) 204.39	82 Lead (Pb) 207.21	83 Bismuth (Bi) 209.00	84 Polonium (Po) 210	85 Astatine (At) 210	86 Radon (Rn) 222
96 Curium m) 244	97 Berkelium (Bk) 245	98 Californium (Cf) 246	99 Einsteinium (Es) 253	100 Fermium (Fm) 255	101 Mendelevium (Md) 256	102 Nobelium (No)		

This pinned the elements into definite position in the table. If two elements, supposedly adjacent in the table, yielded X-rays which differed in wavelength by twice the expected amount, then there must be a gap between them belonging to an unknown element. If they differed by three times the expected amount, there must be two missing elements. If, on the other hand, the two elements' characteristic X-rays differed by only the expected amount, one could be certain that there was no missing element between the two.

It was now possible to give the elements definite numbers. Until then there had always been the possibility that some new discovery might break into the sequence and throw any adopted numbering system out of kilter. Now there could no longer be unsuspected gaps.

Chemists proceeded to number the elements from 1 (hydrogen) to 92 (uranium). These "atomic numbers" were found to be significant in connection with the internal structures of the atoms (see Chapter 6) and to be more fundamental than the atomic weight. For instance, the X-ray data proved that Mendeleev had been right in placing tellurium (atomic number 52) before iodine (53), in spite of tellurium's higher atomic weight.

Moseley's new system proved its worth almost at once. The French chemist Georges Urbain, after discovering "lutetium" (named after the old Latin name of Paris), had later announced that he had discovered another element which he called "celtium." According to Moseley's system, lutetium was element 71 and "celtium" should be 72. But when Moseley analyzed "celtium's" characteristic X-rays, it turned out to be lutetium all over again. Element 72 was not actually discovered until 1923, when the Danish physicist Dirk Coster and the Hungarian chemist Georg von Hevesy detected it in a Copenhagen laboratory and named it "hafnium," from the Latinized name of Copenhagen.

Moseley was not present for this verification of the accuracy of his method: he had been killed at Gallipoli in 1915 at the age of 28 — certainly one of the most valuable lives lost in World War I.

In 1925 Walter Noddack, Ida Tacke, and Otto Berg of Germany filled another hole in the periodic table. After a three-year search through ores containing elements related to the one they were hunting for, they turned up element 75 and named it "rhenium," in honor of the Rhine River. This left only four holes: elements 43, 61, 85, and 87.

It was to take two decades to track those four down. Although chemists didn't realize it at the time, they had found the last of the stable elements. The missing ones were unstable species so rare on the earth today that all but one of them would have to be created in the laboratory to be identified. And thereby hangs a tale.

RADIOACTIVE ELEMENTS

AFTER THE DISCOVERY of X-rays, many scientists were impelled to investigate these new and dramatically penetrating radiations. One of them was the French physicist Antoine-Henri Becquerel. Henri's father, Alexandre Edmond, himself a famous physicist, had been particularly interested in "fluorescence" and had studied a fluorescent substance called potassium uranyl sulfate (a compound containing an atom of uranium). Henri wondered whether the fluorescent radiations of the potassium uranyl sulfate contained X-rays. The way to check this was to expose the sulfate to sunlight (whose ultraviolet light would excite the fluorescence) while the compound lay on a photographic plate wrapped in black paper. Since the sunlight could not penetrate the black paper, it would not itself affect the plate, but if the fluorescence it excited contained X-rays, they *would* penetrate the paper and darken the plate. Becquerel tried the experiment in 1896 and it worked. Apparently there were X-rays in the fluorescence. Becquerel even got the supposed X-rays to pass through thin sheets of aluminum and copper, and that seemed to clinch the matter, for no radiation except X-rays was known to do this.

But then, by a great stroke of good fortune, a siege of cloudy weather intervened. Waiting for the return of sunlight, Becquerel put away his photographic plates, with pinches of sulfate lying on them, in a drawer. After several days he grew impatient and decided to develop his plates anyway, with the thought that even without direct sunlight some trace of X-rays might have been produced. When he saw the developed pictures, Becquerel experienced one of those moments of deep astonishment and delight that are the dream of all scientists. The photographic plate was deeply darkened by strong radiation! Something other than fluorescence or sunlight was responsible for it. Becquerel decided (and experiments quickly proved) that this something was the uranium in the potassium uranyl sulfate.

This discovery further electrified scientists, already greatly excited by the recent discovery of the X-rays. One of the scientists who at once set out to investigate the strange radiation from uranium was a young Polish-born chemist named Marie Sklodowska, who just the year before had married a French chemist named Pierre Curie.

Pierre Curie, in collaboration with his brother Jacques, had discovered that certain crystals, when put under pressure, developed a positive electric charge on one side and a negative charge on the other. This phenomenon is called "piezo-electricity" (from a Greek word meaning "to press"). Marie Curie decided to measure the radiation given off from uranium by means of piezo-electricity. She set up an arrangement whereby this radiation would ionize the air between two electrodes, a current would then flow, and the strength of this small current would be measured by the amount of pressure that had to be placed on a crystal to produce a balancing counter-current. The method worked so well that Pierre Curie dropped his own work at once and, for the rest of his life, joined Marie as an eager second.

It was Marie Curie who suggested the term "radioactivity" to describe the ability of uranium to give off radiations and who went on to demonstrate the phenomenon in a second radioactive substance — thorium. In fast succession, enormously important discoveries were made by other scientists as well. The penetrating radiations from radioactive substances turned out to be even more penetrating and more energetic than X-rays; they are now called "gamma rays." Radioactive elements were found to give off other types of radiation also, which led to discoveries about the internal structure of the atom, but this is a story for another chapter (see Chapter 6). What has the greatest bearing on our discussion of the elements is the discovery that the radioactive elements, in giving off the radiation, changed to other elements — a modern version of transmutation.

Marie Curie was the first to come upon the implications of this phenomenon, and she did so accidentally. In testing pitchblende for its uranium content, to see if samples of the ore had enough uranium to be worth the refining effort, she and her husband found to their surprise that some of the pieces had more radioactivity than they ought to have even if they were made of pure uranium. This meant, of course, that there had to be other radioactive elements in the pitchblende. These unknown elements could only be present in small quantities, because ordinary chemical analysis did not detect them, so they must be very radioactive indeed.

In great excitement, the Curies obtained tons of pitchblende, set up shop in a small shack and under primitive conditions, and with only their unbeatable enthusiasm to drive them on, they proceeded to struggle through the heavy, black ore for the trace quantities of new elements. By July of 1898 they had isolated a trace of black powder 400 times as intensely radioactive as the same quantity of uranium.

This contained a new element with chemical properties like those of tellurium, and it therefore probably belonged beneath it in the periodic table (it was later given the atomic number 84). The Curies named it "polonium," after Marie's native land.

But polonium accounted for only part of the radioactivity. More work followed, and by December of 1898 the Curies had a preparation which was even more intensely radioactive than polonium. It contained still another element, which had properties like those of barium (and was eventually placed beneath barium with the atomic number 88). The Curies called it "radium," because of its intense radioactivity.

They worked on for four more years to collect enough pure radium so that they could see it. Then Marie Curie presented a summary of her work as her Ph.D. thesis in 1903. It was probably the greatest doctor's thesis in scientific history. It earned her not one but two Nobel Prizes; she is to this date the only person ever to win two. Marie and her husband, along with Becquerel, received the Nobel physics prize in 1903 for their studies of radioactivity, and in 1911 Marie alone (her husband having died in a traffic accident in 1906) was awarded the prize in chemistry for the discovery of polonium and radium.

Polonium and radium are far more unstable than uranium or thorium, which is another way of saying they are far more radioactive. More of their atoms break down each second. Their lifetimes are so short that practically all the polonium and radium in the Universe should have disappeared within a matter of a million years or so. Why do we still find them in the billions-of-years-old earth? The answer is that radium and polonium are continually being formed in the course of the breakdown of uranium and thorium to lead. Wherever uranium and thorium are found, small traces of polonium and radium are likewise to be found. They are intermediate products on the way to lead as the end product.

Three other unstable elements on the path from uranium and thorium to lead were discovered by means of the careful analysis of pitchblende or by researches into radioactive substances. In 1899 André Louis Debierne, on the advice of the Curies, searched pitchblende for other elements and came up with one he called "actinium" (from the Greek word for "ray"), which eventually received the atomic number 89. The following year the German physicist Friedrich Ernst Dorn demonstrated that radium, when it broke down, formed a gaseous element. A radioactive gas was something new! Eventually the element was named "radon" (from radium and argon, its chemical cousin) and was given the atomic number 86.

Finally, in 1917 two different groups — Otto Hahn and Lise Meitner in Germany and Frederick Soddy and John A. Cranston in England — isolated from pitchblende element 91, named protactinium.

By 1925, then, the score stood at 88 identified elements — 81 stable and seven unstable. The search for the missing four — numbers 43, 61, 85, 87 — became avid indeed.

Since all the known elements from number 84 to 92 were radioactive, it was confidently expected that 85 and 87 would be radioactive as well. On the other hand, 43 and 61 were surrounded by stable elements, and there seemed no reason to suspect that they were not themselves stable as well. Consequently they should be found in nature.

Element 43, lying just above rhenium in the periodic table, was expected to have similar properties and to be found in the same ores. In fact, the team of Noddack, Tacke, and Berg, who had discovered rhenium, felt certain that they had also detected X-rays of a wavelength that went along with element 43. So they announced its discovery, too, and named it "masurium," after a region in East Prussia. However, their identification was not confirmed, and in science a discovery is not a discovery unless and until it has been confirmed by at least one independent researcher.

In 1926 two University of Illinois chemists, J. A. Harris and B. S. Hopkins, announced that they had found element 61 in ores containing its neighboring elements (60 and 62), and they named their discovery "illinium." The same year, a pair of Italian chemists at the University of Florence, L. Rolla and L. Fernandes, thought they had isolated the same element and named it "florentium." But other chemists could not confirm the work of either group.

A few years later an Alabama Polytechnic Institute physicist named Fred Allison, using a new analytical method of his own devising, reported that he had found small traces of element 87 and of element 85; he called them "virginium" and "alabamine," after his native and adopted States, respectively. But these discoveries could not be confirmed, either, and Allison's analytical method did not seem valid to most chemists.

Events were to show that the "discoverers" of elements 43, 61, 85, and 87 had been mistaken.

The first of the four to be identified beyond doubt was element 43. The American physicist Ernest Orlando Lawrence, who was to receive the Nobel Prize in physics for his invention of the cyclotron (see Chapter 6), made the element in his accelerator by bombarding molybdenum (element 42) with high-speed particles. His bombarded material developed radioactivity, and Lawrence sent it for analysis to the Italian chemist Emilio Gino Segrè, who was interested in the element 43 problem. Segrè and his colleague C. Perrier, after separating the radioactive part from the molybdenum, found that it resembled rhenium in its properties but was not rhenium. They decided it could only be element number 43, and that element number 43, unlike its neighbors in the periodic table, was radioactive. Because it is not being produced as a breakdown product of a higher element, virtually none of it is left in the earth's crust, and so Noddack and company were undoubtedly mistaken in thinking they had found it. Segrè and Perrier eventually were given the privilege of naming element 43: they called it "technetium," from a Greek word meaning "artificial," because it was the first man-made element. (Segrè was later to receive a Nobel Prize for quite another discovery, having to do with another man-made bit of matter — see Chapter 6.)

In 1939 element number 87 was finally discovered in nature. The French chemist Marguerite Perey isolated it from among the breakdown products of uranium. It was present in extremely small amounts, and only improvements in technique enabled it to be found where earlier it had been missed. She later named the new element "francium," after her native land.

Element 85, like technetium, was produced in the cyclotron, by bombardment of bismuth (element 83). In 1940 Segrè, D. R. Corson, and K. R. MacKenzie isolated element 85 at the University of California, Segrè having emigrated from Italy to the United States.

World War II interrupted their work on the element, but after the war they returned to it and in 1947 proposed the name "astatine" for the element, from a Greek word meaning "unstable." (By that time tiny traces of astatine had, like francium, been found in nature among the breakdown products of uranium.)

Meanwhile the fourth and final missing element, number 61, had been discovered among the products of the fission of uranium. (Technetium, too, turned up among these products.) Three chemists at the Oak Ridge National Laboratory, J. A. Marinsky, L. E. Glendenin, and C. D. Coryell, isolated element 61 in 1945. They named it "promethium," after the Greek demigod Prometheus, who had stolen fire for mankind from the sun. Element number 61, after all, had been stolen from the sun-like fires of the atomic furnace.

So the list of elements, from 1 to 92, was at last complete. And yet, in a sense, the strangest part of the adventure had only begun. For scientists had broken through the bounds of the periodic table: uranium was not the end.

A SEARCH for elements beyond uranium — "transuranium elements" — had actually begun as early as 1934. Enrico Fermi in Italy had found that when he bombarded an element with a newly-discovered subatomic particle called the "neutron" (see Chapter 6), this often transformed the element into the one of the next higher atomic number. Could uranium be built up to element 93 — a totally synthetic element that did not exist in nature? Fermi's group proceeded to attack uranium with neutrons, and they got a product which they thought was indeed element 93. They called it "uranium X."

In 1938 Fermi received the Nobel Prize in physics for his studies in neutron bombardment. At the time, the real nature of his discovery, or its consequences for mankind, was not even suspected. Like that other Italian, Columbus, he had found not what he was looking for but something far more important of which he was not aware. That story — the story of fission — we shall leave for a later chapter.

Suffice it to say here that after a series of chases up a number of false trails, it was finally discovered that what Fermi had done was not to create a new element but to split the uranium atom. When physicists turned in 1940 to studies of uranium fission, element 93 cropped up as an almost casual result of their experiments. In the mélange of elements that came out of the splitting of uranium by neutrons, there was one which at first defied identification. Then it dawned on Edwin McMillan of the University of California that perhaps the neutrons released by fission had converted some of the uranium atoms to a higher element, as Fermi had tried to do. Mc-Millan and Philip Abelson, a physical chemist, were able to prove that the unidentified element was in fact number 93. The proof of its existence lay in the nature of its radioactivity, as was to be the case in all subsequent discoveries.

McMillan suspected that another transuranium element might be mixed with number 93. The chemist Glenn Theodore Seaborg, together with his co-workers A. C. Wahl and J. W. Kennedy, soon showed that this was indeed so, and that the element was number 94.

Since uranium, the supposed end of the periodic table, had been named for the most distant known planet, Uranus, elements 93 and 94 were now named for Neptune and Pluto, still more distant planets discovered after Uranus. They were called "neptunium" and "plutonium," respectively. It turned out that they existed in nature, for small traces of neptunium and plutonium were later found in uranium ores. So uranium was not the heaviest natural element after all.

Seaborg and his group at the University of California went on to build more transuranium elements, one after the other. By bombarding plutonium with subatomic particles, in 1944 they created elements 95 and 96, named respectively "americium" (after America) and "curium" (after the Curies.) When they had manufactured a sufficient quantity of americium and curium to work with, they bombarded those elements and successively produced number 97 in 1949 and number 98 in 1950. These they named "berkelium" and "californium," after Berkeley and California. In 1951 Seaborg and Mc-Millan shared the Nobel Prize in chemistry for this train of achievements.

The next elements were discovered in more catastrophic fashion. Elements 99 and 100 emerged in the first hydrogen bomb explosion, detonated in the Pacific in November 1952. Although their existence was detected in the explosion debris, the elements were not confirmed and named until the University of California group made small quantities of both in the laboratory in 1955. The names given them were "einsteinium" and "fermium," for Albert Einstein and Enrico Fermi, both of whom had died within the same year. Then the group bombarded a small quantity of einsteinium and formed element 101, which they called "mendelevium" after Mendeleev.

The next step came through a collaboration between California and the Nobel Institute in Sweden. The Institute carried out a particularly complicated type of bombardment which apparently produced a small quantity of element 102. It was named "nobelium," in honor of the Institute, but the experiment has not been confirmed and so the name is not yet official.

EACH STEP in this climb up the transuranium scale was harder than the one before. At each successive stage the element became harder to accumulate and more unstable. When mendelevium was reached, identification had to be made on the basis of 17 atoms, no more. Fortunately radiation-detecting techniques were marvelously refined by 1955. The Berkeley scientists actually hooked up their instruments to a firebell, so that every time a mendelevium atom was formed, the characteristic radiation it emitted on breaking down announced the event by a loud and triumphant ring of the bell. (The fire department soon put a stop to this.)

How much farther atomic scientists can go is not certain. They are trying to get as far as element number 104 at least, for reasons which I will shortly explain. In 1960 Seaborg announced that more than 25 pounds of plutonium would be subjected to neutron bombardment; this should within a few years produce as much as 100 grams of curium as a basis for manufacturing higher elements.

ELECTRONS

WHEN MENDELEEV and his contemporaries found that they could arrange the elements in a periodic table composed of families of substances showing similar properties, they had no notion as to why the elements fell into such groups or why the properties were related. Eventually a clear and rather simple answer emerged, but it came only after a long series of discoveries which at first seemed to have nothing to do with chemistry.

It all began with studies of electricity. Faraday performed every experiment with electricity he could think of, and one of the things he tried to do was to send an electric discharge through a vacuum. He was not able to get a vacuum good enough for the purpose. But by 1854 a German glass-blower named Heinrich Geissler had invented an adequate vacuum pump and an evacuated glass tube enclosing metal electrodes. When experimenters succeeded in producing electric discharges in the "Geissler tube," they noticed that a green glow appeared on the tube wall opposite the negative electrode. The German physicist Eugen Goldstein suggested in 1876 that this green glow was caused by the impact upon the glass of some sort of radiation originating at the negative electrode, which Faraday had named the "cathode." Goldstein called the radiation "cathode rays."

Were the cathode rays a form of electromagnetic radiation? The English physicist William Crookes and some others said no: they were a stream of particles of some kind. Crookes designed improved versions of the Geissler tube (called "Crookes tubes"), and with these he was able to show that the rays were deflected by a magnet.

This meant that they must be made up of electrically charged particles.

In 1897 the physicist Joseph John Thomson settled the question beyond doubt by demonstrating that the cathode rays could also be deflected by electric charges. What, then, were these cathode "particles?" The only negatively charged particles known at the time were the negative ions of atoms. Experiments showed that the cathode-ray particles could not possibly be such ions, for they were so strongly deflected by an electromagnetic field that they must have an unthinkably high electric charge or else must be extremely light particles with only about 1/2000 the mass of a hydrogen atom. The latter interpretation turned out to fit the evidence best. Physicists had already guessed that the electric current was carried by particles, and so these cathode-ray particles were accepted as the ultimate particles of electricity. They were called "electrons" — a name that had been suggested in 1891 by the Irish physicist George Johnstone Stoney. The electron was finally determined to have 1/1837 the mass of a hydrogen atom. (For establishing its existence, Thomson was awarded the Nobel Prize in physics in 1906.)

The discovery of the electron at once suggested that it might be a sub-particle of the atom — in other words, that atoms were not the ultimate, indivisible units of matter that Democritus and John Dalton had pictured them to be.

This was a hard pill to swallow, but the lines of evidence converged inexorably. One of the most convincing items was Thomson's showing that negatively charged particles which came out of a metal plate when it was struck by ultraviolet radiation (the "photoelectric effect") were identical with the electrons of the cathode rays. The photoelectric electrons must have been knocked out of the atoms of the metal.

SINCE ELECTRONS could easily be removed from atoms (by other means as well as by the photoelectric effect), it was natural to conclude that they were located in the outer regions of the atom. If this was so, there must be a positively charged region within the atom balancing the electrons' negative charges, because the atom as a whole was normally neutral. It was at this point that investigators began to close in on the solution of the mystery of the periodic table.

To remove an electron from an atom takes a little energy. Conversely, when an electron falls into the vacated place in the atom, it must *give up* an equal amount of energy. (Nature is usually symmetrical, especially when it comes to considerations of energy.) This energy is released in the form of electromagnetic radiation. Now since the energy of radiation is measured in terms of wavelength, the wavelength of the radiation emitted by an electron falling into a particular atom will indicate the force with which the electron is held by that atom. The energy of radiation increases with shortening wavelength: the greater the energy, the shorter the wavelength.

We arrive, then, at Moseley's discovery that metals (*i.e.*, the heavier elements) produced X-rays, each at a characteristic wavelength, which decreased in regular fashion as one went up the periodic table. Each successive element, it seemed, held its electrons more strongly than the one before, which is another way of saying that each had a successively stronger positive charge in its internal region.

Assuming that each unit of positive charge corresponded to the negative charge on an electron, it followed that the atom of each successive element must have one more electron. The simplest way of picturing the periodic table, then, was to suppose that the first element, hydrogen, had one unit of positive charge and one electron; the second element, helium, two positive charges and two electrons; the third, lithium, three positive charges and three electrons; and so on all the way up to uranium, with 92 electrons. So the atomic numbers of the elements turned out to represent the number of electrons in their atoms.

One more major clue, and the atomic scientists had the answer to the periodicity of the periodic table. It developed that the electronic radiation of a given element was not necessarily restricted to a single wavelength; it might emit radiations at two, three, four or even more different wavelengths. These sets of radiations were named the K-series, the L-series, the M-series, and so on. The investigators interpreted this to mean that the electrons were arrayed in "shells" around the positively charged core of the atom. The electrons of the innermost shell were most strongly held, and their removal took the most energy. An electron falling into this shell would emit the most energetic radiation, that is, of the shortest wavelengths, or the K-series. The electrons of the next innermost shell were responsible for the L-series of radiations; the next shell produced the M-series, and so on. So the shells were called the K-shell, the L-shell, the M-shell, etc.

In 1916 the American chemist Gilbert Newton Lewis worked out the kinships of properties and the chemical behavior of some of the simpler elements on the basis of their shell structure. There was ample evidence, to begin with, that the innermost shell was limited to two electrons. Hydrogen has only one electron; therefore the shell is unfilled. The atom's tendency is to fill this K-shell, and it can do so in a number of ways. For instance, two hydrogen atoms can pool their single electrons and, by sharing the two electrons, mutually fill their K-shells. This is why hydrogen gas almost always exists in the form of a pair of atoms — the hydrogen molecule. To separate the two atoms and free them as "atomic hydrogen" takes a good deal of energy. (Irving Langmuir of the General Electric Company, who also worked on deciphering the electronic structure of atoms, presented a practical demonstration of the strong tendency of the hydrogen atom to keep its electron shell filled. He made an "atomic hydrogen torch" by blowing hydrogen gas through an electric arc which split the molecules' atoms apart; when the atoms recombined after passing the arc, they liberated the energy they had absorbed in splitting apart, and this was sufficient to yield temperatures up to 3400° C.!)

In helium, element number two, the K-shell is filled with two electrons. Helium atoms therefore are stable and do not combine with other atoms. When we come to lithium, element three, we find that two of its electrons fill the K-shell and the third starts the L-shell. The succeeding elements add electrons to this shell one by one: beryllium has two electrons in the L-shell, boron has three, carbon four, nitrogen five, oxygen six, fluorine seven, and neon eight. Eight is the limit for the L-shell, and therefore neon corresponds to helium in having its outermost electron shell filled. And sure enough, it, too, is an inert gas with properties like helium's.

Every atom with an unsatisfied outer shell has a tendency to enter into combination with other atoms in a manner that leaves it with a filled outer shell. For instance, the lithium atom readily surrenders its one L-shell electron so that its outer shell is the filled K, while fluorine tends to seize an electron to add to its seven and complete the L-shell. Therefore lithium and fluorine have an affinity for each other; when they combine, lithium donates its L-electron to fluorine to fill the latter's L-shell. Since the atoms' interior positive charges do not change, lithium, with one electron subtracted, now carries a net positive charge, while fluorine, with one extra electron, carries a net negative charge. The mutual attraction of the opposite charges holds the two ions together. The compound is called lithium fluoride.

L-shell electrons can be shared as well as transferred. For instance, each of two fluorine atoms can share one of its electrons with the other, so that each atom has a total of eight in its L-shell, counting the two shared electrons. Similarly two oxygen atoms will pool a total of four electrons to complete their L-shells; and two nitrogen atoms will share a total of six. Thus fluorine, oxygen, and nitrogen all form two-atom molecules.

The carbon atom, with only four electrons in its L-shell, will share each of them with a different hydrogen atom, thereby filling the K-shells of the four hydrogen atoms and in turn filling its own L-shell by sharing *their* electrons. This stable arrangement is the methane molecule, CH_4.

In the same way, a nitrogen atom will share electrons with three

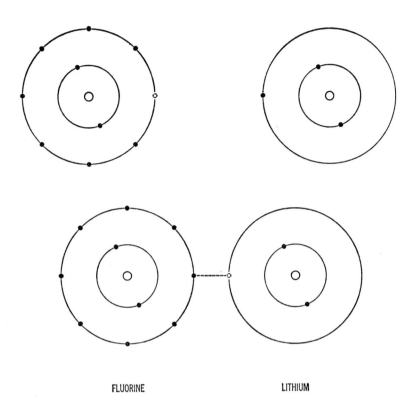

FLUORINE   LITHIUM

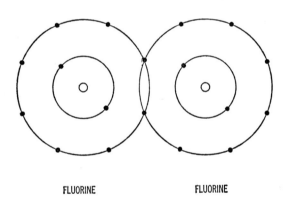

FLUORINE   FLUORINE

Transfer and sharing of electrons. *Lithium transfers the electron in its outer shell to fluorine in the combination of lithium fluoride; each atom then has a full outer shell. In the fluorine molecule (Fl_2) two electrons are shared, filling both atoms' outer shells.*

hydrogen atoms to form ammonia; an oxygen atom will share electrons with two hydrogen atoms to form water; a carbon atom will share electrons with two oxygen atoms to form carbon dioxide; and so on. Almost all the compounds formed by the elements in the first part of the periodic table can be accounted for on the basis of this tendency to complete the outermost shell by giving up electrons, accepting electrons or sharing electrons.

The element after neon, sodium, has eleven electrons, and the eleventh must start a third shell. Then follow magnesium, with two electrons in the M-shell, aluminum with three, silicon with four, phosphorus with five, sulfur with six, chlorine with seven, and argon with eight.

Now each element in this group corresponds to one in the preceding series. Argon, with eight electrons in the M-shell, is like neon (with eight electrons in the L-shell), and it is an inert gas. Chlorine, having seven electrons in its outer shell, resembles fluorine very closely in chemical properties. Likewise, silicon resembles carbon, sodium resembles lithium, and so on.

So it goes right through the periodic table. Since the chemical behavior of every element depends on the configuration of electrons in its outermost shell, all those with, say, one electron in the outer shell will react in much the same way chemically. Thus all the elements in the first column of the periodic table — lithium, sodium, potassium, rubidium, cesium, and even the man-made radioactive element francium — are remarkably alike in their chemical properties. Lithium has one electron in the L-shell, sodium one in the M-shell, potassium one in the N-shell, rubidium one in the O-shell, cesium one in the P-shell, and francium one in the Q-shell. Again, all the elements with seven electrons in their respective outer shells — fluorine, chlorine, bromine, iodine, and astatine — resemble one another. The same is true of the last column in the table — the closed-shell group that includes helium, neon, argon, krypton, xenon, and radon.

The Lewis-Langmuir concept works so well that it still serves in its original form to account for the simple and straightforward types of behavior among the elements. However, refinements had to be introduced to explain certain more complex situations, and that is a matter into which we must now look further.

ONE OF THESE REFINEMENTS dealt with a very puzzling aspect of the periodic table, having to do with the so-called "rare earths" — elements 57 to 71, inclusive.

To go back a bit, the early chemists considered any substance that was insoluble in water and unchanged by heat to be an "earth" (a hangover of the Greek view of "earth" as an element). Such substances included what we would today call calcium oxide, magnesium oxide, silicon dioxide, ferric oxide, aluminum oxide, and so on — compounds which actually constitute about 90 per cent of the earth's crust. Calcium oxide and magnesium oxide are slightly soluble and in solution display "alkaline" properties (that is, opposite to those of acids), and so they were called the "alkaline earths"; when Humphry Davy isolated the metals calcium and magnesium from these earths, they were named alkaline earth metals. The same name was eventually applied to all the elements that fall into the column of the periodic table containing magnesium and calcium: that is, to beryllium, strontium, barium, and radium.

The puzzle to which I have referred began in 1794, when a Finnish chemist, Johan Gadolin, examined an odd rock which had been found near the Swedish hamlet Ytterby and decided that it was a new "earth." Gadolin gave this "rare earth" the name "yttria," after Ytterby. Later the German chemist Martin Klaproth (the discoverer of uranium) found that yttria could be divided into two "earths," for one of which he kept the name yttria, while he named the other "ceria" (after the newly discovered planetoid Ceres). But the Swedish chemist Carl Gustav Mosander subsequently broke these down further into a series of different earths. All eventually proved to be oxides of new elements named the "rare-earth metals." By 1907, 14 such elements had been identified. In order of increasing atomic weight they are:

lanthanum (from a Greek word meaning "hidden")
cerium (from Ceres)
praseodymium (from the Greek for "green twin," after a green line in its spectrum)
neodymium ("new twin")
samarium (from "samarskite," the mineral in which it was found)
europium (from Europe)
gadolinium (in honor of Johan Gadolin)
terbium (from Ytterby)
dysprosium (from a Greek word meaning "hard to get at")
holmium (from Stockholm)
erbium (from Ytterby)
thulium (from Thule, an old name for Scandinavia)
ytterbium (from Ytterby)
lutetium (from Lutetia, an old name for Paris)

On the basis of their X-ray properties, these elements were assigned the atomic numbers from 57 (lanthanum) to 71 (lutetium). As I related earlier, there was a gap at 61 until the missing element, promethium, emerged from the fission of uranium. It made the fifteenth in the list.

Now the trouble with the rare-earth elements is this: they apparently cannot be made to fit into the periodic table. It is fortunate that only four of them were definitely known when Mendeleev proposed the table, for if they had all been on hand, the table might have been altogether too confusing to be accepted. There are times, even in science, when ignorance is bliss.

The first of the rare-earth metals, lanthanum, matches up all right with yttrium, number 39, the element above it in the table. (Yttrium, though found in the same ores as the rare earths and similar to them in properties, is not a rare-earth metal. It is, however, named after Ytterby. Four elements honor that hamlet — which is overdoing it.) The confusion begins with the rare earth after lanthanum, namely,

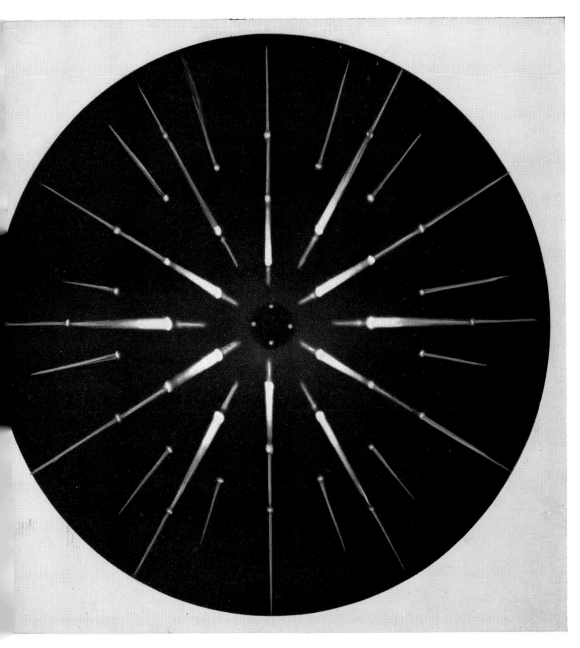

A SINGLE ICE CRYSTAL *photographed by* X-*ray diffraction, showing the symmetry and balance of the physical forces holding the structure together.*

URANIUM ORE. *The black portion is pitchblende (uranium oxide); the inset in the lower left corner is an autoradiograph produced by pitchblende's radioactivity.*

MOLECULAR MODEL *of titanium oxide in crystalline form, which can serve as a transistor. Removal of one of the oxygen atoms (light balls) will make the material semiconducting.*

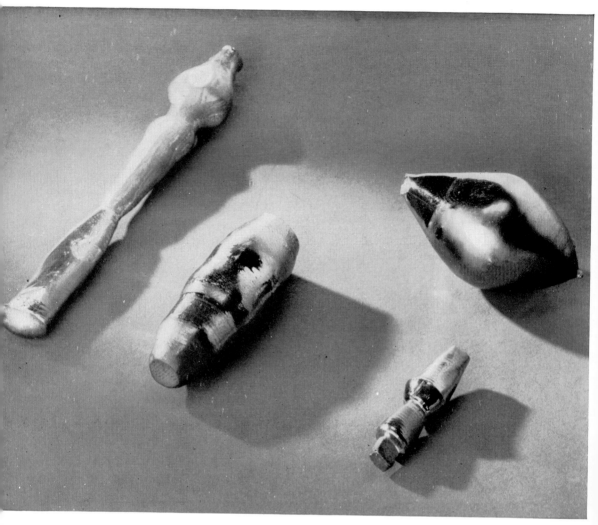

Typical crystals *under study in research on semiconductors and the solid state. These are crystals of bismuth telluride and an indium-antimony alloy.*

cerium, which ought to resemble the element following yttrium, that is, zirconium. But it does nothing of the sort; instead, it resembles yttrium. And the same is true of all 15 of the rare-earth elements: they strongly resemble yttrium and one another (in fact, they are so alike chemically that they could not at first be separated except by the most tedious procedures), but they are not related to any other elements preceding them in the table. We have to skip the whole rare-earth group and go on to hafnium, element 72, to find the element related to zirconium, the one after yttrium.

Baffled by this state of affairs, chemists could do no better than to dump all the rare-earth elements into one box beneath yttrium and list them individually in a kind of footnote to the table.

THE ANSWER to the puzzle finally came with a refinement of the Lewis-Langmuir picture of the electron-shell structure of the elements.

In 1921 C. R. Bury suggested that the shells were not necessarily limited to eight electrons apiece. Eight always sufficed to satisfy the outer shell. But a shell might have a greater capacity when it was not on the outside. As one shell built on another, the inner shells might absorb more electrons, and each succeeding shell might hold more than the one before. Thus the K-shell's capacity would be two electrons, the L-shell's eight, the M-shell's 18, the N-shell's 32, and so on — the step-ups going according to a pattern of successive squares multiplied by two (*i.e.*, 2×1, 2×4, 2×9, 2×16, etc.).

This view was backed up by a detailed study of the spectra of the elements. The Danish physicist Niels Bohr, one of the twentieth century's foremost contributors to understanding of the atom (for which he received the Nobel Prize in physics in 1922), showed that each electron shell was made up of subshells at slightly different energy levels. In each succeeding shell the spread of the subshells was greater, so that soon the shells overlapped. As a result, the outermost subshell of an interior shell (say the M-shell) might actually be farther from the center than the innermost subshell of the next shell beyond it (*i.e.,* the N-shell). This being so, the N-shell's inner subshell might fill with electrons while the M-shell's outer subshell was still empty.

An example will make this clearer. The M-shell, according to the theory, is divided into three subshells, whose capacities are two, six, and ten electrons respectively, making a total of 18. Now argon, with eight electrons in its M-shell, has filled only the two inner subshells. And in fact, the M-shell's third, or outermost, subshell will not get the next electron in the element-building process, because it lies beyond the innermost subshell of the N-shell. That is, in potassium, the element after argon, the nineteenth electron goes not into the outermost subshell of M but into the innermost subshell of N. Potassium, with one electron in its N-shell, resembles sodium, which has one electron in its M-shell. Calcium, the next element (20), has two electrons in the N-shell and resembles magnesium, which has two in the M-shell. But now the innermost subshell of the N-shell, having room for only two electrons, is full. The next electrons to be added can start filling the outermost subshell of the M-shell, which so far has not been touched. Scandium (21) begins the process and zinc (30) completes it. In zinc the outermost subshell of the M-shell has at last acquired its complement of ten electrons. The 30 electrons of zinc are distributed as follows: two in the K-shell, eight in the L-shell, 18 in the M-shell, and two in the N-shell. At this point, electrons can resume the filling of the N-shell. The next electron gives the N-shell three electrons and forms gallium (31), which resembles aluminum, with three in the M-shell.

The point of all this is that elements 21 to 30, formed on the road to filling a subshell which had been skipped temporarily, are "transitional" elements. Note that calcium resembles magnesium and gallium resembles aluminum. Now magnesium and aluminum are adjacent members of the periodic table (numbers 12 and 13). But calcium (20) and gallium (31) are not. Between them lie the transitional elements, and these introduce a complication in the periodic table.

The N-shell is larger than the M-shell and is divided into four subshells instead of three: they can hold 2, 6, 10, and 14 electrons, respectively. Krypton, element 36, fills the two innermost subshells of the N-shell, but here the innermost subshell of the overlapping O-shell intervenes, and before electrons can go on to N's two outer subshells they must fill that one. The element after krypton, rubidium (37), has its 37th electron in the O-shell. The 38th element, strontium, completes the filling of the two-electron O subshell. Thereupon a new series of transitional elements proceeds to fill the skipped third subshell of the N-shell. With cadmium (48) this is completed; now N's fourth and outermost subshell is skipped while electrons fill O's second innermost subshell, ending with xenon (54).

But even now N's fourth subshell must still bide its turn, for by this stage the overlapping has become so extreme that even the P-shell interposes a subshell which must be filled before N's last. After xenon come cesium (55) and barium (56), with one and two electrons respectively in the P-shell. It is still not N's turn: the 57th electron, surprisingly, goes into the third subshell of the O-shell, creating the element lanthanum. Then, and only then, an electron at long last enters the outermost subshell of the N-shell. One by one the rare-earth elements add electrons to the N-shell until element 71, lutetium, finally fills it. Lutetium's electrons are arranged thus: two in the K-shell, eight in the L-shell, 18 in the M-shell, 32 in the N-shell, nine in the O-shell (two subshells full plus one electron in the next subshell), and two in the P-shell (innermost subshell full).

Now at last we begin to see why the rare-earth elements, and some other groups of transitional elements, are so alike. The decisive thing that differentiates elements, as far as their chemical properties are concerned, is the configuration of electrons in their outermost shell. For instance, carbon, with four electrons in its outermost shell, and nitrogen, with five, are completely different in their properties. On the other hand, in sequences where electrons are busy filling inner subshells while the outermost one remains unchanged, the properties vary less. Thus iron, cobalt, and nickel (elements 26, 27, and 28), all of which have the same outer-shell electronic configuration — an N subshell filled with two electrons — are a good deal alike

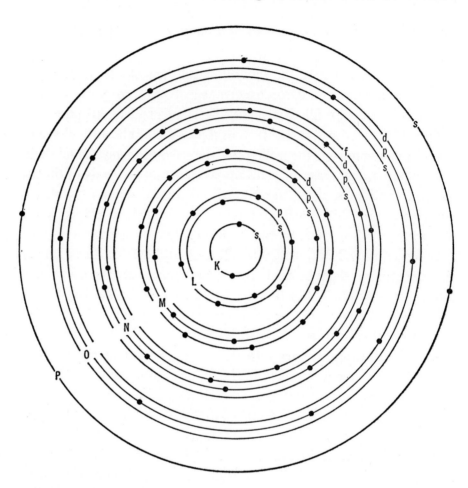

THE ELECTRON SHELLS OF LANTHANUM. *Note that the fourth sub-shell of the N-shell has been skipped and is empty.*

in chemical behavior. Their internal electronic differences (in an M subshell) are largely masked by their surface electronic similarity. And this goes double for the rare-earth elements. Their differences (in the N-shell) are buried under not one but two outer electronic configurations (in the O-shell and the P-shell) which in all these elements are identical. Small wonder that the elements are chemically as alike as peas in a pod.

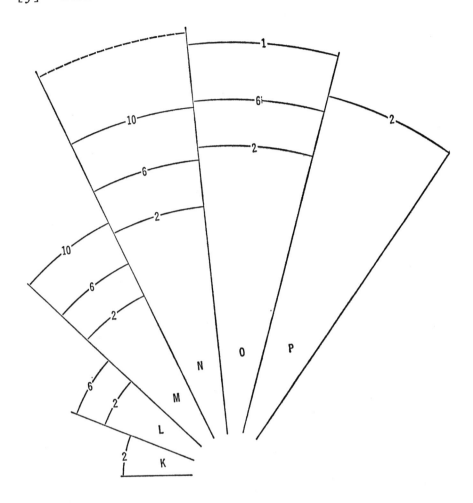

SCHEMATIC REPRESENTATION OF THE OVERLAPPING OF ELECTRON
SHELLS AND SUBSHELLS IN LANTHANUM. *The outermost subshell of
the N-shell has yet to be filled.*

BECAUSE the rare-earth metals have so few uses, and are so
difficult to separate, chemists made little effort to do so — until the
uranium atom was fissioned. Then it became an urgent matter indeed, because radioactive varieties of some of these elements were
among the main products of fission, and in the atomic bomb project
it was necessary to separate and identify them quickly and cleanly.

The problem was solved in short order by use of a chemical technique first devised in 1906 by a Russian botanist named Mikhail Tswett. He named it "chromatography" ("writing in color"). Tswett had found that he could separate plant pigments, chemically very much alike, by washing them down a column of powdered limestone with a solvent. He dissolved his mixture of plant pigments in petroleum ether and poured this on the limestone. Then he proceeded to pour in clear solvent. As the pigments were slowly washed down through the limestone powder, each pigment moved down at a different rate, because they differed in strength of adhesion to the powder. The result was that they separated into a series of bands, each of a different color. With continued washing, the separated substances trickled out separately at the bottom of the column, one after the other.

The world of science for many years ignored Tswett's discovery, possibly because he was only a botanist and only a Russian, while the leaders of research on separating difficult-to-separate substances at the time were German biochemists. But in 1931 a German biochemist, Richard Willstätter, rediscovered the process, whereupon it came into general use. (Willstätter had received the 1915 Nobel Prize in chemistry for his excellent work on plant pigments. Tswett, as far as I know, has gone unhonored.)

Chromatography through columns of powder was found to work on almost all sorts of mixtures — colorless as well as colored. Aluminum oxide and starch proved to be better than limestone for separating ordinary molecules. Where ions are separated, the process is called ion exchange, and compounds known as zeolites were the first efficient agents applied for this purpose. Calcium and magnesium ions could be removed from "hard" water, for instance, by pouring the water through a zeolite column. The calcium and magnesium ions adhere to the zeolite and are replaced in solution by the sodium ions originally present on the zeolite, so "soft" water drips out of the bottom of the column. The sodium ions of zeolite have to be replenished from time to time by pouring in a concentrated solution of salt (sodium chloride). In 1935 a refinement came with the development of "ion-exchange resins." These synthetic substances can be designed for the job to be done. For instance, certain resins will substitute hydrogen ions for positive ions, while others substitute hydroxyl ions for negative ions; a combination of both types will remove most of the salts from sea water. Kits containing such resins were part of the survival equipment on life rafts during World War II.

It was F. H. Spedding at Iowa State College who adapted ion-exchange chromatography to the separation of the rare earths. He found that these elements came out of an ion-exchange column in the reverse order of their atomic number, so that they were not only quickly separated but also identified. In fact, the discovery of promethium, the missing element 61, was confirmed in this way from the tiny quantities found among the fission products.

Thanks to chromatography, purified rare-earth elements can now be prepared by the pound or even by the ton. It turns out that the rare earths are not particularly rare: the rarest of them (excepting promethium) are more common than gold or silver, and the most abundant — lanthanum, cerium, and neodymium — are more plentiful than lead. Together the rare-earth metals make up a larger percentage of the earth's crust than copper and tin combined. So scientists have pretty well dropped the term "rare earths" and now call this series of elements the "lanthanides," after its lead-off member.

As IF TO REWARD the chemists and physicists for their decipherment of the rare-earth mystery, the new knowledge provided a key to the chemistry of the elements at the end of the periodic table, including the man-made ones.

The series of heavy elements in question begins with actinium, number 89. In the table it falls under lanthanum. Actinium has two electrons in the Q-shell, just as lanthanum has two electrons in the P-shell. Actinium's 89th and last electron entered the P-shell, just as lanthanum's 57th and last entered the O-shell. Now the question is: do the elements after actinium continue to add electrons to the P-shell and remain ordinary transition elements? Or do they, perchance, follow the pattern of the elements after lanthanum, where the electrons dive down to fill the skipped subshell below? If the latter is true, then actinium may start a new series of "rare-earth metals."

The natural elements in this series are actinium, thorium, protactinium, and uranium. They were not much studied before 1940. What little was known about their chemistry suggested that they were ordinary transition elements. But when the man-made elements neptunium and plutonium were added to the list and studied intensively, those two showed a strong chemical resemblance to uranium. This prompted Glenn Seaborg to propose that the heavy elements were in fact following the rare-earth pattern and filling the buried, unfilled subshell. As more transuranium elements were added to the list, studies of their chemistry bore out this view, and it is now generally accepted.

The shell being filled is the fourth subshell of the O-shell. Nobelium, element 102 (if its discovery is confirmed), would have 13 electrons in that subshell. There is room for only one more. When and if element 103 is discovered, the subshell will be full and the new list of "rare-earth metals" will be complete. All will share much the same chemical properties, and will resemble lanthanum. With element 104, the 104th electron will have to be added to the P-shell, and its properties should be like those of hafnium. It will be the final touch that clinches the existence of the second rare-earth series, and that is why chemists look forward so eagerly to carrying the list of elements to 104.

They already have one independent confirmation. Ion-exchange chromatography separates the transuranium elements beautifully, and in an exactly analogous manner to the separation of the lanthanides.

In token of the parallelism, the heavier "rare-earth metals" are now called "actinides," just as the members of the first series are called lanthanides.

GASES

FROM THE DAWN of chemistry, it was recognized that many substances could exist in the form of a gas, liquid or solid, depending on the temperature. Water is the most common example: sufficiently cooled, it becomes solid ice, and sufficiently heated, it becomes gaseous steam. Van Helmont (who first used the word "gas") differentiated between substances which were gases at ordinary temperature, such as carbon dioxide, and those which, like steam, were gases only at elevated temperatures. He called the latter "vapors," and we still speak of "water vapor" rather than "water gas."

The study of gases, or vapors, continued to fascinate chemists, partly because they lent themselves to quantitative studies. The rules governing their behavior were simpler and more easily worked out than those governing the behavior of liquids and solids.

In 1787 the French physicist Jacques Alexandre César Charles discovered that when a gas was cooled, each degree of cooling caused its volume to contract by about 1/273 of the volume it had at 0° C., and conversely, each degree of warming caused it to expand by the same 1/273. The expansion with warmth raised no logical difficulties, but if shrinkage with cold were to continue according to Charles' Law (as it is called to this day), at —273° C. a gas should have shrunk to nothing! This paradox did not particularly bother chemists, for they realized that Charles' Law could not hold all the way down and they had no way of getting to very low temperatures to see what happened.

The development of the atomic theory, picturing gases as collections of molecules, presented the situation in new terms. The volume was now seen to depend upon the velocity of the molecules. The higher the temperature, the faster they moved, the more "elbow room" they required, and the greater the volume. Conversely, the lower the temperature, the more slowly they moved, the less room they required, and the smaller the volume. In the 1860's the British physicist William Thomson, who had just been raised to the peerage as Baron Kelvin, suggested that it was the molecules' average energy content that declined by 1/273 for every degree of cooling. Whereas volume could not be expected to disappear completely, energy could. Thomson maintained that at —273° C. the energy of molecules would sink to zero and they would be motionless. Therefore —273° C. must represent the lowest possible temperature. So this temperature (now put at —273.12° C. according to refined modern measurements) would be "absolute zero," or, as it is often stated, "zero Kelvin." On this absolute scale the melting point of ice is 273° K.

Naturally, among physicists there was even more interest in trying to reach absolute zero than in trying to reach the North Pole, for instance. There is something about any distant horizon that calls for conquest. Men had been exploring extremes of coldness even before Thomson defined the ultimate goal. This exploration involved attempts to liquefy gases. Experimenters had found that even at ordinary temperatures some gases could be liquefied by putting them under pressure; they had liquefied chlorine, sulfur dioxide, and ammonia in this way. Now, once liquefied, a gas could act as a cooling agent. When the pressure above the liquid was slowly reduced, the gas evaporated, and the evaporation absorbed heat from the remaining liquid. (When you blow on a moistened finger, the coolness you feel is the effect of the water evaporation drawing heat from the finger.) Of course, the general principle is well known today as the basis of modern refrigeration. An appropriate gas is liquefied by a compressor and then circulated in coils of pipe, where, as the liquid evaporates, it withdraws heat from the surrounding space.

If a liquefied gas is enclosed in a well-insulated container, so that its evaporation draws heat only from the liquid itself, very low temperatures can be attained. By 1835 physicists had reached temperatures as low as —110° C. (163° K.). Such a temperature is low enough to liquefy many gases, and Faraday used this method to cool a number of gases to liquefaction.

Hydrogen, oxygen, nitrogen, carbon monoxide, and some other

common gases, however, defied liquefaction at this temperature even with the use of high pressures.

In 1869 the Irish physicist Thomas Andrews deduced from his experiments that every gas had a "critical temperature" above which it could not be liquefied even under pressure. To liquefy any gas one had to be certain, therefore, that one was working at a temperature below the critical value, or it was labor thrown out. Efforts were made to reach still lower temperatures to conquer the stubborn gases. A "cascade" method, lowering temperatures by steps, turned the trick. First, liquefied sulfur dioxide, cooling through evaporation, was used to liquefy carbon dioxide, then the liquid carbon dioxide to liquefy a more resistant gas, and so on. In 1877 the Swiss physicist Raoul Pictet finally managed to liquefy oxygen, at a temperature of —140° C. (113° K.) and under a pressure of 500 atmospheres (7,500 pounds per square inch). The French physicist Louis Paul Cailletet at about the same time liquefied not only oxygen but also nitrogen and carbon monoxide. Naturally these liquids made it possible to go on at once to still lower temperatures. The liquefaction point of oxygen at ordinary air pressure was eventually found to be —183° C. (90° K.), that of carbon monoxide —190° C. (83° K.), and that of nitrogen —195° C. (78° K.).

Hydrogen resisted all efforts at liquefaction until 1900. The Scottish chemist James Dewar then accomplished the feat by bringing a new stratagem into play. Lord Kelvin and James Prescott Joule had shown that even in the gaseous state a gas could be cooled simply by letting it expand and preventing heat from leaking into the gas from outside. Dewar therefore cooled compressed hydrogen to a temperature of —200° C. in a vessel surrounded by liquid nitrogen, let this super-frigid hydrogen expand and cool further, and repeated the cycle again and again by conducting the ever-cooler hydrogen back through pipes. The compressed hydrogen finally became liquid at a temperature of about —240° C. (33° K.).

By 1895 the British inventor William Hampson and the German physicist Carl Lindé had developed methods of liquefying air on a commercial scale. Pure liquid oxygen, separated from the nitrogen, became a highly useful article. Its main use, in terms of quantity, was in blowtorches, principally for welding. But more dramatic were its services in medicine (*e.g.*, oxygen tents), in aviation, in submarines, and so on.

With the coming of rocketry, liquefied gases suddenly rose to new heights of glamor.

Rockets require an extremely rapid chemical reaction, yielding large quantities of energy. The most convenient type of fuel is a combination of a liquid combustible, such as alcohol or kerosene, and liquid oxygen. Oxygen must be carried by the rocket in any case, because it runs out of any natural supply of oxygen when it leaves the atmosphere. And the oxygen must be in liquid form to be pumped at high speed into the combustion chamber. Consequently liquid oxygen, familiarly called "lox," has come into high demand in rocketry.

The efficiency of a mixture of fuel and oxidizer is measured by a quantity known as the "specific impulse." This represents the number of pounds of thrust produced by the combustion of one pound of the fuel-oxidizer mixture in one second. For a mixture of kerosene and oxygen, the specific impulse is equal to 242. Since the payload a rocket can carry depends on the specific impulse, there has been an avid search for more efficient combinations. The best chemical fuel, from this point of view, is liquid hydrogen. Combined with liquid oxygen, it can yield a specific impulse equal to 350 or so. If liquid ozone or liquid fluorine could be used in place of oxygen, the specific impulse could be raised to something like 370.

So far such combinations have not been achieved. For one thing, liquid hydrogen requires extremely low storage temperatures. For another, liquid ozone and liquid fluorine are dangerous to handle. That does not necessarily mean that the problems can't be solved. If a hydrogen-fluorine combination turns out to be the best possible liquid fuel, ways may be found to make it practicable. Already there are laboratories that can produce as much as 90 gallons of liquid hydrogen per hour; if the hydrogen cannot be efficiently stored, it can at least be replaced as it evaporates.

Research to find better fuels for rockets is being pursued in several directions. For instance, attempts are being made to work out new solid fuels—like gunpowder but much more efficient. Such fuels, it is hoped, would be easy to store and handle, would serve as their own oxidizers, and would burn in a rapid but controlled fashion. Most of the work in this direction is under strict security wraps.

Another possibility is atomic hydrogen, which Langmuir put to use in his blowtorch. It has been calculated that a rocket engine operating on the recombination of hydrogen atoms into molecules could develop a specific impulse of more than 1,300. The main problem is: how store the atomic hydrogen? So far the best hope seems to be to cool the free atoms very quickly and very drastically immediately after they are formed. Researches at the National Bureau of Standards seem to show that free hydrogen atoms are best preserved if trapped in a solid material at extremely low temperatures — say frozen oxygen or argon. If it could be arranged to push a button, so to speak, to let the frozen gases start warming up and evaporating, the hydrogen atoms would be freed and allowed to recombine. If such a solid could hold even as much as 10 per cent of its weight in free hydrogen atoms, the result would be a better fuel than any we now possess. But, of course, the temperature would have to be very low indeed—considerably below that of liquefied hydrogen. These solids would have to be kept at about —272° C., or just one degree above absolute zero.

PHYSICISTS HAVE, in fact, entered that extremely frigid world. They have done so through helium, the last gas to be liquefied. For eight years after hydrogen yielded, helium remained a stubborn holdout against liquefaction at the lowest temperatures attainable. Then in 1908 the Dutch physicist Heike Kammerlingh Onnes finally subdued helium. He carried the Dewar system one step farther. Using liquid hydrogen, he cooled helium gas under pressure to about —255° C. (16° K.), and then let the gas expand to cool itself further. By this method he liquefied the gas. Thereafter, by letting the liquid helium evaporate, he got down to the temperature at which helium could be liquefied under normal atmospheric pressure (4.2° K.) and even to temperatures as low as 1° K. (For his low-temperature work, Onnes received the Nobel Prize in physics in 1913.)

Onnes did more than reach new depths of temperature. He was the first to show that unique properties of matter existed at those depths.

One of these properties is the strange phenomenon called "superconductivity." In 1911 Onnes was testing the electrical resistance of mercury at low temperatures. It was expected that resistance to an electric current would steadily decrease as the removal of heat reduced the normal vibration of the atoms in the metal. But at 4.12° K. the mercury's electrical resistance suddenly disappeared altogether! An electric current coursed through it without any loss of strength whatever. It was soon found that other metals also could be made superconductive. Lead, for instance, became superconductive at 7.22° K. An electric current set up in a lead ring kept at that temperature by liquid helium went on circling through the ring for two and a half years with absolutely no detectable decrease in quantity.

As temperatures were pushed lower and lower, more metals were added to the list of superconductive materials. Tin became superconductive at 3.73° K., aluminum at 1.20° K., uranium at 0.8° K., titanium at 0.53° K. The lowest transition point so far established is that of hafnium, which becomes superconductive at 0.35° K. But iron, nickel, copper, gold, sodium, and potassium must have still lower transition points — if they can be made superconductive at all — because they have not been reduced to this state at the lowest temperatures reached. The highest transition point found for a metal is that of technetium, which becomes superconductive at 11.2° K. A few alloys exhibit superconductivity, and some, particularly those containing niobium, show transition temperatures up to 18° K.

Along with superconductivity goes another property involving magnetism. At the moment that a substance becomes superconductive, it also becomes perfectly "diamagnetic;" that is, it excludes the lines of force of a magnetic field. By making the magnetic field strong enough, however, one can destroy the substance's superconductivity, even at temperatures well below its transition point. It is as if, once enough lines of force have been concentrated in the surroundings, some at last manage to penetrate the substance, and when that happens, gone is the superconductivity as well.

THE OTHER STARTLING PHENOMENON at low temperatures was discovered in helium itself. It is called "superfluidity."

Helium is the only known substance that cannot be frozen solid, even at absolute zero. It can be pressed into the solid state, at temperatures below 1° K., by a pressure of about 25 atmospheres, but only in that way. What is much more surprising is the discovery that at very low temperatures liquid helium shows a change which in a way is the opposite of freezing: it suddenly becomes so fluid that it will climb out of a glass by itself!

In 1935 W. H. Keesom and Miss A. P. Keesom, a brother and sister team working at the Onnes laboratory in Leiden, found that liquid helium at a temperature below 2.2° K. conducted heat almost perfectly. It conducted heat so quickly, in fact, that all parts of the helium were always at the same temperature. It would not boil — as any ordinary liquid will by reason of localized hot-spots forming bubbles of vapor — because there were no localized hot-spots in the liquid helium (if you can speak of "hot-spots" in connection with a liquid below 2° K.). When it evaporated, the top of the liquid simply slipped off quietly — peeling off, so to speak, in sheets.

The Russian physicist Peter Leonidovich Kapitza went on to investigate this property and found that the reason helium conducted heat so well was that it flowed with remarkable ease, carrying the heat from one part of itself to another almost instantaneously. It flowed even more easily than a gas, and it would leak through apertures so tiny that they stopped a gas. Furthermore, the superfluid liquid would form a film on glass and flow along it as quickly as it would pour through a hole. If an open container of the liquid was placed in a larger container filled to a lower level, the fluid would creep up the side of the glass and over the rim into the outer container, until the levels in both were equalized.

Helium is the only substance that exhibits this phenomenon of "superfluidity." In fact, the superfluid behaves so differently from the way helium itself does above 2.2° K. that it has been given a separate name, helium II, to distinguish it from liquid helium above that temperature, called helium I.

SPURRED by the odd phenomena discovered in the neighborhood of absolute zero, physicists have naturally made every effort to get down as close to absolute zero as possible. The evaporation of liquid helium can, under special conditions, produce temperatures as low as 0.5° K. (Temperatures at such a level, by the way, are measured by special methods involving electricity — *e.g.*, by the size of the current generated in a thermocouple, or by the resistance of a wire made of some non-superconductive metal. The measurement of extremely low temperatures is scarcely easier than their attainment.) Temperatures substantially lower than 0.5° have been reached by a technique first suggested in 1925 by the physicist Peter Joseph Wilhelm Debye. A "paramagnetic" substance (*i.e.*, a substance which concentrates lines of magnetic force) is placed almost in contact with liquid helium, separated from it by helium gas, and the temperature of the whole system is reduced to about 1° K. The system is then placed within a magnetic field. The molecules of the paramagnetic substance line up parallel to the field's lines of force and in doing so give off heat. This heat is removed by further slight evaporation of the surrounding helium. Now the magnetic field is removed. The paramagnetic molecules immediately fall into a random orientation. In going from an ordered to a random orientation, the molecules must absorb heat, and the only thing they can absorb it from is the liquid helium. The temperature of the liquid helium therefore drops.

This can be repeated and repeated, each time lowering the temperature of the liquid helium. In this way, a record low temperature of 0.00002° K. was reached in 1957.

Is absolute zero attainable? Well, no heat pump we know of can take out more than a part of the heat in any one operation. And just as no air pump will ever produce a complete vacuum, so no device for lowering temperature, as far as we know, will ever quite get to absolute zero.

ONE OF THE NEW SCIENTIFIC HORIZONS opened up by the work on liquefaction of gases was the development of an interest in producing high pressures. It seemed that putting various kinds of matter (not only gases) under great pressure might bring out some fundamental information about the nature of matter and also about the interior of the earth. At a depth of seven miles, for instance, the pressure is 1,000 atmospheres; at 400 miles, 200,000 atmospheres; at 2,000 miles, 1,400,000 atmospheres; and at the center of the earth, 4,000 miles down, it reaches three million atmospheres.

The best that nineteenth-century laboratories could do was about 3,000 atmospheres, attained by E. H. Amagat in the 1880's. But in 1905 the American physicist Percy Williams Bridgman began to devise new methods which soon reached pressures of 20,000 atmospheres and burst the tiny metal chambers he used for his experiments. He went to stronger materials and eventually succeeded in producing pressures of hundreds of thousands of atmospheres. For his work on high pressure, he received the Nobel Prize in physics in 1946.

Under his ultra-high pressures Bridgman was able to force the atoms and molecules of a substance into more compact arrangements, which were sometimes retained after the pressure was released. For instance, he converted ordinary yellow phosphorus, a nonconductor of electricity, into a black, conducting form of phosphorus. He brought about startling changes even in water. Ordinary ice is less dense than liquid water. Using high pressure, Bridgman produced a series of ices ("ice-II, ice-III," etc.) which were not only denser than the liquid but were ice only at temperatures well above the normal freezing point of water. Ice-VII is a solid at temperatures higher than the boiling point of water (so the phrase "hot ice," you see, can mean something other than stolen diamonds).

The word "diamond" brings up the most glamorous of all the high-pressure feats. Diamond, of course, is crystallized carbon. This was first proved in 1772 by Lavoisier and some fellow French chemists. They pooled their funds to buy a diamond and proceeded to heat it to a high enough temperature to burn it up. (There's devotion to science for you.) The gas that resulted was found to be carbon dioxide. Later the British chemist Smithson Tennant showed that the amount of carbon dioxide measured could be produced only if diamond was pure carbon, and in 1799 the French chemist Guyton de Morveau clinched the case by converting a diamond into a lump of graphite.

That was an unprofitable maneuver, but now why could not matters be reversed? Diamond is 55 per cent denser than graphite. Why not put graphite under pressure and force the atoms composing it into the tight packing characteristic of diamond?

Many efforts were made and, like the alchemists, a number of experimenters reported successes. The most famous was the claim of the French chemist Ferdinand Frédéric Henri Moissan. In 1893 he dissolved graphite in molten cast iron and reported that he found small diamonds in the mass after it cooled. Most of the objects were black, impure, and tiny, but one was colorless and almost a millimeter long. These results were widely accepted, and for a long time Moissan was considered to have manufactured synthetic diamonds. However, his results were never successfully repeated.

In the 1930's chemists worked out the pressure requirements for converting graphite to diamond. It turned out that the conversion called for a pressure of at least 10,000 atmospheres, and even then it would be impracticably slow. Raising the temperature would speed the conversion but would also raise the pressure requirements. At 1500° C. a pressure of at least 30,000 atmospheres would be necessary. All this proved that Moissan and his contemporaries could no more have produced diamonds than the alchemists could have produced gold. (There is some evidence that Moissan was actually a victim of one of his assistants, who, tiring of the tedious experiments, decided to end them by planting a real diamond in the cast-iron mixture.)

Aided by Bridgman's pioneering work in attaining the necessary high temperatures and pressures, scientists at the General Electric Company finally accomplished the feat in 1955. Pressures of 100,000 atmospheres or more were produced, along with temperatures of up to 2500° C. In addition, a small quantity of metal, such as chromium, was used to form a liquid film across the graphite. It was on this film that the graphite turned to diamond.

The synthetic diamonds are too small and impure to be used as gems, but they are now produced commercially as abrasives and cutting tools. A newer product made by the same sort of treatment may, however, replace them. A compound of boron and nitrogen (boron nitride) is very similar in properties to graphite (except that boron nitride is white instead of black). Subjected to the high temperatures and pressures that convert graphite to diamond, the boron nitride undergoes a similar conversion. From a crystal arrangement like that of graphite, the atoms of boron nitride are converted to one like that of diamond. In its new form it is called "borazon." Borazon is about as hard as diamond. In addition it has the great advantage of being more resistant to heat. At a temperature of 900° C., diamond burns up but borazon comes through unchanged.

METALS

MOST OF THE ELEMENTS in the periodic table are metals. As a matter of fact, only about 20 of the 102 elements can be considered definitely non-metallic. Yet the use of metals came relatively late in the history of the human species. One reason is that, with rare exceptions, the metallic elements are combined in nature with other elements and are not easy to recognize or extract. Primitive man at first used only materials that could be manipulated by simple treatments such as carving, chipping, hacking and grinding. This restricted his materials to bones, stones, and wood.

His introduction to metals may have come in the form of discoveries of meteorites, or of small nuggets of gold, or of metallic copper in the ashes of fires built on rocks containing a copper ore. In any case, people who were curious enough (and lucky enough) to find these strange new substances and look into ways of handling them would discover many advantages in them. Metal differed from rock in that it had an attractive luster when polished. It could be beaten into sheets and drawn into wire. It could be melted and poured into a mold to solidify. It was much more beautiful and adaptable than rock, and ideal for ornaments. Metals probably were fashioned into ornaments long before they were put to any other use.

What really brought metals into their own was the discovery that some of them would take a sharper cutting edge than stone could, and they would maintain that edge under conditions that would ruin a stone axe. Moreover, metal was tough. A blow that would splinter a wooden club or shatter a stone axe would only slightly deform a metal object of similar size. These advantages more than compensated for the fact that metal was heavier than stone and harder to obtain.

The first metal obtained in quantity was copper. Copper itself was too soft to make useful weapons or armor, but it was often found alloyed with a little tin in the ore, and in this form (bronze) it was hard enough. Men soon learned to add the tin deliberately. The Bronze Age replaced the Stone Age in Egypt and western Asia about 3500 B.C. and in southeastern Europe by 2000 B.C. Homer's *Iliad* and *Odyssey* commemorate that period of culture.

Iron was known as early as bronze, but for a long time meteorites were the only source. It remained no more than a precious metal, limited to occasional use, until methods were discovered for smelting iron ore and thus obtaining iron in unlimited quantities. Iron-smelting began somewhere in Asia Minor about 1400 B.C. and developed and spread slowly.

An iron-weaponed army could rout a bronze-armed one, for iron swords would cut through bronze. The Hittites of Asia Minor were the first to use iron weapons to any extent, and they had a period of power in western Asia. Then the Assyrians succeeded the Hittites. By 800 B.C. they had a completely ironized army which was to dominate western Asia and Egypt for two and a half centuries. At about the same time, the Dorians brought the Iron Age to Europe by invading Greece and defeating the Achaeans, who committed the error of clinging to the Bronze Age.

IRON IS OBTAINED essentially by heating iron ore (usually a ferric oxide) with carbon. The carbon atoms carry off the oxygen of the ferric oxide, leaving a lump of pure iron behind. In ancient times the temperatures used did not melt the iron, and the product was a tough metal which could be worked into the desired shape by hammering — that is, "wrought iron." Iron metallurgy on a larger scale came into being in the Middle Ages. Special furnaces were used, and higher temperatures that melted the iron. The molten iron could be poured into molds to form castings, so it was called "cast iron." This was much less expensive than wrought iron and much harder, too, but it was brittle and could not be hammered; as was later found, the reason was that the molten iron dissolved enough carbon to constitute 4 to 5 per cent of its own weight.

Steel is iron with a carbon content of between 0.2 and 1.5 per cent. It is harder and tougher and generally stronger than either cast iron or wrought iron. But until the mid-nineteenth century, steel could be made only by the complicated procedure of carefully adding the appropriate quantity of carbon to wrought iron (itself comparatively expensive). Steel was therefore a luxury metal, used only where no substitute could be found — as in swords and springs.

The Age of Steel was ushered in by a British engineer named Henry Bessemer. Originally interested primarily in cannon and projectiles, Bessemer invented a system of rifling intended to enable cannon to shoot farther and more accurately. Napoleon III of France was interested and offered to finance further experiments. But a French artillerist killed the idea by pointing out that the propulsive explosion Bessemer had in mind would shatter the cast-iron cannons used in those days. Bessemer, chagrined, turned to the problem of creating stronger iron. He knew nothing of metallurgy, so he could approach the problem with a fresh mind. Cast iron was brittle because of its carbon content. Therefore the problem was to reduce the carbon.

Why not burn the carbon away by melting the iron and sending a blast of air through it? This seemed at first thought a ridiculous idea. Would not the air blast cool the molten metal and cause it to solidify? Bessemer tried it anyway, and he found that quite the reverse was true. As the air burned the carbon, the combustion gave off heat and the temperature of the iron rose rather than fell. The carbon burned off nicely. By proper controls, steel could be produced in quantity and comparatively cheaply.

In 1856 Bessemer announced his "blast furnace." Iron-makers adopted the method with enthusiasm, then dropped it in anger when they found that inferior steel was being formed. Bessemer discovered that the iron ore used by the industry contained phosphorus (which had been absent from his own ore samples). Although Bessemer explained to the iron-makers that phosphorus had betrayed them, they refused to be twice-bitten. Bessemer therefore had to borrow money and set up his own steel works in Sheffield. Importing phosphorus-free iron ore from Sweden, he speedily produced steel at a price that undersold the other iron-makers.

In 1875 the British metallurgist Sidney Gilchrist Thomas discovered that by lining the interior of the furnace with limestone and magnesia, he could easily remove the phosphorus from the molten iron. After this, almost any iron ore could be used in the manufacture of steel.

The Age of Steel then got under way. The name is no mere phrase. Without steel, skyscrapers, suspension bridges, great ships, railroads, and many other modern constructions would be almost unthinkable, and despite the rise of other metals, steel still remains the preferred metal in a host of everyday uses, from automobile bodies to knives.

With steel cheap and commonplace, it became possible to experiment with the addition of other metals to see if steel could be still further improved. The British metallurgist Robert Abbott Hadfield pioneered in this direction. In 1882 he found that adding manganese to steel to the extent of 13 per cent produced a harder alloy, which could be used in machinery for particularly brutal jobs such as rock-crushing. In 1900 a steel alloy containing tungsten and chromium was found to retain its hardness well at high temperatures, even red heat, and this alloy proved a boon for high-speed tools. Today there are innumerable other alloy steels for particular jobs, employing metals such as molybdenum, nickel, cobalt, and vanadium.

The great difficulty with steel is its vulnerability to corrosion — a process which returns iron to the crude state of the ore whence it came. One way of combating this is to shield the metal by painting it or by plating it with a metal less likely to corrode, such as nickel, chromium, cadmium or tin. A more effective method is to form an alloy that does not corrode. In 1913 the British metallurgist Harry Brearley discovered such an alloy by accident. He was looking for steel alloys that would be particularly suitable for gun barrels. Among the samples he discarded as unsuitable was a nickel-chromium alloy. Months later he happened to notice that these particular pieces in his scrap heap were as bright as ever. That was the birth of "stainless steel." It is too soft for use in large-scale construction, but it serves admirably in cutlery and small appliances where non-rusting is more important than hardness.

Since something like a billion dollars a year is spent over the world in the not too successful effort to keep iron and steel from corroding, the search for a general rust-inhibitor goes on unabated. One interesting recent discovery is that pertechnetates, compounds containing technetium, protect iron against rusting. Of course, this rare, man-made element will never be common enough to be used on any substantial scale, but it offers an invaluable research tool. Its radio-activity allows chemists to follow its fate and to observe what happens to it on the iron surface. If this use of technetium leads to a new understanding which will help solve the corrosion problem, that achievement alone will pay back in a matter of months all the money invested in research on the synthetic elements over the last quarter-century.

WE HAVE SEEN in recent decades the emergence of enormously useful new metals — metals that were completely unknown up to a century or so ago and in some cases up to our own generation. The most striking example is aluminum. Aluminum is the most common of all metals — 60 per cent more common than iron. But it is also exceedingly difficult to extract from its ores. In 1825 Hans Christian Oersted (who had discovered the connection between electricity and magnetism) separated a little aluminum in impure form. Thereafter many chemists tried unsuccessfully to purify the metal, until the French chemist Henri Etienne Sainte-Clair Deville in 1854 finally devised a method of obtaining aluminum in reasonable quantities. Aluminum is so active chemically that he had to use metallic sodium (even more active) to break aluminum's grip on its neighboring atoms. For a while aluminum sold for a hundred dollars a pound, making it practically a precious metal. Napoleon III indulged himself in aluminum cutlery and had an aluminum rattle fashioned for his infant son; and in the United States, as a mark of the nation's great esteem for George Washington, the Washington Monument was capped with a slab of solid aluminum.

In 1886 Charles Martin Hall, a young student of chemistry at Oberlin College, was so impressed by his professor's statement that anyone who could discover a cheap method of making aluminum would make a fortune that he decided to try his hand at it. In a home laboratory in his woodshed, Hall set out to apply Humphry Davy's early discovery that an electric current sent through a molten metal could separate the metal ions by depositing them on the cathode plate. Looking for a material that could dissolve aluminum, he stumbled across cryolite, a mineral found in reasonable quantity only in Greenland. (Nowadays synthetic cryolite is available.) Hall dissolved aluminum oxide in cryolite, melted the mixture, and passed an electric current through it. Sure enough, pure aluminum collected on the cathode. Hall rushed to his professor with his first few ingots of the metal. (To this day they are treasured by the Aluminum Company of America.)

As it happened, a young French chemist named Paul Louis Toussaint Héroult, who was just Hall's age (22), discovered the same process in the same year. (To complete the coincidence Hall and Héroult both died in 1914.)

The Hall-Héroult process made aluminum an inexpensive metal, though it was never to be as cheap as steel, because useful aluminum ore is less common than useful iron ore, and electricity (the key to aluminum) is more expensive than coal (the key to steel). Nevertheless, aluminum has two great advantages over steel. First, it is light — only one-third the weight of steel. Second, in aluminum's case corrosion merely takes the form of a thin, transparent film over its surface, which protects deeper layers from corrosion without affecting the metal's appearance.

Pure aluminum is rather soft, but alloying can take care of that. In 1906 the German metallurgist Alfred Wilm made a tough alloy by adding a bit of copper and a smaller bit of magnesium to the aluminum. He sold his patent rights to the Durener Metal Works in Germany, and they gave the alloy the name "Duralumin."

Engineers quickly realized how valuable a light but strong metal could be in aircraft. After the Germans introduced Duralumin in zeppelins during World War I and the British learned its composition by analyzing the alloy in a crashed zeppelin, use of this new metal spread over the world. Because Duralumin was not quite as corrosion-resistant as aluminum itself, metallurgists covered it with thin sheets of pure aluminum, forming the product called "Alclad."

Today there are aluminum alloys which, weight for weight, are stronger than some steels. Aluminum has tended to replace steel wherever lightness and corrosion-resistance are more important than brute strength. It has become, as everyone knows, almost a universal metal, used in airplanes, rockets, railway trains, automobiles, doors, screens, house siding, paint, kitchen utensils, foil wrapping, and what not.

And now we have magnesium, a metal even lighter than aluminum. Only about one-fourth as abundant as aluminum and more active chemically, magnesium is harder to obtain from ores. But fortunately there is a rich source in the ocean. Magnesium, unlike aluminum or iron, is present in sea water in quantity. The ocean carries dissolved matter to the amount of 3.5 per cent of its mass. Of this dissolved material, 3.7 percent is magnesium ion. The ocean as a whole, therefore, contains about two quadrillion (2,000,000,-000,000,000) tons of magnesium, or all we could use for the indefinite future.

The problem was to get it out. The method chosen was to pump sea water into large tanks and add calcium oxide (also obtained from the sea, *i.e.*, from oyster shells). The calcium oxide reacts with the water and the magnesium ion to form magnesium hydroxide, which is insoluble and therefore precipitates out of solution. The magnesium hydroxide is converted to magnesium chloride by treatment with hydrochloric acid, and the magnesium metal is then separated from the chlorine by means of an electric current.

In January of 1941 the Dow Chemical Company produced the first ingots of magnesium from sea water, and the stage was laid for a tenfold increase in magnesium production during the war years.

If steel was the "wonder metal" of the mid-nineteenth century, aluminum of the early twentieth century, and magnesium of the mid-twentieth century, what will the next new "wonder metal" be? The possibilities are limited. There are only seven really common metals in the earth's crust. Besides iron, aluminum, and magnesium, they are sodium, potassium, calcium, and titanium. Sodium, potassium, and calcium are far too active chemically to be used as construction metals. (For instance, they react violently with water.) That leaves titanium, which is about one-eighth as abundant as iron.

Titanium has an extraordinary combination of good qualities. It is only a little more than half as heavy as steel, stronger, weight for weight, than aluminum or steel, resistant to corrosion, and able to withstand high temperatures. For all these reasons, titanium is now being used in aircraft, ships, and guided missiles wherever these properties can be put to good use.

Why was mankind so slow to discover the value of titanium? The reason is much the same as for aluminum and magnesium. It reacts too readily with other substances, and in its impure forms — combined with oxygen or nitrogen — it is an unprepossessing metal, brittle and seemingly useless. Its strength and other fine qualities emerged only when it was isolated in really pure form (in a vacuum or under an inert gas). If simple, inexpensive ways of purifying can be worked out, titanium may indeed turn out to be the next "wonder metal" — and perhaps the last.

The last, that is, entirely new wonder metal. There is reason to think, however, that the older metals (and some non-metals, too) can be made far more "wonderful" than they are now.

In Oliver Wendell Holmes's poem "The Deacon's Masterpiece" the story is told of a one-hoss shay which was carefully made in such a way as to have no weakest point. In the end, the shay went all at once — decomposing into a powder. But it had lasted a hundred years.

The atomic structure of crystalline solids, both metal and non-metal, is rather like a one-hoss shay situation. A metal's crystals are riddled with sub-microscopic clefts and scratches. Under pressure, a fracture will start at one of these weak points and spread through the crystal. If, like the deacon's wonderful one-hoss shay, a crystal could be built with no weak points, it would have great strength.

Such no-weak-point crystals do form as tiny fibers called "whiskers" on the surface of crystals. Tensile strengths of carbon whiskers have been found to run as high as 1,400 tons per square inch, which is from 15 to 70 times the tensile strength of steel. If methods could be designed for manufacturing defect-free metal in quantity, we would find ourselves with old metals that were newly-wonderful indeed.

CHAPTER

THE
PARTICLES

THE NUCLEAR ATOM

As I POINTED OUT in the preceding chapter, it was known by 1900 that the atom was not a simple, indivisible particle but contained at least one subatomic particle — the electron, identified by J. J. Thomson. Thomson suggested that electrons were stuck like raisins in the positively-charged main body of the atom.

But very shortly it developed that there were also other subparticles within the atom. When Becquerel discovered radioactivity, he identified some of the radiation emitted by radioactive substances as consisting of electrons, but other emissions were discovered as well. The Curies in France and Ernest Rutherford in England found one which was less penetrating than the electron stream. Rutherford called this radiation "alpha rays," or alpha particles, and gave the electron emission the name "beta rays," or beta particles. Meanwhile the French chemist P. Villard discovered a third form of radioactive emission which was named "gamma rays." The gamma rays were quickly identified as radiation resembling X-rays, but with shorter wavelength.

Rutherford learned by experiment that a magnetic field deflected alpha particles much less than it did beta particles. Furthermore, they were deflected in the opposite direction, which meant that the alpha particle had a positive charge, as opposed to the electron's negative one. From the amount of deflection, it could be calculated that the alpha particle must have at least twice the mass of the hydrogen ion, which possessed the smallest known positive charge. The amount of deflection would be affected both by the particle's mass and by its charge. If the alpha particle's positive charge was equal to that of the hydrogen ion, its mass would be two times that of the hydrogen ion; if its charge was double that, it would be four times as massive as the hydrogen ion, and so on.

Rutherford settled the matter in 1909 by isolating alpha particles. He put some radioactive material in a thin-walled glass tube surrounded by a thick-walled glass tube, with a vacuum between. The alpha particles could penetrate the thin inner wall but not the thick outer one. They bounced back from the outer wall, so to speak, and in doing so lost energy and therefore were no longer able to penetrate the thin walls either. Thus they were trapped between. Now Rutherford excited the alpha particles by means of an electric discharge so that they glowed. They then showed the spectral lines of helium. If the alpha particle was helium, its mass must be four times that of hydrogen. This, in turn, meant that its positive charge amounted to two units, taking the hydrogen ion's charge as the unit.

Rutherford later identified another positive particle in the atom. This one had actually been detected, but not recognized, many years before. In 1886 the German physicist Eugen Goldstein, using a cathode-ray tube with a perforated cathode, had discovered a new radiation which streamed through the holes of the cathode in the direction opposite to the cathode rays themselves. He called it

"Kanalstrahlen" ("channel rays"). Since it moved opposite to the negatively-charged cathode rays, Thomson suggested that this radiation be called "positive rays." It turned out that the particles of the "positive rays" could easily pass through matter. They were therefore judged to be much smaller in volume than ordinary ions or atoms. The amount of their deflection by a magnetic field indicated that the smallest of these particles had the same charge and mass as a hydrogen ion, assuming that this ion carried the smallest possible unit of positive charge. The "positive-ray" particle was therefore deduced to be the fundamental positive particle — the opposite number of the electron. Rutherford named it the "proton" (from the Greek word for "first").

The proton and the electron do indeed carry equal, though opposite, electric charges, though the proton is 1,836 times as massive as the electron. It seemed highly likely, then, that an atom was composed of protons and electrons, mutually balancing their charges. It also appeared that the protons were in the interior of the atom, for whereas electrons could easily be peeled off, protons could not. But now the big question was: what sort of structure did these particles of the atom form?

RUTHERFORD HIMSELF came upon the beginning of the answer. Between 1906 and 1908 he kept firing alpha particles at a thin foil of metal (such as gold or platinum) to probe its atoms. Most of the projectiles passed right through undeflected (as bullets might pass through the leaves of a tree). But not all: Rutherford found that on the photographic plate that served as his target behind the metal, there was an unexpected scattering of hits around the central spot, and some particles bounced back! It was as if some of the bullets had not passed through leaves alone but had ricocheted off something more substantial.

Rutherford decided that what they had hit was some sort of dense core which occupied only a very small part of the volume of the atom. Most of an atom's volume, it seemed, must be occupied by electrons. As alpha particles charged through the foil of metal, they usually encountered only electrons, and they brushed aside this froth of light particles, so to speak, without being deflected. But once in a while an alpha particle might happen to hit an atom's denser core, and then it was deflected. That this happened only very occasionally showed that the atomic cores must be very small indeed, because a projectile passing through the metal foil must encounter many thousands of atoms.

It was logical to suppose that the hard core was made up of protons. Rutherford pictured the protons of an atom as crowded into a tiny "atomic nucleus" at the center. (It has since been demonstrated that this nucleus has a diameter only about 1/100,000 that of the whole atom.)

This, then, is the basic model of the atom: a positively charged nucleus taking up very little room but containing almost all the mass of the atom, surrounded by a froth of electrons which takes up nearly all the volume of the atom but contains practically none of its mass. For his extraordinary pioneering work on the ultimate nature of matter, Rutherford received the Nobel Prize in chemistry in 1908.

It now became possible to describe specific atoms and their behavior in more definite terms. For instance, the hydrogen atom possesses but a single electron. If this is removed, the proton that remains immediately attaches itself to some neighboring molecule. But when the bare hydrogen nucleus does not find an electron to share in this fashion, it acts as a proton — that is to say, a subatomic particle — and in that form it can penetrate matter and react with other nuclei if it has enough energy.

Helium, with two electrons, does not give one up so easily. As I mentioned in the preceding chapter, its two electrons form a closed shell, and the atom is therefore inert. If helium is stripped of both electrons, however, it becomes an alpha particle — that is, a subatomic particle carrying two units of positive charge.

The third element, lithium, has three electrons in its atom. Stripped of one or two, it is an ion. If all three of its electrons are removed, it, too, becomes a bare nucleus, carrying a three-unit positive charge.

The number of units of positive charge in the nucleus of an atom has to be exactly equal to the number of electrons it normally contains, for the atom as a whole is ordinarily neutral. And, in fact, the atomic numbers of the elements are based on their units of positive charge rather than of negative charge, because the number of an atom's electrons may easily be made to vary in ion formation, whereas the number of its protons can be altered only with great difficulty.

This scheme of the construction of atoms had hardly been worked out when a new conundrum arose. The number of units of positive charge on a nucleus did not balance at all with the nucleus's weight, or mass, except in the case of the hydrogen atom. The helium nucleus, for instance, had a positive charge of two but was known to have four times the mass of the hydrogen nucleus. And the situation got worse and worse as one went down the table of elements, until, by the time uranium was reached, one had a nucleus with a mass equal to 238 protons but a charge equal to only 92.

How could a nucleus containing four protons (as the helium nucleus was supposed to) have only two units of positive charge? The first, and simplest, guess was that two units of its charge were neutralized by the presence in the nucleus of negatively-charged particles of negligible weight. Naturally the electron sprang to mind. Everything could be straightened out if one assumed that the helium nucleus consisted of four protons and two neutralizing electrons, leaving a net positive charge of two — and so on all the way to uranium, whose nucleus would have 238 protons and 146 electrons, netting 92 units of positive charge. The whole idea was given encouragement by the fact that radioactive nuclei were actually known to emit electrons — *i.e.*, beta particles.

This view of matters prevailed for more than a decade, until the true answer came in a roundabout way from other investigations. But in the meantime some serious objections to the hypothesis arose. For one thing, if the nucleus was built essentially of protons, with the light electrons contributing practically nothing to the mass, how was it that the relative masses of the various nuclei did not come to whole numbers? According to the measured atomic weights, the nucleus of the chlorine atom, for instance, had a mass 35 and a half times that of the hydrogen nucleus. Did that mean it contained 35 and a half protons? No scientist (then or now) could accept the idea of half a proton.

Actually, this particular question had an answer which was discovered even before the main issue was solved. It makes an interesting story in itself.

ISOTOPES

As EARLY AS 1816 an English physician named William Prout had suggested that all atoms were built up from the hydrogen atom. As time went on and the atomic weights were worked out, Prout's theory fell by the wayside, because it developed that many elements had fractional weights (taking oxygen as the standard at 16). Chlorine, as I have mentioned, has an atomic weight of about 35 and a half — 35.457, to be exact. Other examples are antimony, 121.76; barium, 137.36; boron, 10.82; calcium, 112.41.

Around the turn of the century there came a series of puzzling observations which were to lead to the explanation. The Englishman William Crookes (he of the Crookes tube) separated from uranium a small quantity of a substance which proved much more radioactive than uranium itself. He suggested that uranium was not radioactive at all — only this impurity, which he called "uranium X." Henri Becquerel, on the other hand, discovered that the purified, feebly radioactive uranium somehow increased in radioactivity with time. After it was left standing for a while, the active "uranium X" could be extracted from it, again and again. In other words, uranium was converted by its own radioactivity to the still more active uranium X.

Then Rutherford similarly separated a strongly radioactive "thorium X" from thorium and found that thorium, too, went on producing more "thorium X." It was already known that the most famous radioactive element of all, radium, broke down to the radioactive gas radon. So Rutherford and his assistant, the chemist Frederick Soddy, concluded that radioactive atoms, in the process of emitting their particles, generally transformed themselves into other varieties of radioactive atoms.

Chemists began searching for such transformations and came up with quite an assortment of new substances, giving them names such as radium A, radium B, mesothorium I, mesothorium II, actinium C, and so on. All of them were grouped into three series, depending on their atomic ancestry. One series arose from the breakdown of uranium, another from that of thorium, and a third from that of actinium (later it turned out that actinium itself had a predecessor, named "protactinium"). Altogether, some 40 members of these series were identified — each distinguished by its own peculiar pattern of radiation. But the end product of all three series was the same: each chain of substances eventually broke down to the same stable element — lead.

Now obviously these 40 substances could not all be separate elements; between uranium (92) and lead (82) there were only ten places in the periodic table, and all but two of these belonged to known elements. The chemists found, in fact, that though the substances differed in radioactivity, some of them were identical with one another in chemical properties. For instance, "radiothorium," one of the disintegration products of thorium, showed precisely the same chemical behavior as thorium. "Radium D" behaved chemically exactly like lead; in fact, it was often called "radiolead." All this suggested that the substances in question were actually varieties of the same element — radiothorium a form of thorium, radiolead a member of a family of leads, and so on.

In 1913 Soddy gave clear expression to this idea and developed it further. He showed that when an atom emitted an alpha particle it changed into an element two places lower in the list of elements;

when it emitted a beta particle, it changed into an element one place higher. On this basis, "radiothorium" would indeed fall in thorium's place in the table, and so would the substances called "uranium X_1" and "uranium Y": all three would be varieties of element 90. Likewise, "radium D," "radium B," "thorium B," and "actinium B" all would share lead's place as varieties of element 82.

To the members of a family of substances sharing the same place in the periodic table Soddy gave the name "isotopes" (from Greek words meaning "same position"). Soddy received the Nobel Prize in chemistry in 1921.

The proton-electron model of the nucleus fitted in beautifully with Soddy's isotope theory. Removal of an alpha-particle from a nucleus would reduce the positive charge of that nucleus by two — exactly what was needed to move it two places down in the periodic table. On the other hand, the ejection of an electron (beta particle) from a nucleus would leave a proton unneutralized and thus increase the nucleus's positive charge by one unit. That amounted to raising the atomic number by one, so the element would move to the next higher position in the periodic table.

How is it that when thorium breaks down to "radiothorium," after going through not one but three disintegrations, the product is still thorium? Well, in the process the thorium atom loses an alpha particle, then a beta particle, then a second beta particle. If we accept the proton building-block idea, this means it has lost four electrons (two supposedly contained in the alpha particle) and four protons. (The actual situation differs from this picture, but in a way which does not affect the result.) The thorium nucleus started with 232 protons and 142 electrons (supposedly). Having lost four protons and four electrons, it is reduced to 228 protons and 138 electrons. This still leaves the atomic number 90, the same as before. So "radiothorium," like thorium, has 90 planetary electrons circling around the nucleus. Since the chemical properties of an atom are controlled by the number of its planetary electrons, thorium and "radiothorium" behave the same chemically, regardless of their difference in atomic weight (232 against 228).

The isotopes of an element are identified by their atomic weight, or "mass number." Thus ordinary thorium is called thorium 232, while "radiothorium" is thorium 228. Similarly, the radioactive isotopes of lead are known as lead 210 ("radium D"), lead 214 ("radium B"), lead 212 ("thorium B"), and lead 211 ("actinium B").

The notion of isotopes was found to apply to stable elements as well as to radioactive ones. For instance, it turned out that the three radioactive series I have mentioned ended in three different forms of lead. The uranium series ended in lead 206, the thorium series in lead 208, and the actinium series in lead 207. Each of these was an "ordinary," stable isotope of lead, but the three leads differed in atomic weight.

Proof of the existence of stable isotopes came from a device invented by an assistant of J. J. Thomson named Francis William Aston. It was an arrangement which separated isotopes very sensitively by virtue of the difference in deflection of their ions by a magnetic field; Aston called it a "mass spectrograph." In 1919, using this instrument, he showed that neon was made up of two varieties of atom, one with a mass number of 20, the other with a mass number of 22. Neon 20 was the common isotope; neon 22 came with it in the ratio of one atom in ten. (Later a third isotope, neon 21, was discovered, amounting to only one atom in 400 in the neon of the atmosphere.)

Now the reason for the fractional atomic weights of the elements at last became clear. Neon's atomic weight of 20.183 represented the composite weight of the three differently-weighted isotopes making up the element as it was found in nature. Each individual atom had an integral mass number but the average mass number — the atomic weight — was fractional.

Aston proceeded to show that several common stable elements were indeed mixtures of isotopes. He found that chlorine, whose fractional weight of 35.457 had given physicists such a bad time, was made up of chlorine 35 and chlorine 37, in the ratio of four to one. Aston was awarded the Nobel Prize in chemistry in 1922.

Thus, after a century of false trails, Prout's idea was finally vindicated. The elements *were* built of uniform building blocks — if not of hydrogen atoms, at least of units with hydrogen's mass. The reason the elements did not bear this out in their weights was that they were mixtures of isotopes containing different numbers of building blocks. In fact, even oxygen, whose atomic weight of 16 was used as the standard for measuring the relative weights of the elements, was not a completely pure case. For every 10,000 atoms of common oxygen 16, there were 20 atoms of an isotope with a weight equal to 18 units and four with the mass number 17.

Actually there are a few elements consisting of a "single isotope." (This is a misnomer: to speak of an element as having only one isotope is like saying a woman has given birth to a "single twin.") The elements of this kind include beryllium, all of whose atoms have the mass number nine; fluorine, made up solely of fluorine 19; aluminum, solely aluminum 27, and a number of others. A nucleus with a particular structure is now called a "nuclide." One can properly say that an element such as aluminum is made up of a single nuclide.

EVER SINCE RUTHERFORD identified the first nuclear particle (the alpha particle), physicists have busied themselves poking around in the nucleus, trying either to change one atom into another or to break it up to see what it is made of. At first they had only the alpha particle to work with. Rutherford made excellent use of it.

One of the fruitful experiments Rutherford and his assistants carried out involved firing alpha particles at a screen coated with zinc sulfide. Each hit produced a tiny scintillation, so that the arrival of single particles could be witnessed and counted with the naked eye. Pursuing this technique, the experimenters put up a metal disk which would block the alpha particles from reaching the zinc sulfide screen so that the scintillations stopped. When hydrogen was introduced into the apparatus, scintillations appeared on the screen despite the blocking metal disk. Moreover, these new scintillations differed in appearance from those produced by alpha particles.

Since the metal disk stopped alpha particles, some other radiation must be penetrating it to reach the screen. The radiation, it was decided, must consist of fast protons. In other words, the alpha particles would now and then make a square hit on the nucleus of a hydrogen atom and send it careening forward, as one billiard ball might send another forward upon striking it. The struck protons, being relatively light, would shoot forward at great velocity and so could penetrate the metal disk and strike the zinc sulfide screen.

Then came a much more unexpected development. When the same experiment was performed with nitrogen instead of hydrogen as the target of the alpha-particle bombardment, the zinc sulfide screen still showed scintillations exactly like those produced by protons. Rutherford could only conclude that the bombardment had knocked protons out of the nitrogen nucleus.

To try to find out just what had happened, Rutherford turned to the "Wilson cloud chamber." This device, now familiar to every high-school student of physics, had been invented in 1895 by the Scottish physicist Charles Thomson Rees Wilson. A glass container fitted with a piston is filled with moisture-saturated air. When the piston is pulled outward, the air abruptly expands and therefore cools. At the reduced temperature it is supersaturated with the moisture. Now any charged particle will cause the water vapor to condense on it. If a particle dashes through the chamber, ionizing atoms in it, a foggy line of droplets will mark its wake.

The nature of this track can tell a great deal about the particle. The light beta particle leaves a faint, wavering path; the particle is knocked about even in passing near electrons. The much more massive alpha particle makes a straight, thick track. If it strikes a nucleus and rebounds, the path has a sharp bend in it. If it picks up two electrons and becomes a neutral helium atom, its track ends. Aside from the size and character of its track, there are other ways of identifying a particle in the cloud chamber. Its response to an applied magnetic field tells whether it is positively or negatively charged, and the amount of curve indicates its mass and energy. By now

233

physicists are so familiar with photographs of all sorts of tracks that they can read them off as if they were primer print. For the development of his cloud chamber, Wilson shared the Nobel Prize in physics in 1927.

What, then, did Rutherford see when he attacked nitrogen nuclei with alpha particles in a Wilson cloud chamber? The alpha particle would start off with its customary straight track. Then, occasionally, this would end suddenly in a fork. Plainly this event represented a collision with a nitrogen nucleus. One branch of the fork would be a comparatively thin track representing a proton shooting off. The other branch, a short, really heavy track, apparently represented what was left of the nitrogen nucleus, rebounding from the collision. But there was no sign of the alpha particle itself. It seemed that it must have been absorbed by the nitrogen nucleus, and this supposition was later verified by the British physicist Patrick Maynard Stuart Blackett, who is supposed to have taken more than 20,000 photographs in the process of collecting eight such collisions (surely an example of superhuman patience, faith, and persistence). For this and other work in the field of nuclear physics, Blackett received the Nobel Prize in physics in 1948.

The fate of the nitrogen nucleus could now be deduced. When it absorbed the alpha particle, its mass number of 14 and positive charge of seven were raised to 18 and nine, respectively. But since the combination immediately lost a proton, the mass number dropped to 17 and the positive charge to eight. Now the element with a positive charge of eight is oxygen, and the mass number 17 belongs to the isotope oxygen 17. In other words, Rutherford had transmuted nitrogen into oxygen. This was the first man-made transmutation in history. The dream of the alchemists had been fulfilled, though in a manner they could not possibly have foreseen.

Alpha particles from radioactive sources had limits as projectiles: they were not nearly energetic enough to break into nuclei of the heavier elements, whose high positive charges exercise a strong repulsion against positively-charged particles. But the nuclear fortress had been breached, and more energetic attacks were to come.

234

NEW PARTICLES

T HE MATTER OF ATTACKS on the nucleus brings us back to the question of the make-up of the nucleus. So far the model picturing it as composed of protons and electrons had stood up fairly well. But now came a series of discoveries which did not fit into the picture. In 1930 two German physicists reported that they had released from the nucleus a mysterious new radiation of unusual penetrating power. They had produced it by bombarding beryllium atoms with alpha particles. Two years later this discovery was followed up by the French physicists Frédéric and Irène Joliot-Curie. (Irène was the daughter of Pierre and Marie Curie, and Joliot had added her name to his on marrying her.) They used the new-found radiation from beryllium to bombard paraffin, a waxy substance composed of hydrogen and carbon. The radiation knocked protons out of the paraffin.

The English physicist James Chadwick quickly suggested that the radiation consisted of particles. To determine their size, he bombarded boron atoms with them, and from the increase in mass of the new nucleus he calculated that the particle added to the boron had a mass about equal to the proton. Yet the particle itself could not be detected in a Wilson cloud chamber. Chadwick decided that the explanation must be that the particle had no electric charge (an uncharged particle produces no ionization and therefore condenses no water droplets).

So Chadwick concluded that a completely new particle had turned up — a particle with just about the same mass as a proton but without any charge, or, in other words, electrically neutral. The possibility of such a particle had already been suggested, and a name had even been proposed — the "neutron." Chadwick accepted that name. For his discovery of the neutron, he was awarded the Nobel Prize in physics in 1935.

The new particle at once solved certain doubts that theoretical

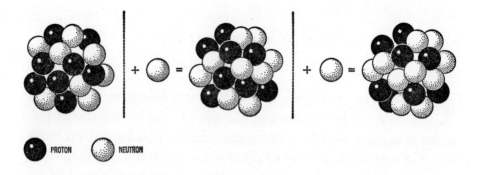

NUCLEAR MAKEUP OF OXYGEN 16, OXYGEN 17 AND OXYGEN 18. *They contain eight protons each, and in addition eight, nine, and ten neutrons, respectively.*

physicists had had about the proton-electron model of the nucleus. The German theoretical physicist Werner Heisenberg announced that the concept of a nucleus consisting of protons and neutrons, rather than protons and electrons, gave a much more satisfactory picture — more in accord with what the mathematics of the case said the nucleus should be like.

Furthermore, the new model fitted the facts of the periodic table of elements just as neatly as the old one had. The helium nucleus, for instance, would consist of two protons and two neutrons, which explained its mass of four and nuclear charge of two units. And the concept accounted for isotopes in very simple fashion. For example, the chlorine-35 nucleus would have 17 protons and 18 neutrons; the chlorine-37 nucleus, 17 protons and 20 neutrons. This would give both the same nuclear charge, and the extra weight of the heavier isotope would lie in its two extra neutrons. Likewise, the three isotopes of oxygen would differ only in their numbers of neutrons: oxygen 16 would have eight protons and eight neutrons; oxygen 17, eight protons and nine neutrons; oxygen 18, eight protons and ten neutrons.

In short, every element could be defined simply by the number of protons in its nucleus, which is equivalent to the atomic number. All the elements except hydrogen, however, also had neutrons in the nucleus, and the mass number of a nuclide was the sum of its protons and neutrons. Thus the neutron joined the proton as a basic building block of matter. For convenience, both are now called "nucleons."

THE PROTON-NEUTRON MODEL of the nucleus is not likely to be seriously upset in the future. At first it left unexplained the fact that radioactive nuclei emitted electrons, but that question was soon cleared up, as I shall explain shortly.

Nevertheless, in a very important respect the discovery of the neutron disappointed physicists. They had been able to think of the universe as being built of just two fundamental particles — the proton and the electron. Now a third had to be added. To scientists, every retreat from simplicity is regrettable.

The worst of it was that, as things turned out, this was only the beginning. Simplicity's backward step quickly became a headlong rout. There were more particles to come.

For many years physicists had been studying the mysterious "cosmic rays" from space, first discovered in 1911 by the Austrian physicist Victor Francis Hess on balloon flights high in the atmosphere. The American physicist Robert Andrews Millikan, who collected a great deal of information on this radiation (and gave it the name "cosmic rays"), decided that it must be a form of electromagnetic radiation. It had extremely high penetrating power; some of it could even pass through several feet of lead. To Millikan this suggested that the radiation was like the penetrating gamma rays, but with an even shorter wavelength.

Other physicists, notably Arthur Holly Compton at the University of Chicago, contended that the cosmic rays were particles. There was a way to investigate the question. If they were charged particles, they should be deflected by the earth's magnetic field as they approached the earth from outer space. Compton studied the measurements of cosmic radiation at various latitudes and found that it did indeed curve with the magnetic field: it was weakest near the magnetic equator and strongest near the poles, where the magnetic lines of force dipped down to the earth. (Hess, Millikan, and Compton all received Nobel awards in physics, the latter two mainly for other work besides that on cosmic rays.)

The "primary" cosmic particles, as they enter our atmosphere, carry fantastically high energies. Most of them are protons, but some are nuclei of heavier elements, all the way up to iron. When the primary particles hit atoms and molecules of the air, they smash these nuclei and produce all sorts of "secondary" particles. It is this secondary radiation (still very energetic) that we detect near the earth, but balloons sent to the upper atmosphere have recorded the primary radiation.

Now it was in the cosmic rays that the next new particle — after the neutron — was discovered. This discovery had actually been predicted by a theoretical physicist. Paul Adrien Maurice Dirac had reasoned, from a mathematical analysis of the properties of subatomic particles, that each particle should have an "anti-particle." (Scientists like Nature to be not only simple but also symmetrical.) Thus there ought to be an "anti-electron," exactly like the electron except that it had a positive instead of a negative charge, and an "anti-proton" with a negative instead of a positive charge.

Dirac's theory did not make much of a splash in the scientific world when he proposed it in 1930. But sure enough, two years later the "anti-electron" actually turned up. The American physicist Carl David Anderson was working with Millikan on the problem of whether cosmic rays were electromagnetic radiation or particles. By then most people were ready to accept Compton's evidence that they were charged particles, but Millikan was an extraordinarily hard loser and he was not satisfied that the issue was settled. Anderson undertook to find out whether cosmic rays entering a Wilson cloud chamber would be bent by a strong magnetic field. To slow down the rays sufficiently so that the curvature, if any, could be detected, Anderson placed in the chamber a lead barrier about a quarter of an inch thick. He found that the cosmic radiation crossing the chamber after it came through the lead did make a curved track. But he also found something else. In their passage through the lead, the energetic cosmic rays knocked particles out of the lead atoms. One of these particles made a track just like that of an electron. But it curved in the wrong direction! Same mass but opposite charge. There it was — Dirac's "anti-electron." Anderson called his discovery the "positron."

The positron had only an instant of existence. As soon as it encountered an electron, the two annihilated each other, leaving pure energy in the form of gamma rays in their place. This confirmed Albert Einstein's remarkable suggestion that matter could be converted into energy and vice versa. Indeed, Anderson soon succeeded in detecting the reverse phenomenon: gamma rays suddenly disappearing and giving rise to an electron-positron pair. (Anderson, along with Hess, received the Nobel Prize in physics in 1936.)

The Joliot-Curies shortly afterward came across the positron in another connection, and in so doing made an important discovery. Bombarding aluminum atoms with alpha particles, they found that the procedure produced not only protons but also positrons. This in itself was interesting but not fabulous. When they stopped the bombardment, however, the aluminum kept right on emitting positrons! The emission faded off with time. Apparently they had created a new radioactive substance in the target.

The Joliot-Curies interpreted what had happened in this way. When an aluminum nucleus absorbed an alpha particle, the addition of two protons changed aluminum (atomic number 13) to phosphorus (atomic number 15). Since the alpha particle contained four nucleons altogether, the mass number would go up by four — from aluminum 27 to phosphorus 31. Now if the reaction knocked a proton out of this nucleus, the reduction of its atomic number and mass number by one would change it to another element —namely, silicon 30.

Since an alpha particle is the nucleus of helium and a proton the nucleus of hydrogen, we can write the following equation of this "nuclear reaction":

aluminum 27 + helium 4 → silicon 30 + hydrogen 1

Notice that the mass numbers balance: 27 plus 4 equals 30 plus 1. So do the atomic numbers, for aluminum's is 13 and helium's 2, making 15 together, while silicon's atomic number of 14 and hydrogen's 1 also add up to 15. This balancing of both mass numbers and atomic numbers is a general rule of nuclear reactions.

The Joliot-Curies assumed that neutrons as well as positrons had been formed in the reaction. If phosphorus 31 emitted a neutron instead of a proton, the atomic number would not change, though the mass number would go down one. In that case the element would remain phosphorus but would be phosphorus 30. This equation would read:

$$\text{aluminum } 27 + \text{helium } 4 \rightarrow \text{phosphorus } 30 + \text{neutron } 1$$

Since the atomic number of phosphorus is 15 and that of the neutron is 0, again the atomic numbers on both sides of the equation also balance.

Both processes — alpha-absorption followed by proton-emission, and alpha-absorption followed by neutron-emission — take place when aluminum is bombarded by alpha particles. But there is one important distinction between the two results. Silicon 30 is a perfectly well-known isotope of silicon, making up a little more than 3 per cent of the silicon in nature. But phosphorus 30 does not exist in nature. The only known natural form of phosphorus is phosphorus 31. Phosphorus 30, in short, is a radioactive isotope with a brief lifetime which exists today only when it is produced artificially; in fact, it was the first such isotope made by man. The Joliot-Curies received the Nobel Prize in chemistry in 1935 for their discovery of artificial radioactivity.

The unstable phosphorus 30 that the Joliot-Curies had produced by bombarding aluminum quickly broke down by emitting positrons. Since the positron, like the electron, has practically no mass, this emission did not change the mass number of the nucleus. However, the loss of one positive charge did reduce its atomic number by one, so that it was converted from phosphorus to silicon.

Where does the positron come from? Are positrons among the

components of the nucleus? The answer is no. What happens is that a proton within the nucleus changes to a neutron by shedding its positive charge, which is released in the form of a speeding positron.

Now the emission of beta particles — the puzzle we encountered earlier in the chapter — can be explained. This comes about as the result of a process just the reverse of the decay of a proton into a neutron. That is, a neutron changes into a proton. The proton-to-neutron change releases a positron, and, to maintain the symmetry, the neutron-to-proton change releases an electron (the beta particle). The release of a negative charge is equivalent to the gain of a positive charge and accounts for the formation of a positively-charged proton from an uncharged neutron. But how does the uncharged neutron manage to dig up a negative charge and send it forth in the form of an energetic particle? Well, in a sense we can consider the electron it emits a form of energy created in the conversion process. (I will go into the question of the creation of matter and energy in more detail in the next chapter.)

When a neutron in an atom's nucleus changes to a proton, the mass number remains unchanged. But the nucleus has gained a proton (*i.e.*, one unit of positive charge), so its atomic number increases by one. That is why the emission of a beta particle from the nucleus signals its conversion to the next higher element.

ONCE THE JOLIOT-CURIES had created the first artificial radioactive isotope, physicists proceeded merrily to produce whole tribes of them. In fact, radioactive varieties of every single element in the periodic table have now been formed in the laboratory. In the modern periodic table each element is really a family, with stable and unstable members, some found in nature, some only in the laboratory.

For instance, hydrogen comes in three varieties. First there is ordinary hydrogen, containing a single proton. In 1932 the chemist Harold Urey succeeded in isolating a second. He did it by slowly evaporating a large quantity of water, working on the theory that he would be left in the end with a concentration of the heavier form of hydrogen that was suspected to exist. Sure enough, when he examined the last few drops of unevaporated water spectroscopically, he found a faint line in the spectrum in exactly the position predicted for "heavy hydrogen."

Heavy hydrogen's nucleus is made up of one proton and one neutron. Having a mass number of two, the isotope is hydrogen 2. Urey named the atom "deuterium," from a Greek word meaning "second," and the nucleus a "deuteron." A water molecule containing deuterium is called "heavy water." Because deuterium has twice the mass of ordinary hydrogen, heavy water has a higher boiling point: whereas ordinary water boils at 100° C., heavy water boils at 101.42° C. Deuterium occurs in nature in the ratio of one part to 6,000 parts of ordinary hydrogen. For his discovery of deuterium, Urey received the Nobel Prize in chemistry in 1934.

The deuteron turned out to be a valuable particle for bombarding nuclei. In 1934 the English physicists M. L. E. Oliphant and P. Harteck, attacking deuterium itself with deuterons, produced a third form of hydrogen, made up of one proton and two neutrons. The reaction went:

hydrogen 2 + hydrogen 2 → hydrogen 3 + hydrogen 1

The new "superheavy" hydrogen was named "tritium," from the Greek word for "third." It proved to be radioactive, emitting an electron and changing to helium 3, a stable but rare isotope of helium.

Helium 3 differs from ordinary helium 4 in some interesting ways, particularly in the fact that it does not display the same properties of superconductivity and superfluidity in the liquid state, discussed

NUCLEI OF ORDINARY HYDROGEN, DEUTERIUM, AND TRITIUM.

LINEAR ACCELERATOR *at the University of California Radiation Laboratory in Berkeley.*

THE SOVIET UNION'S PHASOTRON, *which accelerates particles to 10 billion electron-volts.*

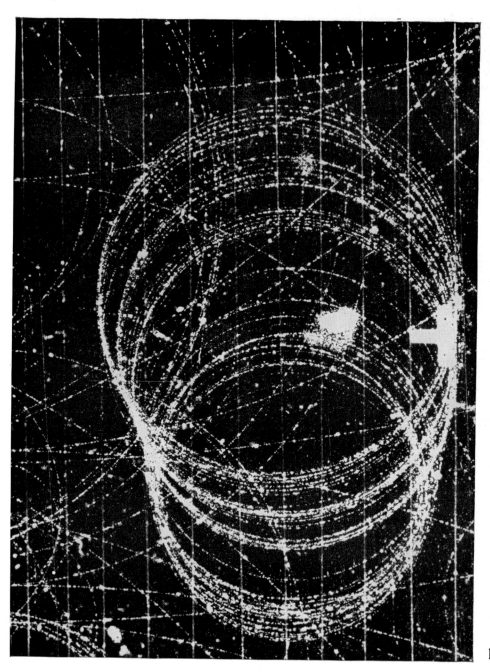

TRACKS OF ELECTRONS AND POSITRONS *formed in a cloud chamber by high-energy gamma rays. The circular pattern was made by an electron revolving in the magnetic field.*

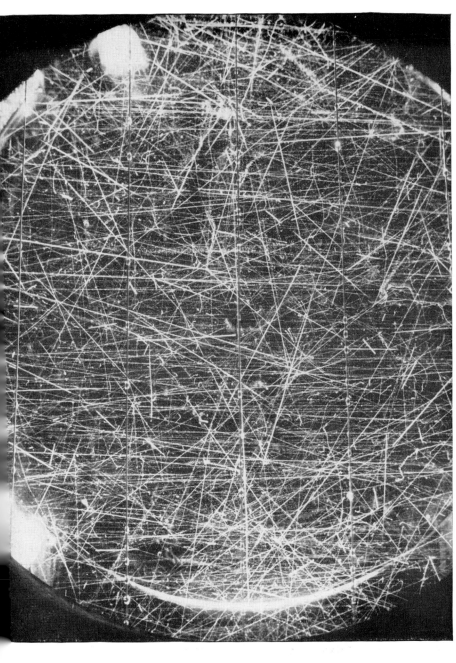

TRACKS OF NUCLEAR PARTICLES *produced by 1.2 Bev protons from the Cosmotron smashing atoms in a brass target.*

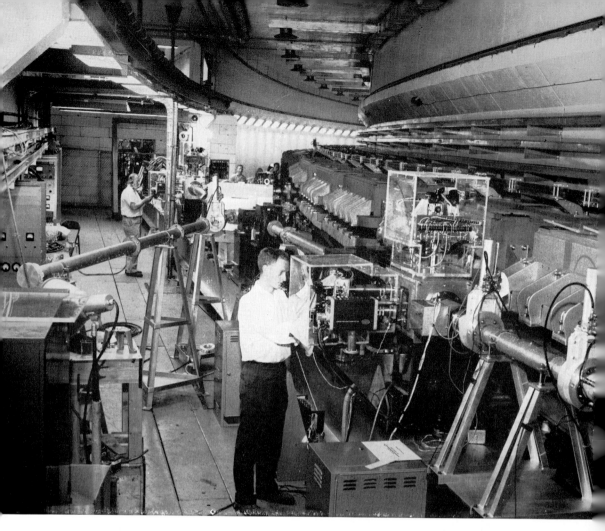

BROOKHAVEN'S NEW SYNCHROTRON, *which went into operation July 29, 1960, and produced a proton beam with an energy of more than 30 Bev. Using the "strong-focusing" principle, it is called the Alternating Gradient Synchrotron (AGS). The pipe running diagonally from the upper left to the lower right of the picture is the channel through which the protons are injected from a linear accelerator into the circular synchrotron.*

LINEAR ACCELERATOR *for the Brookhaven AGS. This accelerator injects protons at 50 Mev into the synchrotron.*

in the preceding chapter. These two are not the only isotopes of helium. Physicists have created two radioactive forms: helium 5, one of the most unstable nuclei known, and helium 6, also very unstable.

And so it goes. By now the list of isotopes of the elements has grown to more than a thousand altogether. Many of them have been created by new forms of atomic artillery far more potent than the alpha particles from radioactive sources which were the only projectiles at the disposal of Rutherford and the Curies.

PARTICLE ACCELERATORS

DIRAC HAD PREDICTED not only an anti-electron (the positron) but also an anti-proton. But to produce an anti-proton would take vastly more energy. The energy needed was proportional to the mass of the particle. Since the proton was 1,836 times as massive as the electron, the formation of an anti-proton called for at least 1,836 times as much energy as the formation of a positron. The feat had to wait for the development of a super atomic cannon for accelerating subatomic particles.

At the time of Dirac's prediction, the first atomic cannons had just been invented. In 1928 the English physicists John D. Cockroft and Ernest Walton, working in Rutherford's laboratory, developed a "voltage multiplier," a device for building up electric potential, which could drive the charged proton up to an energy of nearly 400,000 electron-volts. (One electron-volt is equal to the energy developed by an electron accelerated across an electric field with a potential of one volt.) With protons accelerated in this machine they were able to break up the lithium nucleus.

Meanwhile the American physicist Robert Jemison Van de Graaf was creating another type of accelerating machine. Essentially it operated by separating electrons from protons and depositing them at opposite ends of the apparatus by means of a moving belt. In this way the "Van de Graaf electrostatic generator" developed a very high electric potential between the opposite ends; Van de Graaf got it up to eight million volts. The machine can easily accelerate protons to a speed amounting to four million electron-volts (physicists invariably abbreviate million electron-volts now to "Mev").

The dramatic pictures of the Van de Graaf electrostatic generator producing huge sparks caught the popular imagination and introduced the public to "atom-smashers."

The energy that can be reached in such a machine is restricted by practical limits on the attainable potential. However, another scheme for accelerating particles shortly made its appearance. Suppose that, instead of firing particles with one big shot, you accelerated them with a series of small pushes. If each successive push was timed just right, it would increase the speed each time, just as pushes on a child's swing will send it higher and higher if they are applied "in phase" with the swing's oscillations.

This idea gave birth, in 1931, to the "linear accelerator." The particles are driven down a tube divided into sections. The driving force

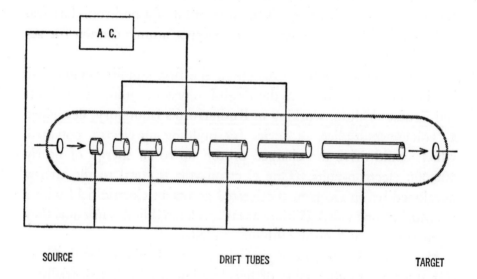

SOURCE   DRIFT TUBES   TARGET

PRINCIPLE OF THE LINEAR ACCELERATOR. *A high-frequency alternating charge alternately pushes and pulls the charged particles in the successive drift tubes, accelerating them in one direction.*

is an alternating electric field, so managed that as the particles enter each successive section, they get another push. Since the particles speed up as they go along, each section must be longer than the one before, so that the particles will take the same time to get through it and will be in phase with the timing of the pushes.

It is not easy to keep the timing just right, and anyway there is a limit to how long a tube you can make practicably, so the linear accelerator did not catch on in the 1930's. One of the things that pushed it into the background was that Ernest Orlando Lawrence of the University of California conceived a better idea.

Instead of driving the particles down a straight tube, why not whirl them around in a circular path? A magnet could bend them in such a path. Each time they completed a half circle, they would be given a kick by the alternating field, and in this setup the timing would not be so difficult to control. As the particles speeded up, their path would be bent less sharply by the magnet, so they would move in ever wider circles and perhaps take the same time for each round trip. At the end of their spiraling flight, the particles would emerge from the circular chamber (actually divided into semi-circular halves, called "dees") and attack their target.

Lawrence's compact new device was named the "cyclotron." His first model, less than a foot in diameter, could accelerate protons to energies of nearly one and a quarter Mev. By 1939 the University of California had a cyclotron, with magnets five feet across, capable of raising particles to some 20 Mev, twice the speed of the most energetic alpha particles emitted by radioactive sources. In that year Lawrence received the Nobel Prize in physics for his invention.

The cyclotron itself had to stop at about 20 Mev, because at that energy the particles were traveling so fast that their mass increased — an effect predicted by Albert Einstein's theory of relativity (see Chapter 7). This increase in mass would cause the particles to start lagging and falling out of phase with the electrical kicks. But there was a cure for this trouble, and it was worked out in 1945 independently by the Soviet physicist V. I. Veksler and the California physicist Edwin M. McMillan. The cure was simply to synchronize

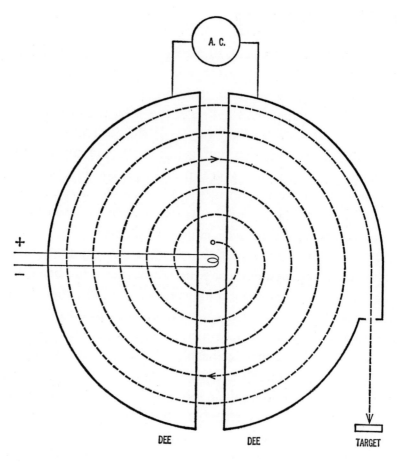

A. C.

+
−

DEE   DEE   TARGET

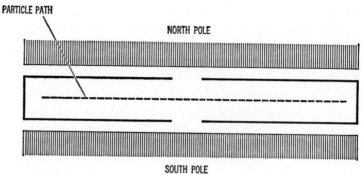

PARTICLE PATH

NORTH POLE

SOUTH POLE

PRINCIPLE OF THE CYCLOTRON, *shown in top view* (above) *and side view* (below). *Particles injected from the source are given a kick in each dee by the alternating charge and are bent in their spiral path by a magnet.*

2 4 6

the alternations of the electric field with the increase in mass of the particles. This modification of the cyclotron was called the "synchrocyclotron." By 1946 the University of California had built one which accelerated particles to energies of 200 to 400 Mev. Later larger synchrocyclotrons in the United States and in the Soviet Union raised the energies to 700 to 800 Mev.

Meanwhile the acceleration of electrons had been getting separate attention. To be useful in smashing atoms, the light electrons had to be raised to much higher speeds than protons (just as a ping-pong ball has to be moving much faster than a golf ball to do as much damage). The cyclotron would not work for electrons, because at the high velocities needed to make the electrons effective, their increase in mass was too great. So in 1940 the University of Illinois physicist D. W. Kerst designed an electron-accelerating device which balanced the increasing mass with an electric field of increasing strength. The electrons were kept in the same circular path instead of spiraling outward. This instrument was named the "betatron," after beta particles. Betatrons now generate electron velocities up to 300 Mev. They have been joined by another instrument of slightly different design called the "electron synchrotron."

Taking a leaf from the betatron and electron synchrotron, physicists working with protons began about 1947 to build "proton synchrotrons," which likewise kept their particles in a single circular path. With this instrument they set out for the goal of 1,000 Mev, or a billion electron-volts — abbreviated to Bev. (In Great Britain a billion is a million million, so Bev does not mean the same thing as in the United States; for 1,000 Mev the British use the shorthand Gev, the G coming from "giga," Greek for "giant.")

In 1952 the Brookhaven National Laboratory on Long Island completed a proton synchrotron which reached two to three Bev. They called it the "Cosmotron," because it had arrived at the main energy range of particles in the cosmic rays. Two years later the University of California brought in its "Bevatron," capable of producing particles of between five and six Bev. Then in 1957 the Soviet Union announced its "Phasotron" had got to 10 Bev.

But by now these machines seem puny in comparison with accelerators of a newer type, called the "strong-focusing synchrotron." The limitation on the Bevatron type is that particles in the stream fly off into the walls of the channel in which they travel. The new type counteracts this tendency by means of alternating magnetic fields of different shape which keep focusing the particles in a narrow stream. The idea was first suggested by the Greek engineer Nicholas Christofilos.

In November 1959 the European Committee for Nuclear Research (CERN), a cooperative agency of 12 nations, completed in Geneva a strong-focusing synchrotron which reached 24 Bev and produced large pulses of particles (containing 10 billion protons) every three seconds. This synchrotron is nearly three city blocks in diameter, and one round trip through it is two-fifths of a mile. In the three-second period during which the pulse builds up, the protons travel half a million times around that track. The instrument has a magnet weighing 3,500 tons and cost $30 million.

It is not, however, the last word. Brookhaven is completing an even larger machine, and the U.S.S.R. has announced plans for one that will attain 50 Bev.

Meanwhile, the linear accelerator has undergone a revival. Improvements in technique have removed the difficulties that plagued the early models. For extremely high energies, a linear accelerator has some advantages over the cyclic type. It can accelerate electrons more powerfully and focus beams on targets more sharply. Stanford University is planning a linear accelerator two miles long which will reach energies of perhaps 45 Bev.

WITH THE BEVATRON, man at last came within reach of creating the anti-proton. The California physicists set out deliberately to produce and detect it. In 1955 Owen Chamberlain and Emilio G. Segrè, after bombarding copper with protons of 6.2 Bev hour after hour, definitely caught the anti-proton — in fact, 60 of them. It was far from easy to identify them. For every anti-proton produced, 40,000 particles of other types came into existence. But by an elaborate system of detectors, so designed and arranged that only an anti-proton could touch all the bases, they recognized the particle beyond question. For their achievement, Chamberlain and Segrè received the Nobel Prize in physics in 1959.

The anti-proton is as evanescent as the positron — at least in our universe. Within a tiny fraction of a second after it is created, the particle is snatched up by some normal, positively charged nucleus. There the anti-proton and one of the protons of the nucleus annihilate each other, turning into energy and minor particles.

Once in a while a proton and an anti-proton have only a near-collision instead of a direct one. When that happens, they mutually neutralize their respective charges. The proton is converted to a neutron, which is fair enough. But the anti-proton becomes an "anti-neutron"! What can an "anti-neutron" be? The positron is the opposite of the electron by virtue of its opposite charge, and the anti-proton likewise, but what is the uncharged anti-neutron the opposite of?

Here we have to digress a little into the subject of the spin of particles. Every known type of particle spins on its axis, like a top or the earth or the sun or our Galaxy or, for all we know, the Universe itself. In spinning, the particle generates a tiny magnetic field; such fields have been measured and thoroughly explored, notably by the American physicist Isidor Isaac Rabi, who received the Nobel Prize in physics in 1944 for his work on this phenomenon.

Now it is easy to understand how a charged particle sets up a

AN ATOM OF HYDROGEN AND AN ATOM OF ITS ANTI-MATTER COUNTERPART, *consisting of an anti-proton and a positron.*

2 4 9

magnetic field, but not so easy to see why the uncharged neutron should. Yet it unquestionably does. The most direct evidence of this is that when a neutron beam strikes magnetized iron, it behaves differently from the way it does when the iron is not magnetized. The neutron's magnetism remains a mystery; physicists can do no better than to guess that the neutron may contain positive and negative charges which add up to zero but which somehow manage to set up a magnetic field when the particle spins.

In any case, the spin of the neutron gives us the answer to the question as to what the anti-neutron is. It is simply a neutron with its spin-direction reversed; its south magnetic pole, say, is up instead of down. Actually the proton and anti-proton and the electron and positron show exactly the same pole-reversed phenomenon.

Naturally some intriguing thoughts arise from the discovery that the three chief particles making up matter — the proton, the neutron and the electron — all have anti-particles. Were particles and anti-particles created in equal numbers at the beginning of the Universe? If so, does the Universe contain worlds, remote from ours, which are made up of anti-particles? Such a world would be like ours and follow exactly the same laws with only one trifling difference: the plus and minus signs would be reversed. It would be a mirror-image of our world. Of course, if the two worlds ever came together — matter encountering anti-matter — they would instantly destroy each other.

Astronomers have lately taken to looking speculatively at distant galaxies to see if they can find anything odd about them. An individual galaxy composed of anti-matter would not betray itself in any way we can recognize. But two colliding galaxies might. Fred Hoyle believes that the tremendous output of radio energy from the two colliding galaxies in Cygnus (see Chapter 2), may just possibly signify a meeting of matter and anti-matter. He also points out that Messier 87, a galaxy which has a bright jet of luminosity sticking out of its globular main body, may represent a collision of matter with a small cloud of anti-matter, or vice versa.

Maurice Goldhaber of Brookhaven suggests that the original cosmic egg from which the universe was born may have been formed of equal parts of matter and anti-matter which promptly split into two universes — a "cosmon" made of normal matter and an "anticosmon" made of anti-matter. They may have been pushed apart by some kind of repulsion between them. (If anti-matter, why not anti-gravity?) So somewhere, entirely beyond our reach or observation, there may be an anti-universe made up almost entirely of anti-matter.

THE VAST ENERGY produced by mutual annihilation between particles and anti-particles brings up the question of the even vaster energies discovered in the cosmic rays. Most of the cosmic-ray particles have energies between one and ten Bev. But a few run much higher — 20 Bev, 30 Bev, 40 Bev, and physicists at the Massachusetts Institute of Technology have even detected some with the colossal energy of five billion Bev! Numbers such as this are more than the mind can grasp, but we may get some idea of what that energy means when we calculate that the amount of energy represented by five billion Bev would be enough to enable a single sub-microscopic particle to raise a one-pound weight two inches!

Ever since cosmic rays were discovered, people have wondered where they came from and how they arise. The simplest concept is that somewhere in the Galaxy, perhaps in our sun, perhaps farther away, there are nuclear reactions going on which shoot forth particles with the huge energies we find them possessing. But there is no known nuclear reaction that could produce anything like five billion Bev. The most energetic one we can conceive of would be the mutual annihilation of heavy nuclei of matter and anti-matter, and this would liberate at most 250 Bev.

The alternative is to suppose that some force in space accelerates the cosmic particles. They may come originally from explosions such as supernovae and gradually be speeded up as they travel through space. The most popular theory at present is that they are accelerated by cosmic magnetic fields, acting like gigantic synchrotrons. Magnetic fields do exist in space, and our Galaxy as a whole is thought to possess one.

Traveling through this field, the cosmic particles would be slowly accelerated in a curved path. As they gained energy, their paths would swing out wider and wider until the most energetic ones would whip right out of the Galaxy. However, most of the particles would never reach this escape trajectory, because they would lose energy by collisions with other particles or with large bodies.

STRANGE PARTICLES

THE DISCOVERY of the anti-particles did not disturb physicists; on the contrary, it was a pleasing confirmation of the symmetry of the universe. What did disturb them was a quick succession of discoveries showing that the proton, the electron, and the neutron were not the only "elementary particles" they had to worry about.

The first of these complications had arisen even before the neutron was discovered. It had to do with the emission of beta particles by radioactive nuclei. The particle emitted by a radioactive nucleus generally carries a considerable amount of energy. Where does the energy come from? It is created by conversion of a little of the nucleus's mass into energy; in other words, the nucleus always loses a little mass in the act of expelling the particle. Now physicists had long been troubled by the fact that often the beta particle emitted in a nucleus's decay did not carry enough energy to account for the amount of mass lost by the nucleus. What was the reason for this deficiency, or, to put it another way, what happened to the missing energy?

In 1931 the Austrian physicist Wolfgang Pauli (who was to receive the Nobel Prize in physics in 1945 for his "exclusion principle," having to do with the distribution of electrons in the atom) suggested a solution for the riddle of the missing energy. His solution was very simple: another particle carrying the missing energy came out of the nucleus along with the beta particle. This mysterious second particle had rather strange properties. It had no charge and practically no mass; all it had was a certain amount of energy. It looked, in fact, like a fictional item created just to balance the energy books.

And yet, no sooner had it been proposed than physicists were sure that the particle existed. When the neutron was discovered and found to break down into a proton, releasing an electron which, as in beta decay, also carried a deficiency of energy, they were still surer. Enrico Fermi in Italy gave the putative particle a name — "neutrino," Italian for "little neutral one."

The neutron furnished physicists with another piece of evidence for the existence of the neutrino. As I have mentioned, every particle has a spin. The amount of spin is expressed in units of one-half — plus or minus, depending on the direction of the spin. Now the proton, the neutron, and the electron each has the spin $\frac{1}{2}$. If, then, the neutron, with spin $\frac{1}{2}$, gives rise to a proton and an electron, each with spin $\frac{1}{2}$, what happens to the law of conservation of angular momentum? There is a $\frac{1}{2}$ spin missing somewhere. The proton and the electron may total their spins to 1 (if both spin in the same direction) or to 0 (if their spins are opposite), but any way you slice it their spins cannot add up to $\frac{1}{2}$. Again, however, the neutrino comes to the rescue. Let the spin of the neutron be $+\frac{1}{2}$. Let the proton's spin be $+\frac{1}{2}$ and the electron's $-\frac{1}{2}$, for a net of 0. Now give the neutrino the spin $+\frac{1}{2}$ and the books are neatly balanced.

$$+\tfrac{1}{2}\ (n) = +\tfrac{1}{2}\ (p) -\tfrac{1}{2}\ (e)\quad +\tfrac{1}{2}\ (neutrino).$$

There is still some more balancing to do. A single particle (the neutron) has formed two particles (the proton and the electron), and if we include the neutrino, actually three particles. It seems more reasonable to suppose that the neutron is converted into two particles and an anti-particle, or a net of one particle. In other words, what we really need to balance the books is not a neutrino but an anti-neutrino.

The neutrino itself would arise from the conversion of a proton into a neutron. There the products would be a neutron (particle), a positron (anti-particle), and a neutrino (particle). This, too, balances the books.

To summarize, then, neutrinos are produced in any process involving the conversion of protons to neutrons. The most important of these are the nuclear reactions that go on in the sun and other stars. Stars therefore emit fast floods of neutrinos, and it is estimated that perhaps 6 to 8 per cent of their energy is carried off in this way. Anti-neutrinos are produced in any process involving the conversion of neutrons to protons. The most important of these are natural radioactivity and uranium fission (which I shall discuss in more detail in Chapter 9).

Naturally physicists could not rest content until they had actually tracked down the neutrino; scientists are never happy to accept phenomena or laws of nature entirely on faith (as concepts such as the "soul" must be). But how detect an entity as nebulous as the neutrino — an object with no mass, no charge, and practically no propensity to interact with ordinary matter? It was calculated that the average neutrino could pass untouched through 50 light-years of lead!

Still, there was some slight hope. Although the probability of a neutrino reacting with any particle is exceedingly small, it is not quite zero. Since 50 light-years of lead is just a measure of the average, there will be some neutrinos that react with a particle before they go that far, and a few — an almost unimaginably small proportion of the total number — that will be stopped within the equivalent of one-tenth of an inch of lead.

In 1953 a group of physicists led by Clyde L. Cowan and Frederick Reines of the Los Alamos Scientific Laboratory set out to try the next-to-impossible. They erected their apparatus for detecting neutrinos next to a large fission reactor of the Atomic Energy Commission on the Savannah River in Georgia. The reactor would furnish streams of neutrons, which, hopefully, would release floods of anti-neutrinos. To catch them, the experimenters used large tanks of water. The plan was to let the anti-neutrinos bombard the protons (hydrogen nuclei) in the water and detect the results of the capture of an anti-neutrino by a proton.

What would happen? When a neutron breaks down, it yields a proton, an electron, and an anti-neutrino. Now a proton's absorption of an anti-neutrino should produce essentially the reverse. That is to say, the proton should be converted to a neutron, emitting a positron in the process. So there were two things to be looked for: (1) the creation of neutrons, and (2) the creation of positrons. The neutrons could be detected by dissolving a cadmium compound in the water, for when cadmium absorbs neutrons, it emits gamma rays of a certain characteristic energy. And the positrons could be identified by their annihilating interaction with electrons, which would yield certain other gamma rays. If the experimenters' instruments detected gamma rays of exactly these two telltale energies, and separated by the proper time interval, they could be certain that they had caught anti-neutrinos.

The experimenters arranged their ingenious detection devices, waited patiently, and in 1956, exactly a quarter-century after Pauli's invention of the particle, they finally trapped the anti-neutrino. The newspapers and even some learned journals called it simply the "neutrino." The neutrino itself has not yet been detected (at this moment of writing) but there can no longer be any doubt of its existence.

OUR LIST of "elementary" particles has grown, then, to eight: proton, neutron, electron, neutrino, and their respective anti-particles. Be patient: we have only begun to count. A fantastic new crop of particles materialized before physicists had had time to digest the ones they had.

The new particles came from the simple question: what holds the nucleus together? How do all those protons — up to 92 of them in the natural elements — stick together in the nucleus despite the fact that ordinarily protons repel one another so strongly?

The search for the nuclear "cement" has engrossed physicists, and still engrosses them, perhaps more than any other single problem in modern physics. The first fruitful lead came in 1932 when Werner Heisenberg suggested that the protons were held together by "exchange forces." He pictured the protons and neutrons in the nucleus as continually interchanging identity, so that any given particle was first a proton, then a neutron, then a proton, and so on. This might keep the nucleus stable in the same way that you might be able to hold a hot potato by tossing it quickly from hand to hand. Before a proton could "realize" (so to speak) that it was a proton and try to flee its neighbor protons, it had become a neutron and could stay where it was. Naturally it could get away with this only if the changes took place exceedingly quickly, say within a trillionth of a trillionth of a second.

In 1935 the Japanese physicist Hideki Yukawa tried to work out this notion mathematically. His reasoning led to the conclusion that the transfer of charge back and forth between the proton and neutron had to be conveyed by a particle with a certain mass. This mass could be calculated from the range of the nuclear force field — obviously a very short range indeed. The mass would be in inverse ratio to the range: the greater the mass, the shorter the range. It turned out that the mass of the appropriate particle lay somewhere between that of the proton and the electron; Yukawa estimated it to be between 200 and 300 times the mass of an electron.

Barely a year later this very kind of particle was discovered. At the California Institute of Technology Carl Anderson (the discoverer of the positron), investigating the tracks left by secondary cosmic rays, came across a short track which was more curved than a proton's and less curved than an electron's. In other words, the particle had an intermediate mass. Soon more such tracks were detected, and the particles were named "mesotrons," or "mesons" for short.

The meson proved to have a mass about 200 times that of the electron and to be extremely unstable, as Yukawa had predicted. But in other respects it failed to fill the specifications of a cementing particle. For one thing, it showed no strong tendency to be absorbed by atomic nuclei. How could mesons be the cement that held nuclei together if they avoided nuclei?

Then in 1947 the British physicist C. F. Powell discovered another type of meson in cosmic-ray photographs. It was a little more massive — about 270 times the mass of an electron. Powell named this one the "pi-meson" and the earlier one the "mu-meson" (they are now usually called "pion" and "muon," respectively). The pi-meson was found to react strongly with nuclei and to be just the particle predicted by Yukawa. (He was awarded the Nobel Prize in physics in 1949.) In fact, bombardment of atoms by cosmic particles gives rise to as many as 20 pi-mesons per collision. So it now appears that even protons and neutrons are not the simple particles they were thought to be but may have nuclei of some sort surrounded by clouds of mesons, just as atoms have nuclear cores surrounded by clouds of electrons.

The pi-mesons and mu-mesons themselves break down into electrons (or positrons) and neutrinos. All the mesons have short lives, breaking down in a millionth of a second or even less. Both pions and muons come in positively charged and negatively charged forms, and the pion also has a neutral variety.

THE PIONS AND MUONS, it developed, were only forerunners — the advance scouts of an army, so to speak. Now came a parade of new particles, discovered by the increasingly sophisticated eyes of the physicists in cosmic-ray photographs and the products of giant accelerators such as the Brookhaven Cosmotron. There were heavier mesons named "K-mesons" (with 966 times the mass of the electron); there were "hyperons," subdivided into types called the "lambda particle," the "sigma particle," and the "xi particle" (with masses 2,180, 2,330 and 2,585 times that of an electron, respectively). These could exist in charged or uncharged forms and as particles or anti-particles. Thus, in 1959, the "xi-zero," an uncharged xi particle, was detected, as well as the "anti-lambda."

With their new particles, physicists have had fun creating odd kinds of "atoms." By bombarding atoms with mesons they have produced "mesonic atoms," in which mesons take the place of electrons and circle close to the nucleus. Then there is "positronium" — a positron and electron circling around a mutual center of gravitation just before they annihilate each other. And a "hyper-fragment" — a nucleus in which a hyperon has replaced a proton or neutron. All these abnormal "atoms" are extremely evanescent, existing for a millionth, or a billionth, or even only a trillionth of a second before the meson is absorbed into the nucleus, or the electron and positron cancel each other, or the hyperon converts itself into an ordinary nucleon.

All in all, nuclear physics is currently a wonderland — or a jungle, if you prefer — awaiting further exploration. At the latest count there were some 29 or 30 particles, detected or predicted, and no one could say that this was the end.

THE K-MESONS and the hyperons introduced physicists to a fourth field of force different from the three already known: gravitational, electromagnetic, and nuclear.

Of these three, gravitational force is by all odds the weakest, electromagnetic force comes next, and the nuclear force is still stronger — some 130 times as strong as electromagnetic forces. But the nuclear force, as I have mentioned, acts only over an extremely short distance. Whereas the electromagnetic and gravitational forces decrease only as the square of the distance, nuclear forces drop off so rapidly with distance that the force between two nucleons falls almost to zero if they are separated by a distance greater than their own diameter. (This is as if the earth's gravity were to become practically zero 4,000 miles above the surface.) Consequently interactions between particles under the influence of nuclear forces must take place very quickly.

For instance, imagine a pi-meson and a proton approaching each other. If the nuclear force is to cause them to interact, it must do so while they are within a proton's width of each other. A proton's

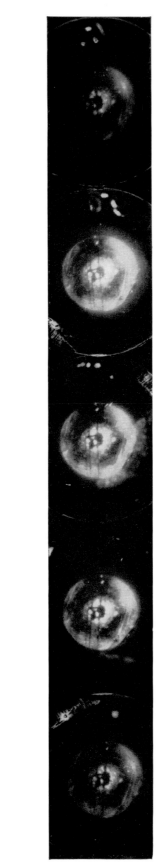

RADIOACTIVE TRACERS in a sample of material here make their own picture by means of a technique called "tracer micrography," developed by the U.S. National Bureau of Standards. Electrons emitted by the radioactive atoms are focused by a magnetic lens upon a photographic film, which thus shows the distribution of the radioactive material in the sample.

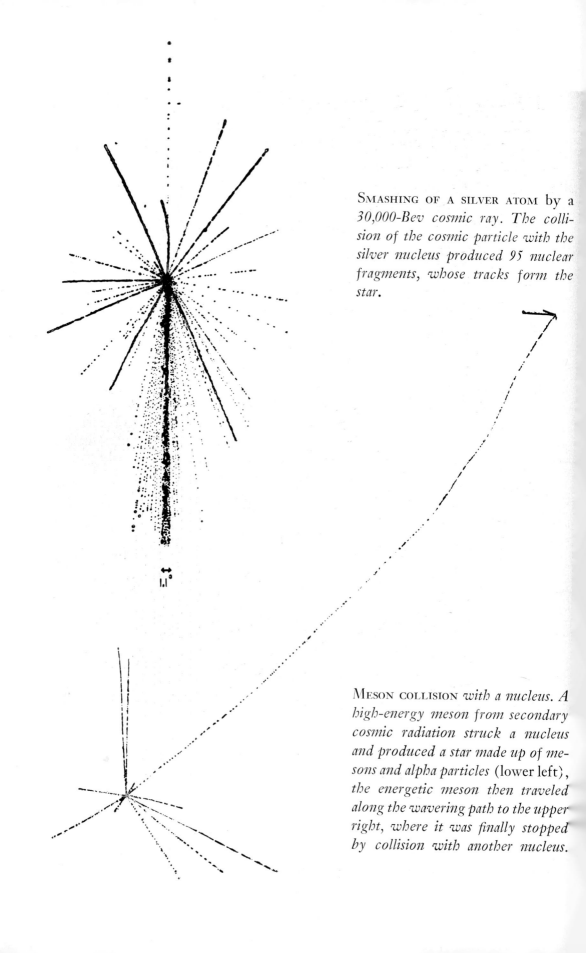

SMASHING OF A SILVER ATOM by a
30,000-Bev cosmic ray. The collision of the cosmic particle with the
silver nucleus produced 95 nuclear
fragments, whose tracks form the
star.

MESON COLLISION with a nucleus. A
high-energy meson from secondary
cosmic radiation struck a nucleus
and produced a star made up of mesons and alpha particles (lower left),
the energetic meson then traveled
along the wavering path to the upper
right, where it was finally stopped
by collision with another nucleus.

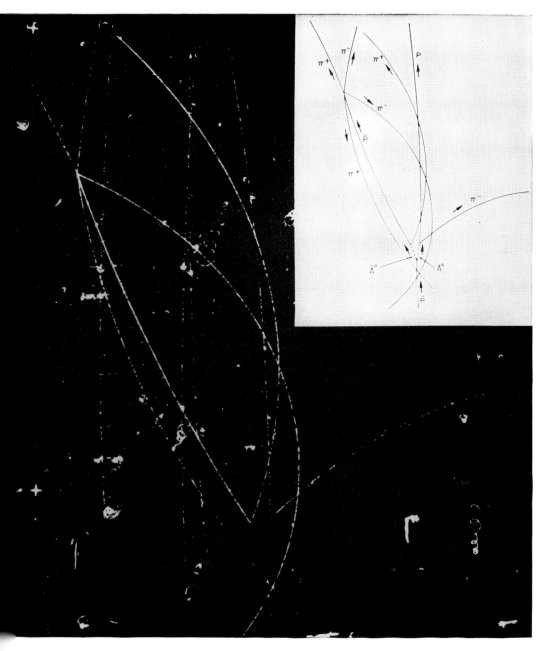

ANTI-PROTONS AND LAMBDA PARTICLES *produced this picture in the large bubble chamber at the University of California's Radiation Laboratory. As the diagram shows, an anti-proton (p̄) from the Bevatron entered at the bottom; where its track ends there is a gap* (dashed lines) *which represents the travel of the undetectable neutral lambda and anti-lambda particles. The anti-lambda then decayed into a positive pi-meson and an anti-proton, which went on to produce four pi-mesons* (upper left); *the lambda decayed into a proton and a negative pi-meson* (right side of the fork).

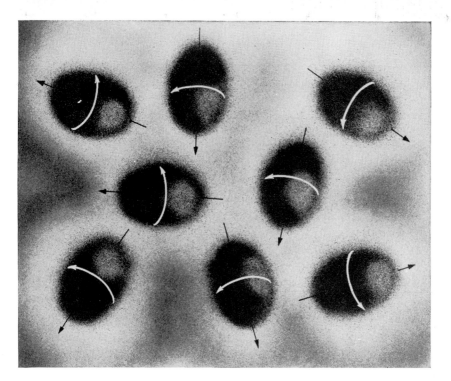

SPINNING PROTONS *in this schematic drawing are oriented in random directions. The white arrow shows the direction of the spin.*

PROTONS LINED UP *by a steady magnetic field. Those oriented in the opposite-to-normal direction* (arrows pointing downward) *are in the excited spin state.*

PARTICLE	SYMBOL	MASS	LIFETIME IN SECONDS
PHOTON	γ	0	Stable
NEUTRINO	ν	0	Stable
ANTI-NEUTRINO	$\bar{\nu}$	0	Stable
ELECTRON	e^-	1	Stable
POSITRON	e^+	1	Stable
PROTON	p	1836	Stable
ANTI-PROTON	$\bar{p}$	1836	Stable
NEUTRON	n	1839	1010
ANTI-NEUTRON	$\bar{n}$	1839	1010
MU MESONS	μ^- μ^+	206	2.22×10^{-6}
PI MESONS	π^- π^+	273	2.56×10^{-8}
NEUTRAL PI MESON	π°	264	$< 10^{-15}$
K MESONS	K^- K^+	967	1.2×10^{-8}
NEUTRAL K MESON$_1$	K_1°	~ 973	10^{-10}
NEUTRAL K MESON$_2$	K_2°	~ 973	$\sim 8 \times 10^{-8}$
HYPERONS — LAMBDA	Λ°	2182	2.6×10^{-10}
ANTI-LAMBDA	$\bar{\Lambda}^\circ$	2182	2.6×10^{-10}
SIGMA POSITIVE	Σ^+	2328	$\sim 8 \times 10^{-11}$
ANTI-SIGMA POSITIVE	$\bar{\Sigma}^+$	2328	$\sim 8 \times 10^{-11}$
SIGMA NEGATIVE	Σ^-	2342	1.7×10^{-10}
ANTI-SIGMA NEGATIVE	$\bar{\Sigma}^-$	2342	1.7×10^{-10}
NEUTRAL SIGMA	Σ°	2326	$< 10^{-11}$
NEUTRAL ANTI-SIGMA	$\bar{\Sigma}^\circ$	2326	$< 10^{-11}$
XI NEGATIVE	Ξ^-	2585	$\sim 10^{-10}$
ANTI-XI NEGATIVE	$\bar{\Xi}^-$	2585	$\sim 10^{-10}$
XI NEUTRAL	Ξ°	....	....
ANTI-XI NEUTRAL	$\bar{\Xi}^\circ$	....	....

A LIST OF IDENTIFIED SUBATOMIC PARTICLES.

width is about 0.0000000000001 centimeter. Flying mesons are traveling at almost the speed of light, which is 30 billion centimeters a second. Thus the pi-meson will be within the influence of the nuclear force for only about 0.0000000000000000000001 second (a hundred billionth of a trillionth of a second). And yet, even in this short time, the nuclear force brings about an interaction. The pi-meson and the proton can react to produce a lambda-hyperon and a K-meson.

This is an example of what physicists call a "strong interaction." A "weak interaction" is one that requires a considerably longer time. An example of such an interaction is the breakdown of a K-meson or a hyperon. This takes one ten-billionth of a second or so. That may seem a breathlessly short time, but compared to the time it takes for a pi-meson and proton to interact, it is very long. It is, in fact, about a trillion times as long as the physicists had expected, considering the speed of most nuclear interactions.

They concluded that the "weak interactions" were governed by forces much weaker than the nuclear forces, and they took to calling the particles that broke down as a result of weak interactions "strange particles." This name applied not only to K-mesons and hyperons but also to the light mesons and to neutrinos, which likewise were involved in weak interactions.

Physicists began to study weak interactions with increasing fascination. And in time they came to a discovery which rocked physics to its foundations.

This involved a property of particles called "parity." It is a strictly mathematical property which cannot be described in concrete terms; suffice it to say that the property refers to a mathematical function which has to do with the wave characteristics of a particle and its position in space. Parity has two possible values — "odd" and "even." The key point we must bear in mind is that parity has been considered a basic property which, like energy or momentum, is subject to the law of conservation — in any reaction or change, parity must be conserved. That is to say, when particles interact to form new particles, the parity on both sides of the equation (so it was thought) must balance, just as mass numbers must, or atomic numbers, or angular momentum.

Let me illustrate. If an odd-parity particle and an even-parity particle interact to form two other particles, one of the new particles must be odd-parity and the other even-parity. If two odd-parity particles form two new particles, both of the new ones must be odd or both even. Conversely, if an even-parity particle breaks down to form two particles, both must be even-parity or both must be odd-parity. If it forms three particles, either all three have even parity or one has even-parity, and the other two have odd-parity. (You may be able to see this more clearly if you consider the odd and even numbers, which follow similar rules. For instance, an even number can only be the sum of two even numbers or of two odd numbers, but never the sum of an even number and an odd one.) This is what is meant by the "conservation of parity."

The beginning of the trouble came when it was found that K-mesons sometimes broke down to two pi-mesons (which, since the pi-meson has odd-parity, added up to even-parity) and sometimes gave rise to three pi-mesons (adding up to odd-parity). Physicists concluded that there were two types of K-mesons, one of even-parity and one of odd-parity; they named the two the "theta-meson" and the "tau-meson," respectively.

Now in every respect except the parity result, the two mesons were identical: the same mass, the same charge, the same stability, the same everything. It was hard to believe that there could be two particles with exactly the same properties. Was it possible that the two were actually the same, and that there was something wrong with the idea of the conservation of parity? In 1956 two young Chinese physicists working in the United States, Tsung Dao Lee and Chen Ning Yang, made precisely that suggestion. They proposed that although the conservation of parity held in strong interactions, it might break down in weak interactions, such as the decay of K-mesons.

As they worked out this possibility mathematically, it seemed to them that if the conservation of parity broke down, the particles involved in weak interactions should show a "handedness." Let me explain.

Your right hand and left hand are opposites. One can be considered the mirror image of the other: in a mirror the right hand looks like a left hand. If all hands were symmetrical in every respect, the mirror image would be no different from the direct image, and there would be no such distinction as "right" and "left" hand. Very well, then, let us apply this to a group of particles emitting electrons. If electrons come out in equal numbers in all directions, the particle in question has no "handedness." But if most of them tend to go in a preferred direction — say up rather than down — then the particle is

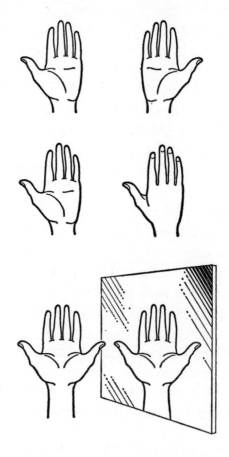

Mirror-image asymmetry and symmetry *illustrated by hands.*

not symmetrical. It shows a "handedness": if we look at the emissions in a mirror, the preferred direction will be reversed.

The thing to do, therefore, was to observe a collection of particles that emit electrons in a weak interaction (say some particle that decays by beta-emission) and see if the electrons came out in a preferred direction. Lee and Yang asked an experimental physicist at Columbia University, Chien-Shiung Wu, to perform the experiment.

She set up the necessary conditions. All the electron-emitting atoms had to be lined up in the same direction if a uniform direction of emission was to be detected; this was done by means of a magnetic field and the material was kept at a temperature near absolute zero.

Within 48 hours the experiment yielded the answer. The electrons were indeed emitted asymmetrically. The conservation of parity did break down in weak interactions. The "theta-meson" and the "tau-meson" were one and the same particle, breaking down with odd parity in some cases, with even parity in others. Other experimenters soon confirmed the overthrow of parity, and for their bold conjecture the theoretical physicists Lee and Yang received the Nobel Prize in physics in 1957.

If symmetry breaks down with respect to weak interactions, perhaps it will break down elsewhere. The Universe as a whole may be left-handed (or right-handed) after all. Alternatively, there may be two universes, one left-handed, the other right-handed; one composed of matter and the other of anti-matter.

INSIDE THE NUCLEUS

Now THAT SO MUCH has been learned about the general make-up and nature of the nucleus, there is great curiosity as to its structure, particularly the fine structure inside. First of all, what is its shape? Because it is so small and so tightly packed with neutrons and protons, physicists naturally assume that it is spherical. The fine details of the spectra of atoms suggest that many nuclei have a spherical distribution of charge. Some do not: they behave as if they have two pairs of magnetic poles, and these nuclei are said to have "quadrupole moments." But their deviation from the spherical is not very large — never more than that of the planet Jupiter, for instance. It seems safe, therefore, to picture all nuclei as more or less spherical in shape.

As for the internal structure of the nucleus, the simplest model pictures it as a tightly packed collection of particles much like a drop of liquid, where the particles (molecules) are packed closely with little space between, where the density is virtually even throughout, and where there is a sharp surface boundary.

This "liquid-drop model" was first worked out in detail in 1936 by the Danish physicist Niels Henrik David Bohr. It suggests a possible explanation of the absorption and emission of particles by some nuclei. When a particle enters the nucleus, one can suppose, it distributes its energy of motion among all the closely packed particles, so that no one particle receives enough energy immediately to break away. After perhaps a quadrillionth of a second, when there has been time for billions of random collisions, some particle accumulates sufficient energy to fly out of the nucleus.

The model could also account for the emission of alpha particles by the heavy nuclei — that is, the unstable elements with atomic numbers above 83. In these large nuclei the short-range nuclear forces may not reach all the way across the nucleus; hence the force of repulsion between positive particles can take effect. As a result, portions of the nucleus in the form of the two-proton, two-neutron alpha particle (a very stable combination) may break off spontaneously from the surface of the nucleus. After the nucleus has decayed to a size such that the nuclear force overwhelms the force of repulsion, the nucleus becomes stable.

The liquid-drop model suggests another form of nuclear instability. When a large drop of liquid suspended in another liquid is set wobbling by currents in the surrounding fluid, it tends to break up into smaller spheres, often into roughly equal halves. We can think of the fission of uranium as closely analogous to this process. The fissionable nucleus, when struck by a neutron, begins to wobble, in a manner of speaking. It may stretch out into the shape of a dumbbell (as a liquid drop would), and in that case the nuclear attractive forces would not reach from one end of the dumbbell to the other, with the result that the repulsive force would drive the two portions apart. Bohr offered this explanation when nuclear fission was discovered.

Other nuclei besides uranium 235 ought to be (and proved to be) subject to fission if they receive enough input of energy. In fact, if a nucleus is large enough for the repulsive forces to become important, it ought occasionally to fission even without the input of energy. (This is like saying that the drop-like nucleus is always vibrating and wobbling, and every once in a while the vibration is strong enough to produce the dumbbell and bring about the break.)

In 1940 two Russian physicists, G. N. Flerov and K. A. Petrjak, discovered indeed that the heavier isotope of uranium, U-238, sometimes fissions spontaneously, without the addition of any particle. Uranium exhibits instability mainly by emitting alpha particles, but in a pound of uranium there are four spontaneous fissions per second while about eight million nuclei are emitting alpha particles.

Spontaneous fission also takes place in uranium 235, in protactinium, in thorium, and, more frequently, in the transuranium elements. As nuclei get larger and larger, the probability of spontaneous fission increases. In the heaviest elements of all — einsteinium, fermium, and mendelevium — it becomes the most important method of breakdown, far outweighing alpha-particle emission.

Another popular model of the nucleus likens it to the atom as a whole, picturing the nucleons within the nucleus, like the electrons around the nucleus, as occupying shells and subshells, each affecting the others only slightly. This is called the "shell model."

How can there be room for independent shells of nucleons in the tiny, tightly packed nucleus? Well, however it is managed, the evidence suggests that there is some "empty space" there. For instance, in a mesonic atom the meson may actually circle in an orbit within the nucleus for a short time. And Robert Hofstadter of Stanford

University, probing nuclei with 500-Mev electrons from Stanford's linear accelerator, found that the nucleus consists of a high-density core surrounded by a "skin" of gradually decreasing density. The thickness of the skin is about half the radius of the nucleus, so that it actually makes up seven-eighths of the volume.

By analogy with the situation in the atom's electronic shells, one may suppose that the nuclei with filled outer nucleonic shells should be more stable than those whose outer shells are not filled. The University of Chicago physicist Maria Goeppert-Mayer has shown that nuclei containing 2, 8, 20, 50, 82 or 126 protons or neutrons are particularly stable. These "shell numbers" are sometimes called the "magic numbers." Among the magic-number nuclei are helium 4 (two protons and two neutrons), oxygen 16 (eight protons and eight neutrons), and calcium 40 (20 protons and 20 neutrons) — all especially stable and more abundant in the universe than other nuclei of similar size. The most striking example of all is tin (50 protons), which has no fewer than ten stable isotopes. Apparently the possession of 50 protons so stabilizes the nucleus that a wide assortment of neutron numbers becomes possible.

Useful as these models are, they are inconsistent with one another, and physicists are not much satisfied with any so far proposed. They want to see more clearly into the nucleus, and they await with high excitement the completion of the great new accelerators with which they expect to continue its dissection.

CHAPTER

7

THE WAVES

LIGHT

OF ALL THE HELPFUL ATTRIBUTES OF NATURE, the one that man probably appreciates most is light. According to the Bible, the first words of God were, "Let there be light," and the sun and the moon were created primarily to serve as sources of light: "And let them be for lights in the firmament of the heaven to give light upon the earth."

The scholars of ancient and medieval times were completely in the dark as to the nature of light. They speculated that it consisted of particles emitted by the glowing object, or perhaps by the eye itself. The only facts about it that they were able to establish were that light traveled in a straight path, that it was reflected from a mirror at an angle equal to that at which the beam struck the mirror, and that a light beam was bent ("refracted") when it passed from air into glass, water or some other transparent substance.

The first important experiments on the nature of light were conducted by Isaac Newton in 1666. He let a beam of sunlight, entering a dark room through a chink in a blind, fall obliquely on one face of a triangular glass prism. The beam was bent when it entered the glass and then bent still farther in the same direction when it emerged from a second face of the prism. Newton caught the emerging beam on a white screen to see the effect of the reinforced refraction. He found that instead of forming a spot of white light, the beam was now spread out in a band of colors — red, orange, yellow, green, blue, and violet, in that order.

Newton deduced that ordinary white light was a mixture of different kinds of light which, separately, affect our eyes so as to produce the sensation of different colors. The spread-out band of its components was called a "spectrum," from a Latin word meaning "ghost."

Newton decided that light consisted of tiny particles ("corpuscles") traveling at enormous speed. This would explain why light traveled in straight lines and cast sharp shadows. It was reflected by a mirror because the particles bounced off the surface, and it was bent on entering a refracting medium (such as water or glass) because the particles traveled faster in such a medium than in air.

Still, there were some awkward questions. Why should the particles of green light, say, be refracted more than those of yellow light? Why was it that two beams of light could cross without affecting each other — that is, without the particles colliding?

In 1678 the Dutch physicist Christian Huyghens (a versatile scientist who had built the first pendulum clock and done important work in astronomy) suggested an opposing theory: namely, that light consisted of tiny waves. If it was made up of waves, there was no difficulty about explaining the different amount of refraction of different kinds of light through a refracting medium, provided it was assumed that light traveled more slowly through the refracting medium than through air. The amount of refraction would vary with the length of the waves: the shorter the wavelength, the greater the refraction. This meant that violet light (the most refracted) had a shorter wavelength than blue light, blue shorter than green, and so on. It was this difference in wavelength that distinguished the colors to the eye. And, of course, if light consisted of waves, two beams could cross without trouble. (After all, sound waves and water waves crossed without losing their identity.)

But Huyghens' wave theory was not very satisfactory either. It didn't explain why light-rays traveled in straight lines and cast sharp shadows, nor why light waves could not go around obstacles, as water waves and sound waves could. Furthermore, if light consisted of waves, how could it travel through a vacuum, as it certainly did in coming to us through space from the sun and stars? What medium was it waving?

FOR ABOUT A CENTURY the two theories contended with each other. Newton's "corpuscular theory" was by far the more popular, partly because it seemed on the whole more logical, and partly because it had the support of Newton's great name. But in 1801 an English physician and physicist, Thomas Young, performed an experiment which swung opinion the other way. He projected a narrow beam of light through two closely spaced holes toward a screen behind. If light consisted of particles, presumably the two beams emerging through the holes would simply produce a brighter region on the screen where they overlapped and less bright regions where they did not. But this was not what Young found. The screen showed a series of bands of light, each separated from the next by a dark band. It seemed that in these dark intervals, the light of the two beams together added up to darkness!

The wave theory would easily explain this. The bright bands represented the reinforcement of waves of one beam by waves of the other; in other words, there the two sets of waves were "in phase," both peaks together and strengthening each other. The dark bands, on the other hand, represented places where the waves were "out of phase," the trough of one canceling the peak of the other. Instead of reinforcing each other, the waves at these places interfered with each other, leaving the net light energy at those points zero.

From the width of the bands and the distance between the two holes through which the beams issued, it was possible to calculate the length of light waves, say of red light or violet or colors between. The wavelengths turned out to be very small indeed. The wavelength of red light, for example, came to about 0.000075 centimeter. (Nowadays the wavelengths of light are expressed in a convenient unit suggested later by the Swedish astronomer Anders Jonas Ångstrom. The unit, called the angstrom — abbreviated Å — is one hundred-millionth of a centimeter. Thus the wavelength of red light is about 7500 angstrom units, the wavelength of violet light is about 3900 angstrom units, and the other wavelengths of the visible spectrum lie between these numbers.)

The shortness of the wavelengths is very important. The reason light waves travel in straight lines and cast sharp shadows is that they are incomparably smaller than ordinary objects; waves can curve around an obstruction only when that obstruction is not much larger than the wavelength. Even bacteria, for instance, are vastly wider than a wavelength of light, so light can define them sharply under a microscope. Only objects somewhere near a wavelength of light in size (for example, viruses and other submicroscopic particles) are small enough for light waves to pass around them.

It was the French physicist Augustin Jean Fresnel who showed (in 1818) that if an interfering object is small enough, a light wave will indeed travel around it. In that case the light produces what is called a "diffraction" pattern. For instance, if a piece of glass is scratched with many very fine parallel lines, each line acts as a tiny obstacle, diffracting light that falls upon it. Such an arrangement is called a "diffraction grating." Since the amount of diffraction depends on the wavelength, a spectrum is produced. From the amount by which any color or portion of the spectrum is diffracted, and from the known separation of the scratches on the glass, the wavelength can again be calculated.

Fresnel was the first to work out the mathematics of wave motion systematically. His experimental and theoretical work established the wave theory of light, and the corpuscular theory retired — apparently for good.

LIGHT OBVIOUSLY TRAVELS at tremendous speeds. If you put out a light, it gets dark everywhere at once, as nearly as can be made out. This is not quite as true for sound, for instance. If you watch a man in the distance chopping wood, you don't hear the stroke until some moments after the axe strikes. Sound has clearly taken a certain amount of time to travel to the ear. In fact, its speed of travel is easy to measure: it amounts to 1,090 feet per second, or about 750 miles per hour, in the air at sea level.

Galileo was the first to try to measure the speed of light. Standing on one hill while an assistant stood on another, he would uncover a lantern; as soon as the assistant saw the flash, he would signal by uncovering a light of his own. Galileo did this at greater and greater distances, assuming that the time it took the assistant to make his response would remain uniform and therefore any increase in the interval between his uncovering his own lantern and seeing the responding flash would represent the time taken by the light to cover the extra distance. The idea was sound, but of course light travels much too fast for Galileo to have detected any difference by this crude method.

In 1676 the Danish astronomer Olaus Roemer did succeed in timing the speed of light — on an astronomical distance scale. Studying Jupiter's eclipses of its four large satellites, Roemer noticed that the interval between successive eclipses became longer when the earth was moving away from Jupiter and became shorter when it was moving toward Jupiter in its orbit. Presumably the difference in eclipse times reflected the difference in distance between the earth and Jupiter; that is, it would be a measure of the difference in the time that light took to travel between Jupiter and the earth. From a rough estimate of the size of the earth's orbit, and from the maximum discrepancy in the eclipse timing, which Roemer took to represent the

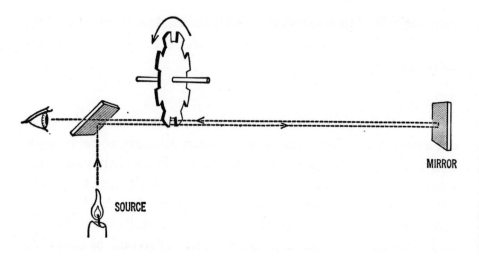

FIZEAU'S ARRANGEMENT FOR MEASURING THE SPEED OF LIGHT. *Light reflected by the semi-mirror near the source passes through a gap in the rapidly spinning toothed wheel to a distant mirror* (right), *and is reflected back to the next tooth or the next gap.*

time it took light to cross the full width of the earth's orbit, he calculated the speed of light. His estimate came to 192,000 miles per second — remarkably close to what we now consider the true value.

Nearly two centuries later scientists began to get more accurate measurements by applying refinements of Galileo's idea. In 1849 the French physicist Armand Hippolyte Louis Fizeau set up an arrangement whereby a light was flashed to a mirror five miles away and reflected back to the observer. The elapsed time for the ten-mile round trip of the flash was not much more than one 20,000th of a second, but Fizeau was able to measure it by placing a rapidly rotating toothed wheel in the path of the light beam. When the wheel turned at a certain speed, the flash going out between two teeth would hit the next tooth when it came back from the mirror, and so Fizeau, behind the wheel, would not see it. When the wheel was speeded up, the returning flash would not be blocked but would come through the next gap between teeth. Thus, by controlling and measuring the speed of the turning wheel, Fizeau was able to calcu-

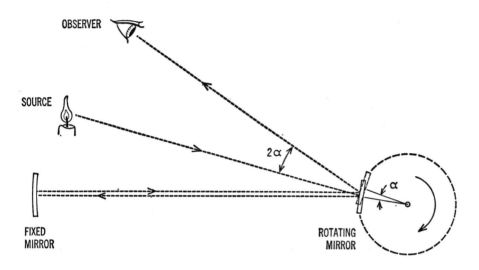

OBSERVER

SOURCE

2α

α

FIXED
MIRROR

ROTATING
MIRROR

FOUCAULT'S METHOD. *The amount of rotation of the mirror, instead of Fizeau's toothed wheel, gave the speed of the light's travel.*

late the elapsed time, and therefore the speed of travel, of the flash of light.

A year later the French physicist Jean Bernard Léon Foucault refined the measurement by using a rotating mirror instead of a toothed wheel. Now the elapsed time was measured by a slight shift in the angle of reflection by the rapidly turning mirror. Foucault got a value of 187,000 miles per second for the speed of light in air. In addition, Foucault used his method to determine the speed of light through various liquids. He found the speed to be markedly less than the speed of light in air. This fitted Huyghen's wave theory, too.

Real precision in the measurement of light's velocity came with the work of the German-born American physicist Albert Abraham Michelson, who over a period of more than 40 years, starting in 1879, applied the Fizeau-Foucault approach with greater and greater refinement. He eventually sent light through a vacuum rather than through air (even air slows it up slightly), using evacuated steel pipes up to a mile long for the purpose. He measured the speed of light in a vacuum to be 186,284 miles per second. He was also able to show that all wavelengths of light traveled at the same speed in a vacuum.

In recent years still more precise measurements have placed the speed of light at 186,282 miles per second. For these measurements scientists have had the benefit of extremely accurate "atomic clocks" called "masers," which tick off time by the regular vibrations of molecules.

With an accurate value for the speed of light, it has become possible to get direct and precise measurements of distances in the solar system by means of radar (since radio waves travel with the speed of light). Radio physicists have already bounced radar waves off the moon, the planet Venus, and the sun.

THROUGH ALL the mounting evidence of the wave nature of light, a nagging question kept bothering the physicists. How was light transmitted through a vacuum? Other kinds of waves — sound, for instance — required a material medium. (We could never hear an explosion on the moon or anywhere else in space, however loud, because sound waves cannot travel across space.) Yet here was light traveling through a vacuum more easily than through matter, and reaching us from galaxies billions of light-years away.

The classical scientists were always uncomfortable about the notion of "action at a distance." Newton, for instance, worried about how the force of gravity could operate through space. As a possible explanation, he revived the Greeks' idea of an "ether" filling the heavens and speculated that perhaps the force of gravity might somehow be conducted by the ether.

Trying to account for the travel of light waves through space, physicists decided that light, too, must be conducted by the supposed ether. They began to speak of the "luminiferous ether." But this idea at once ran into a serious difficulty. Light waves are transverse waves: that is, they undulate at right angles to the direction of travel, like the ripples on the surface of water, in contrast to the "longitudinal" motion of sound waves. Now physical theory said that only a *solid* medium could convey transverse waves. (Transverse water waves travel on the water surface, a special case, but cannot penetrate the body of the liquid.) Therefore the ether had to be solid, not gaseous or liquid. Not only must it be solid, but it must be extremely rigid; to transmit waves at the tremendous speed of light, it had to be far more rigid than steel. What is more, this rigid ether had to permeate ordinary matter — not merely the vacuum of space but gases, water, glass, and all the other transparent substances through which light could travel.

To cap it all, this solid, super-rigid material had to be so frictionless, so yielding, that it did not interfere in the slightest with the motion of the smallest planetoid or the flicker of an eyelid!

And yet, despite all the contradictions, the concept of the ether gained more and more adherents as physics advanced. Faraday resorted to the ether to account for the transmission of electrical and magnetic forces. When James Clerk Maxwell, working out the mathematical implications of Faraday's ideas about electrical and magnetic fields, discovered that there must be a great variety of other "electromagnetic radiations" besides light (later found in the form of radio, X-rays, etc.), the ether became even more important. If there was no ether, how could one account for the transmission of all these phenomena — light, other electromagnetic waves, magnetism, gravity, and the rest?

THEN, AT THE HEIGHT OF ITS POWER, the ether theory met its Waterloo. It was done in unexpectedly as a result of an experiment undertaken to test another classical question as knotty as "action at a distance" — namely, the question of "absolute motion."

By the nineteenth century it had become perfectly plain that the earth, the sun, the stars, and in fact all objects in the universe were in motion. Where, then, could you find a fixed reference point, one which was at "absolute rest," to determine "absolute motion" — the foundation on which Newton's laws of motion were based? There was one possibility. Newton had suggested that the fabric of space

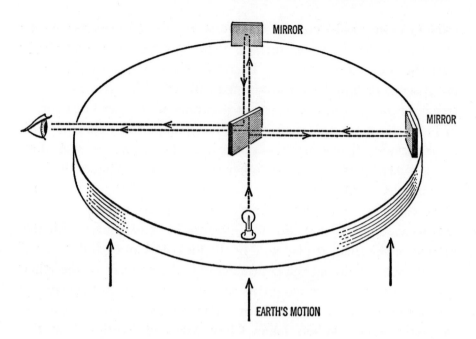

MICHELSON'S INTERFEROMETER. *The semi-mirror* (center) *splits the light beam, reflecting one half and letting the other half go straight ahead. If the two reflecting mirrors* (at right and straight ahead) *are at different distances, the returning beams of light will arrive at the observer out of phase.*

itself (the ether, presumably) was at rest, so that one could speak of "absolute space." If the ether was motionless, perhaps one could find the "absolute motion" of an object by determining its motion in relation to the ether.

In the 1880's Albert Michelson (the measurer of the speed of light) conceived an ingenious scheme to do just that. If the earth was moving through a motionless ether, he reasoned, then a beam of light sent in the direction of its motion and reflected back should travel a shorter distance than one sent out at right angles and reflected back. To make the test, Michelson invented the "interferometer," a device with a semi-mirror which lets half of a light beam through in the forward direction and reflects the other half at right angles. Both beams are then reflected back by mirrors to an eyepiece at the source. If one beam has traveled a slightly longer distance than the other, they arrive out of phase and form interference bands. This instrument is an extremely sensitive measurer of differences in length — so sensitive, in fact, that it can measure the growth of a plant from second to second.

Michelson's plan was to point the interferometer in various directions with respect to the earth's motion and detect the effect of the ether by the amount by which the split beams were out of phase on their return.

So in 1887, with the help of a fellow physicist, Edward Williams Morley, Michelson set up the experiment. Stationing the instrument on a stone floating on mercury, so that it could be turned in any direction easily and smoothly, they projected their beam in various directions with respect to the earth's motion. They discovered practically no difference! The interference bands were virtually the same no matter in what direction they pointed the instrument or however many times they performed the experiment. (It should be said here that more recent experiments along the same line with still more delicate instruments have shown the same negative results.)

The foundations of physics tottered. Either the ether was moving with the earth, which made no sense at all, or there was no such thing as the ether. In either case there was no "absolute motion" or "absolute space." "Classical" physics — the physics of Newton — had had the rug pulled out from under it. Newtonian physics still held in the ordinary world: planets still moved in accordance with his law of gravitation, and objects on earth still obeyed his law of inertia and of action-and-reaction. It was just that the classical explanations were incomplete, and physicists must be prepared to find phenomena which did not obey the classical "laws." The observed phenomena, both old and new, would remain, but the theories accounting for them would have to be broadened and refined.

Modern theoretical physics dates from the "Michelson-Morley experiment," probably the most important experiment-that-didn't-work in the whole history of science. Michelson was awarded the

Nobel Prize in physics in 1907 — the first American scientist to receive a Nobel Prize.

RELATIVITY

In 1893 THE IRISH PHYSICIST George Francis Fitzgerald came up with a novel explanation to account for the negative results of the Michelson-Morley experiment. He suggested that all matter contracted in the direction of its motion, and that the amount of contraction increased with the rate of motion. According to this interpretation, the interferometer was always shortened in the direction of the earth's "true" motion by an amount which exactly compensated for the difference in distance that the light beam would have to travel. Moreover, all possible measuring devices, including human sense organs, would be "foreshortened" in just the same way. Fitzgerald's explanation almost made it look as if Nature conspired to keep man from measuring absolute motion by introducing an effect that just cancelled out any differences he might try to use to detect that motion.

This frustrating phenomenon became known as the "Fitzgerald contraction." Fitzgerald worked out an equation for it. An object moving at seven miles per second (about the speed of our fastest present rockets) would contract by only about two parts per billion in the direction of flight. But at really high speeds the contraction would be substantial. At 93,000 miles per second (half the speed of light) it would be 15 per cent; at 163,000 miles per second (seven-eighths the speed of light), 50 per cent. That is, a one-foot ruler moving past us at 163,000 miles per second would seem only six inches long to us — provided we knew a method of measuring its length as it flew by. And at the speed of light, 186,282 miles per second, its length in the direction of motion would be zero. Since presumably there can be no length shorter than zero, it would follow that the speed of light in a vacuum is the greatest possible velocity in the Universe.

The Dutch physicist Hendrik Antoon Lorentz soon carried Fitz-gerald's idea one step farther. Thinking about cathode rays, on which he was working at the time, he reasoned that if the charge of a charged particle was compressed into a smaller volume, the mass of the particle should increase. Therefore a flying particle foreshort-ened in the direction of its travel by the Fitzgerald contraction would have to increase in mass.

Lorentz presented an equation for the mass increase which turned out to be very similar to Fitzgerald's equation for shortening. At 93,000 miles per second, an electron's mass would be increased by 15 per cent; at 163,000 miles per second, by 100 per cent (that is, its mass would be doubled); and at the speed of light, its mass would be infinite. Again it seemed that no speed greater than that of light could be possible, for how could mass be more than infinite?

The Fitzgerald length affect and the Lorentz mass effect are so closely connected that the equations are often lumped together as the "Lorentz-Fitzgerald equations."

If the Fitzgerald contraction could not be measured, the Lorentz mass effect could be — indirectly. The ratio of an electron's mass to its charge can be determined from its deflection by a magnetic field. As an electron's velocity increased, the mass would increase, but there was no reason to think that the charge would; therefore its mass-charge ratio should increase. By 1900 the German physicist W. Kauffman discovered that this ratio increased with velocity in such a way as to indicate that the electron's mass increased just as predicted by the Lorentz-Fitzgerald equations. Later and better measurements showed the agreement to be just about perfect.

WHILE THE FOUNDATIONS of physics were still rocking, a second explosion took place.

This time the innocent question that started all the trouble had to do with the radiation emitted by matter when it is heated. (Al-though the radiation in question is usually in the form of light, physi-cists speak of the problem as "black-body radiation." All this means is that they are thinking of an ideal body which absorbs light perfectly — without reflecting any of it away, as a perfectly black body would do — and also radiates perfectly.) The Austrian physicist Josef Stefan showed in 1879 that the total radiation emitted by a body depended only on its temperature (not at all on the nature of its substance), and that in ideal circumstances the radiation was proportional to the fourth power of the absolute temperature: *i.e.*, doubling the absolute temperature would increase its total radiation 16-fold. It was also known that as the temperature rose, the predominant radiation moved toward shorter wavelengths. As a lump of steel is heated, for instance, it starts by radiating chiefly in the invisible infrared, then glows dim red, then bright red, then orange, then yellow-white, and finally, if it could somehow be kept from vaporizing at that point, it would be blue-white.

Now in 1893 the German physicist Wilhelm Wien (who received the Nobel Prize in physics in 1911) worked out a theory of the energy distribution of black-body radiation; that is, of the amount of energy radiated at each particular wavelength range. It provided a formula which accurately described the distribution of energy at the violet end of the spectrum, but not at the red end. On the other hand, the English physicists Lord Rayleigh and James Jeans worked up an equation which described the distribution at the red end of the spectrum but failed completely at the violet end. In short, the best theories available could explain one-half of the radiation or the other, but not both at once.

The German physicist Max Karl Ernst Ludwig Planck tackled the problem. He found that in order to make the equations fit the facts, he had to introduce a completely new notion. He suggested that radiation consisted of small units or packets, just as matter was made up of atoms. He called the unit of radiation the "quantum" (after the Latin word for "how much?"). Planck argued that radiation could be absorbed only in whole numbers of quanta. Furthermore he suggested that the amount of energy in a quantum depended on the wavelength of the radiation. The shorter the wavelength, the more energetic the quantum; or, to put it another way, the energy content of the quantum is inversely proportional to the wavelength.

Now the quantum could be related directly to the "frequency" of a given radiation (that is, the number of waves emitted per second). Like the quantum's energy content, the frequency is inversely proportional to the radiation's wavelength. And if both the frequency and the quantum's energy content were inversely proportional to the wavelength, then the two were directly proportional to each other. Planck expressed this by means of his now-famous equation:

$$e = h\nu$$

The symbol "*e*" stands for the quantum energy, "*ν*" (the Greek letter "nu") for the frequency, and "*h*" for "Planck's constant," which gives the proportional relation between quantum energy and frequency.

The value of *h* is extremely small, and so is the quantum. The units of radiation are so small, in fact, that light looks continuous to us, just as ordinary matter seems continuous. But at the beginning of the twentieth century the same fate befell radiation as had befallen matter at the beginning of the nineteenth: both now had to be accepted as discontinuous.

Planck's quanta cleared up the connection between temperature and the wavelengths of emitted radiation. A quantum of violet light was twice as energetic as a quantum of red light, and naturally it would take more heat energy to produce violet-quanta than red-quanta. Equations worked out on the basis of the quantum explained the radiation of a black body very neatly at both ends of the spectrum.

Eventually Planck's quantum theory was to do a great deal more: it was to explain the behavior of atoms, of the electrons in atoms, and of nucleons in the atoms' nuclei. Planck was awarded the Nobel Prize in physics in 1918. It was certainly one of the most justified of all the Nobel awards, for with "quantum mechanics" physics entered a new world.

PLANCK'S THEORY made little impression on physicists when it was first announced in 1900. It was too revolutionary to be accepted at once. Planck himself seemed appalled at what he had done. But five years later a young German physicist named Albert Einstein verified the existence of his quanta.

The physicist Philipp Lenard had found that when light struck certain metals, it caused the metal surface to emit electrons, as if the force of the light kicked electrons out of the atoms. The phenomenon acquired the name "photoelectric effect." When physicists began to experiment with it, they found, to their surprise, that increasing the intensity of the light did not give the kicked-out electrons any more energy. But changing the wavelength of light did affect them: blue light, for instance, caused the electrons to fly out at greater speed than yellow light did. A very dim blue light would kick out fewer electrons than a bright yellow light would, but those few "blue-light" electrons would travel with greater speed than any of the "yellow-light" electrons. On the other hand, red light, no matter how bright, failed to knock out any electrons at all from some metals.

None of this could be explained by the old theories of light. Why should blue light do something red light couldn't do?

Einstein found the answer in Planck's quantum theory. To absorb enough energy to leave the metal surface, an electron had to be hit by a quantum of a certain minimum size. In the case of an electron held only weakly by its atom (*e.g.*, in cesium) even a quantum of red light would do. Where atoms held electrons more strongly, yellow light was required, or blue light, or even ultraviolet. And in any case, the more energetic the quantum, the more speed it would give to the electron it kicked out.

Here was a case where the quantum theory explained a physical phenomenon with perfect simplicity, whereas the pre-quantum view of light had remained helpless. Other applications of quantum mechanics followed thick and fast. For his explanation of the photoelectric effect (not for his theory of relativity) Einstein was awarded the Nobel Prize in physics in 1921.

In his "Special Theory of Relativity," presented in 1905, Einstein proposed a new fundamental view of the universe based on an extension of the quantum theory. He suggested that light traveled through space in quantum form (the "photon"), and thus he resurrected the concept of light consisting of particles. But this was a new kind of particle. It had properties of a wave as well as of a particle, and sometimes it showed one set of properties and sometimes the other.

This has been made to seem a paradox, or even a kind of mysticism, as if the true nature of light passes all possible understanding. That is not so. To illustrate with an analogy, a man may have many aspects: husband, father, friend, businessman. Depending on circumstances and on his surroundings, he behaves like a husband, father, friend or businessman. You would not expect him to exhibit his husbandly behavior toward a customer or his businesslike behavior toward his wife, and yet that makes him neither a paradox nor more than one man.

In the same way, radiation has both corpuscular and wave properties. In some capacities the corpuscular properties are particularly pronounced; in others, the wave properties. This dual character gives a more satisfactory account of radiation than either set of properties alone can.

The discovery of the wave nature of light had led to all the triumphs of nineteenth-century optics, including spectroscopy. But it had also required physicists to imagine the existence of the ether. Now Einstein's particle-wave view kept all the nineteenth-century victories (including Maxwell's equations) but made it unnecessary to assume that the ether existed. Radiation could travel through a vacuum by virtue of its particle attributes, and the ether idea, killed by the Michelson-Morley experiment, could now be buried.

Einstein introduced a second important idea in his Special Theory of Relativity: that the speed of light in a vacuum never varied, regardless of the motion of its source. In Newton's view of the universe, a light beam from a source moving toward an observer should seem to travel more quickly than one from a source moving in any other direction. In Einstein's view, this did not happen, and from that assumption he was able to derive the Lorentz-Fitzgerald equations. He showed that the increase of mass with velocity, which Lorentz had applied only to charged particles, could be applied to all objects of any sort. He reasoned further that increases in velocity would not only foreshorten length and increase mass but also slow the pace of time: in other words, clocks would slow down along with the shortening of yardsticks.

THE MOST FUNDAMENTAL ASPECT of Einstein's theory was its denial of the existence of "absolute space" and "absolute time." This may sound like nonsense: how can the human mind learn anything at all about the Universe if it has no point of departure? Einstein answered that all we needed to do was to pick a "frame of reference" to which the events of the Universe could be related. Any frame of reference (the earth motionless, or the sun motionless, or we ourselves motionless, for that matter) would be equally valid, and we could simply choose the frame that was most convenient. It is more convenient to calculate planetary motions in a frame of reference in which the sun is motionless than in one in which the earth is motionless — but no more "true."

Thus measurements of space and time are "relative" to some arbitrarily chosen frame of reference — and that is the reason for naming Einstein's idea the "theory of relativity."

To illustrate. Suppose we on the earth were to observe a strange planet ("Planet X"), exactly like our own in size and mass, go whizzing past us at 163,000 miles per second relative to ourselves. If we could measure its dimensions as it shot past, we would find that it was foreshortened by 50 per cent in the direction of its motion. It would be an ellipsoid rather than a sphere and would, upon further measurement, seem to have twice the mass of the earth.

Yet to an inhabitant of Planet X, it would seem that he himself and his own planet were motionless. The earth would seem to be moving past *him* at 163,000 miles per second, and it would appear to have an ellipsoidal shape and twice the mass of *his* planet.

One is tempted to ask which planet would *really* be foreshortened and doubled in mass, but the only possible answer is: that depends on the frame of reference. If you find that frustrating, consider that a man is small compared to a whale and large compared to a beetle. Is there any point in asking which a man is *really*, large or small?

For all its unusual consequences, relativity explains all the known phenomena of the universe at least as well as pre-relativity theories do. But it goes farther: it explains easily some phenomena which the Newtonian outlook explained poorly or not at all. Consequently Einstein has been accepted over Newton, not as a replacement so much as a refinement. The Newtonian view of the universe can still be used as a simplified approximation which works well enough in ordinary life and even in ordinary astronomy, as in placing satellites in orbit. But when it comes to accelerating particles in a synchrotron, for example, we find that we must take account of the Einsteinian increase of mass with velocity to make the machine work.

The one aspect of relativity that still provokes arguments among physicists is Einstein's notion of the slowing of clocks. A clock in motion, he said, keeps time more slowly than a stationary one. In fact, all phenomena that change with time change more slowly when moving than when at rest, which is the same as saying that time itself is slowed. At ordinary speeds the effect is negligible, but at 163,000 miles per second a clock would seem (to an observer watching it fly past) to take two seconds to tick off one second. And at the speed of light, time would stand still.

Suppose a clock flew past at 163,000 miles per second and maintained that speed for what seemed to us an hour. The clock would register only half an hour. Now if the clock were brought to rest, it would resume telling time at the usual rate, but it would be half an hour slow!

The worst of it comes when we think of a man traveling with the flying clock. To him, that clock would seem to be telling normal time and it would seem to him that it was our clock that was slow and our clock that would have to be half an hour slow when the two clocks were brought together.

If, as Einstein maintained, either clock could validly be considered at rest, we have the peculiar situation of two clocks, each of which can legitimately be accused of being half an hour slower than the other. This is the famous "clock paradox." Theoretical physicists are still having serious fun with it today.

The controversy arises over what happens when the clock is brought to rest. As long as it is moving with constant velocity, there is no problem about the slowing of its rate. But some physicists produce a line of argument to show that when the clocks are brought together, they will register the same time. Others insist that there is some way of defining motion so that you can tell whether an object is "really" moving or not, and that this can be done in such a way as not to introduce the old notion of "absolute space."

The theoretical arguments no doubt will rage on for a long time to come, but in the meantime the question as to whether a fast-moving clock actually does slow down may be settled by experiment. Suppose a clock were mounted in a satellite and sent around the earth at a speed of, say, five miles per second. At that speed, according to the theory of relativity, the clock would lose one 20,000th of a second per day in comparison with a clock on the earth. "Masers" (atomic clocks) keep time so accurately that they could easily show such a discrepancy. Very well, then, we can synchronize two masers, put one in the satellite, keep one on the ground, bring down the flying maser after a while, and see which maser, if either, has lost time. This experiment is being planned for the day when it becomes possible to bring satellites safely back to earth.

If it turns out that motion will really slow down clocks and leave a permanent mark in the form of lost time, that could have an interesting effect on the possible adventures of future generations of men in space. If a speed near that of light could be maintained, time would slow for the space voyagers. They might reach a distant destination and return in what seemed to them weeks, though on the earth many centuries would have passed. If time really slows in motion, a person might journey even to a distant star in his own life-time. But of course he would have to say good-bye to his own generation and the world he knew. He would return to a world of the future.

IN THE SPECIAL THEORY OF RELATIVITY Einstein did not deal with gravitation. That subject was treated in his "General Theory of Relativity," published in 1915. The General Theory presented a completely altered view of gravitation. It was viewed as a property of space, rather than as a force between bodies. As the result of the presence of matter, space became curved, and bodies followed the line of least resistance among the curves, so to speak. Strange as Einstein's idea seemed, it was able to explain something which the Newtonian law of gravity had not been able to explain.

The greatest triumph of Newton's law of gravity had come in 1846. The planet Uranus, discovered in 1781, had a slightly erratic orbit around the sun. A half century of observation made that unmistakable. Astronomers decided that some still undiscovered planet beyond it must be exerting a gravitational pull on it. The British astronomer John Couch Adams and the French astronomer Urbain Jean Joseph Leverrier calculated the position of this hypothetical planet, using Newton's theories as a basis. In 1846 the German astronomer Johann Gottfried Galle pointed his telescope at the spot indicated by Leverrier and, sure enough, there was a new planet — since named Neptune.

After that, nothing seemed capable of shaking Newton's law of gravity. And yet one planetary motion remained unexplained. The planet Mercury's point of nearest approach to the sun ("perihelion") changed from one trip to the next; it was never in the same place twice in the planet's "yearly" revolutions around the sun. Astronomers were able to account for most of this irregularity as due to "perturbations" of its orbit by the pull of the neighboring planets. But after all perturbations had been allowed for, there was still an unexplained shift of the perihelion amounting to 43 seconds of arc per century. This is not much: in 4,000 years it adds up only to the width of the moon. It was enough, however, to upset astronomers.

Leverrier suggested that this deviation might be caused by a small, undiscovered planet closer to the sun than Mercury. For decades astronomers searched for the supposed planet (called "Vulcan"), and many were the reports of its discovery. All the reports turned out to be mistaken. Finally it was agreed that Vulcan did not exist.

Then Einstein's General Theory of Relativity supplied the answer. It showed that the perihelion of any revolving body should have a motion beyond that predicted by Newton's law. When this new calculation was applied to Mercury, the planet's shift of perihelion fitted it exactly.

More impressive were two unexpected new phenomena which only Einstein's theory predicted. First, Einstein maintained that an intense gravitational field should slow down the vibrations of atoms. The slowing down would be evidenced by a shift of spectral lines toward the red. Casting about for a gravitational field strong enough to produce this effect, astronomers thought of the dense white-dwarf stars. They looked at the spectra of white dwarfs and did indeed find the predicted shift of lines.

The verification of Einstein's second prediction was even more dramatic. His theory said a gravitational field would bend light rays. Einstein calculated that a ray of light just skimming the sun's surface would be bent out of a straight line by 1.75 seconds of arc. How could that be checked? Well, if stars beyond the sun and just off its edge could be observed during an eclipse of the sun, and their positions compared with what they were against the background when the sun did not interfere, any shift resulting from bending of their

THE GRAVITATIONAL BENDING OF LIGHT WAVES, *postulated by Einstein in the General Theory of Relativity.*

light should show up. Since Einstein had published his paper on general relativity in 1915, the test had to wait until after the end of World War I. In 1919 the British Royal Astronomical Society organized an expedition to make the test by witnessing a total eclipse visible from the island of Principe, a small Portuguese-owned island off West Africa. The stars did shift position. Einstein had been verified again. (Probably no theory in the history of man has ever been tested with more publicity and with more eyes watching.)

Scientists never feel really comfortable about a theory until they have been able to check it by controlled experiments. They have now begun to get apparent confirmation of Einstein's General Theory in the laboratory. In 1959 a German physicist named R. L. Mössbauer deduced from the theory that an increase in gravity should reduce the wavelength of gamma rays slightly. In 1960 two Harvard University physicists, Glen A. Ribka and Robert V. Pound, put this prediction to a test. They projected a beam of gamma rays of sharply defined wavelength 75 feet downward (toward the center of the earth). The wavelength of the gamma rays did shorten by a detectable amount with the very slight increase in the strength of the gravitational field represented by that small approach to the earth's center.

There are other possible tests which scientists hope to carry out. A satellite in the proper type of orbit around the sun might show a perihelion advance large enough to check the theory. Another experiment would be to place masers (atomic clocks) in satellites to try to detect the relative effects of motion in slowing time and of reduced gravitation (away from the earth) in speeding time up.

HEAT

So far in this chapter I have been neglecting a phenomenon that usually accompanies light in our everyday experience. Almost all luminous objects, from a star to a candle, give off heat as well as light.

Heat was not studied, other than qualitatively, before modern times. It was enough for a person to say, "It is hot," or "It is cold," or "This is warmer than that." To subject temperature to quantitative measure, it was first necessary to find some measurable change that seemed to take place uniformly with change in temperature. One such change was found in the fact that substances expand when warmed and contract when cooled.

Galileo was the first to try to make use of this fact to measure temperature. In 1603 he inverted a tube of heated air into a bowl of water. As the air in the tube cooled to room temperature, it contracted and drew water up the tube, and there Galileo had his "thermometer" (from Greek words meaning "heat measure"). When the temperature of the room changed, the water level in the tube changed. If the room warmed, the air in the tube expanded and pushed the water level down; if it grew cooler, the air contracted and the water level moved up. The only trouble was that the basin of water into which the tube had been inserted was open to the air and the air pressure kept changing. That also shoved the water level up and down, independently of temperature, confusing the results.

By 1654 the Grand Duke of Tuscany, Ferdinand II, had evolved a thermometer which was independent of air pressure. It contained a liquid sealed into a bulb to which a straight tube was attached. The contraction and expansion of the liquid itself was used as the indication of temperature change. Liquids change their volume with temperature much less than gases do, but by using a sizable reservoir of liquid and a filled bulb, so that the liquid could expand only up a very narrow tube, the rise and fall within that tube, for even tiny volume changes, could be made considerable.

The English physicist Robert Boyle did much the same thing about the same time, and he was the first to show that the human body had a constant temperature, markedly higher than the usual room temperature.

The first liquids used in thermometry were water and alcohol. Since water froze and alcohol boiled away, the French physicist

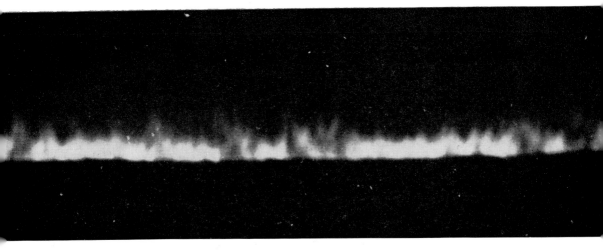

MAGNETIC DOMAINS *photographed with an electron microscope by a special technique. The line of light shows the fine edge of a thin, magnetized piece of steel; the faint areas represent the deflection of electrons by the magnetic domains.*

CONTOUR MAP *of a polished piece of metal, made by means of the interference effect of light waves. The contour lines here show differences on only one-millionth of an inch.*

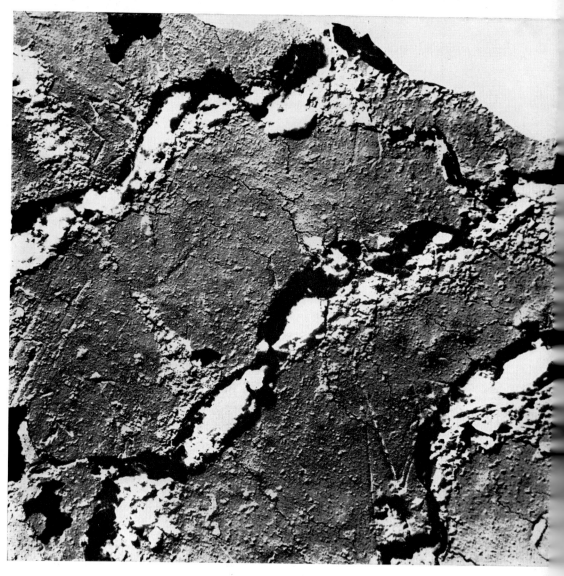

SURFACE OF A HUMAN HAIR, *photographed with an electron microscope.*

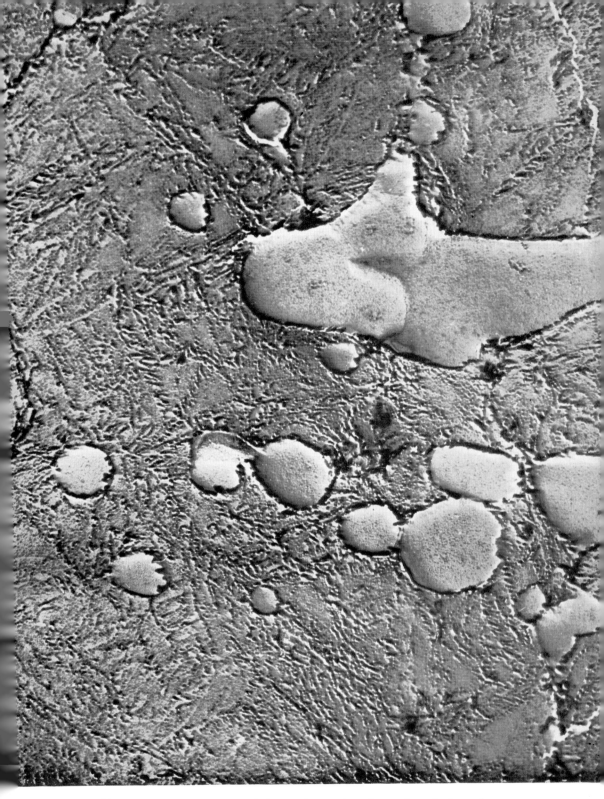

ELECTRON MICROGRAPH *of the surface of a piece of etched steel.*

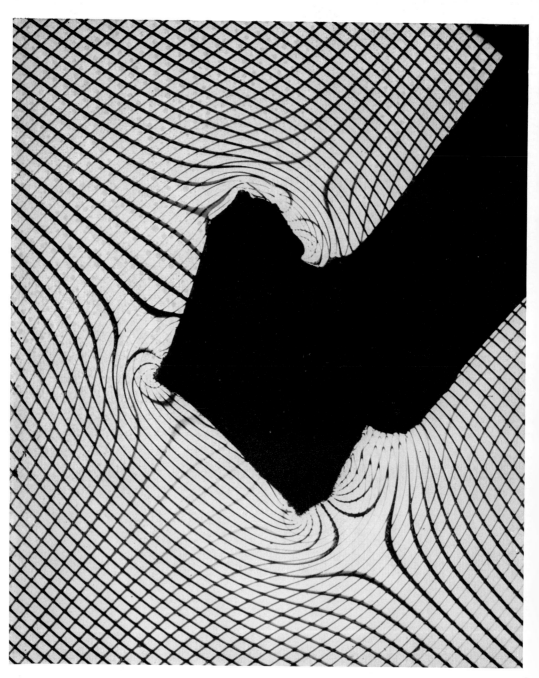

ELECTRIC FIELD *around a charged crystal is photographed with the electron microscope by means of a shadow technique. The method uses a fine wire mesh; the distortion of the net, caused by deflection of electrons, shows the shape and strength of the electric field.*

Guillaume Amontons resorted to mercury. In his device, as in Galileo's, the expansion and contraction of air caused the mercury level to rise or fall.

Then in 1714 the German physicist Gabriel Daniel Fahrenheit combined the advances of the Grand Duke and of Amontons by enclosing mercury in a tube and using its own expansion and contraction with temperature as the indicator. Furthermore, Fahrenheit put a graded scale on the tube to allow the temperature to be read quantitatively.

There is some argument as to exactly how Fahrenheit arrived at the particular scale he used. He set zero, according to one account, at the lowest temperature he could get in his laboratory, attained by mixing salt and melting ice. He then set the freezing point of pure water at 32 and its boiling point at 212. This had two advantages. First, the range of temperature over which water was liquid came to 180 degrees, which seemed a natural number to use in connection with "degrees." (It is the number of degrees in a semicircle.) Secondly, body temperature came near a round 100 degrees; normally it is 98.6° Fahrenheit, to be exact.

In 1742 the Swedish astronomer Anders Celsius adopted a different scale. In its final form, this set the freezing point of water at 0 and its boiling point at 100. Because of the hundredfold division of the temperature range in which water was liquid, this is called the "centigrade scale," from Latin words meaning "hundred steps." Most people still speak of measurements on this scale as "degrees centigrade," but scientists have recently renamed the scale after the inventor, following the Fahrenheit precedent. Officially, then, one should speak of the "Celsius scale" and of "degrees Celsius." The symbol C. still holds.

It was Celsius' scale that won out in most of the civilized world. Scientists, particularly, found the Celsius scale convenient, and the Fahrenheit scale is used today only for non-scientific purposes in the English-speaking countries, including, of course, the United States.

TEMPERATURE measures the intensity of heat but not its quantity. Heat will always flow from a place of higher temperature to a place of lower temperature until the temperatures are equal, just as water will flow from a higher level to a lower one until the levels are equal. This is true regardless of the relative amounts of heat contained in the bodies involved. Although a bathtub of lukewarm water contains far more heat than a burning match, when the match is placed near the water, heat goes from the match to the water, not vice versa.

The Scottish chemist Joseph Black was the first to make clear the distinction between temperature and heat. In 1760 he announced that various substances were raised in temperature by different amounts when a given amount of heat was poured into them. To raise the temperature of a gram of iron by one degree Celsius takes three times as much heat as to warm a gram of lead by one degree. And beryllium requires three times as much heat as iron. To put it another way, at any given temperature beryllium holds nine times as much heat as the same mass of lead. Clearly temperature is no measure of total heat.

Furthermore, Black showed it was possible to pour heat into a substance without raising its temperature at all. When ice is heated, it begins to melt, but it doesn't rise in temperature. Heat will eventually melt all the ice, but the temperature of the ice itself never goes above 0° C. The same thing happens in the case of boiling water at 100° C. As heat is poured into the water, more and more of it boils away as vapor, but the temperature of the liquid doesn't change.

The development of the steam engine (see Chapter 8), which came at about the same time as Black's experiments, intensified the interest of scientists in heat and temperature. They began to speculate about the nature of heat, as earlier they had speculated about the nature of light.

In the case of heat, as of light, there were two theories. One held that heat was a material substance which could be poured or shifted from one substance to another. It was named "caloric," from the

Latin for "heat." According to this view, when wood was burned the caloric in the wood passed into the flame and from that into a kettle above the flame and from that into the water in the kettle. As water filled with caloric, it was converted to steam.

In the late eighteenth century two famous observations gave rise to the theory that heat was a form of vibration. One was published by the American physicist and adventurer Benjamin Thompson, a Tory who fled the country during the Revolution, was given the title Count Rumford, and then proceeded to knock around Europe. While supervising the boring of cannon in Bavaria in 1798, he noticed that quantities of heat were being produced. He found that enough heat was being generated to bring 18 pounds of water to the boiling point in less than three hours. Where was all the caloric coming from? Thompson decided that heat must be a vibration set up and intensified by the mechanical friction of the borer against the cannon.

The next year the chemist Humphry Davy performed an even more significant experiment. Keeping two pieces of ice below the freezing point, he rubbed them together, not by hand but by a mechanical contrivance, so that no caloric could flow into the ice. By friction alone, he melted some of the ice. He, too, concluded that heat must be a vibration and not a material. Actually, this experiment should have been conclusive, but the caloric theory, though obviously wrong, hung on to the middle of the nineteenth century.

Nevertheless, although the nature of heat was misunderstood, scientists learned some important things about it, just as the investigators of light turned up interesting facts about the reflection and refraction of light beams before they knew its nature. Jean Baptiste Joseph Fourier and Nicolas Léonard Sadi Carnot in France studied the flow of heat and made important advances. In fact, Carnot is usually considered the founder of the science of "thermodynamics" (from Greek words meaning "movement of heat"). He placed the working of steam engines on a firm theoretical foundation.

Carnot did his work in the 1820's. By the 1840's, physicists were concerned with the manner in which the heat that was put into steam could be converted into the mechanical work of moving a piston. Was there a limit to the amount of work that could be obtained from a given amount of heat? And what about the reverse process: how was work converted to heat?

Several physicists tackled the problem, and the one whose name is particularly notable is the Englishman James Prescott Joule. Joule inherited a brewery but chose to invest his independent means in physical research, becoming thereby the most eminent brewer in history.

Joule spent 35 years altogether converting various kinds of work into heat. He measured the amount of heat produced by an electric current. He heated water and mercury by stirring them with paddle wheels, or by forcing water through narrow tubes. He heated air by compressing it, and so on. In every case he calculated how much mechanical work had been done on the system and how much heat was obtained as a result. He found that a given amount of work, of any kind, always produced a given amount of heat.

Since heat could be converted into work, it must be considered a form of "energy" (from Greek words meaning "containing work"). Electricity, magnetism, light, and motion could all be used to do work, so they, too, were forms of energy. And work itself, being convertible into heat, was a form of energy.

What Joule's experiments showed above all was that when one form of energy was converted into another, no new energy was created and no old energy destroyed. The first person actually to put this notion into words was Heinrich von Helmholtz. In 1847 von Helmholtz enunciated the "law of conservation of energy," which states that energy can be converted from one form to another but cannot be created or destroyed. Whenever a certain amount of energy seems to disappear in one place, an equivalent amount must appear in another. This is also called "the first law of thermodynamics." It remains a foundation block of modern physics, undisturbed by either the quantum theory or relativity.

Now, although any form of work can be converted entirely into heat, the reverse is not true. When heat is turned to work, some of it is unusable and is unavoidably wasted. In running a steam engine, the heat of the steam is converted into work only until the temperature of the steam is reduced to the temperature of the environment; after that, although there is much remaining heat in the cold water formed from the steam, no more of it can be converted to work. Even in the temperature range at which work can be extracted, some of the heat doesn't go into work but is used up in heating the engine and the air around it, in overcoming friction between the piston and the cylinder, and so on.

In any energy conversion — e.g., electric energy into light energy, or magnetic energy into energy of motion — some of the energy is wasted. It is not lost; that would be against the first law. But it is converted to heat that is dissipated in the environment.

The fraction of any form of energy that can be converted into other useful forms of energy and directly or eventually into work is the "free energy." The portion that is unavoidably lost as non-useful heat is called the "entropy" — a term first used in 1850 by the German physicist Rudolf Julius Emmanuel Clausius.

Clausius pointed out that in any process involving a flow of energy there is always some loss, so that the entropy of the universe is continually increasing. This continual increase of entropy is called the "second law of thermodynamics." It is sometimes referred to as the "running-down of the universe" or the "heat-death of the universe." Fortunately, the quantity of "free," or usable, energy (supplied almost entirely by the stars, which are, of course, "running down" at a tremendous rate) is so vast that there is enough for all purposes for many billions of years.

A CLEAR UNDERSTANDING of the nature of heat finally came with the understanding of the atomic nature of matter. It developed from the realization that the molecules composing a gas were in continual motion, bouncing off one another and off the walls of their container. In the 1870's James Clerk Maxwell and Ludwig Boltzmann worked out the mathematics that described this behavior of molecules and established the "kinetic theory of gases." ("Kinetic" comes from a Greek word meaning "motion.") The theory showed heat to be equivalent to the motion of molecules. Thus the caloric theory of heat received its deathblow. Heat was seen to be a vibrational phenomenon: the movement of molecules in gases and liquids, or the jittery to-and-fro trembling of molecules in solids.

When a solid is heated to a point where the to-and-fro trembling is strong enough to break the bonds that hold neighboring molecules together, the solid melts and becomes a liquid. The stronger the bond between neighboring molecules in a solid, the more heat is needed to make it vibrate violently enough to break the bond. This means that the substance has a higher melting point.

In the liquid state the molecules can move freely past one another. When the liquid is heated further, the movements of the molecules finally become sufficiently energetic to send them free of the body of the liquid altogether, and then the liquid boils. Again the boiling point is higher where the intermolecular forces are stronger.

In converting a solid to a liquid, all of the energy of heat goes into breaking the intermolecular bonds. This is why the heat absorbed by melting ice does not raise the ice's temperature. The same is true of a liquid being boiled.

Now we can distinguish between heat and temperature easily. Heat is the total energy contained in the molecular motions of a given quantity of matter. Temperature represents the average speed of molecular motion in that matter. Thus a quart of water at 60° C. contains twice as much heat as a pint of water at 60° C. (twice as many molecules are vibrating), but the quart and pint have the same temperature, for the average speed of molecular motion is the same in each case.

There is energy in the very structure of a chemical compound — that is, in the bonding forces that hold an atom or ion or molecule to its neighbor. If these bonds are broken and rearranged into new bonds involving less energy, the excess of energy will make its appearance as heat or light or both. Sometimes the energy is released so quickly that an explosion is the result.

It is possible to calculate the chemical energy contained in any substance and show what the amount of heat released in any reaction must be. For instance, the burning of coal involves breaking the bonds between carbon atoms in the coal and the bonds between the oxygen molecules' atoms, with which the carbon recombines. Now the energy of the bonds in the new compound (carbon dioxide) is less than that of the bonds in the original substances that formed it. This difference, which can be measured, is released as heat and light.

In the 1870's the American physicist Josiah Willard Gibbs worked out the theory of "chemical thermodynamics" in such detail that he created the science of physical chemistry almost single-handed. In fact, it was Gibbs who developed the theory of thermodynamics so fully that free energy is often called "Gibbs free energy" (or simply "G") in his honor.

MASS TO ENERGY

WITH THE DISCOVERY of radioactivity in 1896, a totally new question about energy arose at once. The radioactive substances uranium and thorium were giving off particles with astonishing energies. Moreover, Marie Curie found that radium was continually emitting heat in substantial quantities: an ounce of radium gave off 4,000 calories per hour, and this would go on hour after hour, week after week, decade after decade. The most energetic chemical reaction known could not produce a millionth of the energy liberated by radium. And, what was no less surprising, this production of energy, unlike chemical reactions, did not depend on temperature: it went on just as well at the very low temperature of liquid hydrogen as it did at ordinary temperatures!

Quite plainly an altogether new kind of energy, very different from chemical, was involved here. Fortunately physicists did not have to wait long for the answer. Once again, it was supplied by Einstein's Special Theory of Relativity.

2 9 7

Einstein's mathematical treatment of energy showed that mass could be considered a form of energy — a very concentrated form, for a very small quantity of mass would be converted into an immense quantity of energy.

Einstein's equation relating mass and energy is now one of the most famous equations in the world. It is:

$$e = mc^2$$

Here "e" represents energy (in ergs), "m" represents mass (in grams) and "c" represents the speed of light (in centimeters per second).

Since light travels at 30 billion centimeters per second, the value of c^2 is 900 billion billion. This means that the conversion of one gram of mass to energy will produce 900 billion billion ergs. The erg is a small unit of energy not translatable into any common terms, but we can get an idea of what this number means when we are told that the energy in one gram of mass is sufficient to keep a 1,000-watt electric-light bulb running for 2,850 years. Or, to put it another way, the complete conversion of a gram of mass into energy would yield as much as the burning of 2,000 tons of gasoline.

Einstein's conversion destroyed one of the sacred conservation laws of science. Lavoisier's "law of conservation of mass" had stated that matter could neither be created nor destroyed. Actually, every energy-releasing chemical reaction changes a small amount of mass into energy: the products, if they could be weighed with utter precision, would not quite equal the original matter. But the mass lost in ordinary chemical reactions is so small that no technique available to the chemists of the nineteenth century could conceivably have detected it. Physicists, however, were now dealing with a completely different phenomenon, the nuclear reaction of radioactivity rather than the chemical reaction of burning coal. Nuclear reactions released so much energy that the loss of mass was large enough to be measured.

By postulating the interchange of mass and energy, Einstein merged the laws of conservation of energy and of mass into one law

— the conservation of mass-energy. The first law of thermodynamics not only still stood: it was more unassailable than ever.

THE CONVERSION OF MASS to energy was confirmed experimentally by Francis W. Aston through his mass spectrograph. This could measure the mass of atomic nuclei very precisely by the amount of their deflection by a magnetic field. What Aston did was to show that the various nuclei were not exact multiples of the masses of the neutrons and protons that composed them.

Let us take a simple example. We start by assuming the mass of oxygen 16 to be exactly 16.00000. Its nucleus contains eight protons and eight neutrons. Now it turns out from mass-spectrographic measurements that on the basis of oxygen 16 having a mass of 16, the mass of a proton is 1.008145 and that of a neutron 1.008986. Eight protons, then, should add up to a mass of 8.065160 and eight neutrons to a mass of 8.071888. Together the 16 nucleons should have a mass of 16.137048. But the mass of the oxygen 16 nucleus is only 16.00000. What has happened to the missing 0.137048?

Aston called this mass that had disappeared the "packing fraction." It had been converted into energy in the original process of combining the eight protons and eight neutrons into the oxygen 16 nucleus. And to break that nucleus down into individual protons and neutrons would take an amount of energy equivalent to the mass of 0.137048.

Aston determined the packing fraction, or "binding energy," of many nuclei, and he found that it increased rather quickly from hydrogen up to elements in the neighborhood of iron and then decreased, rather slowly, for the rest of the periodic table. In other words, the binding energy per nucleon was highest in the middle of the periodic table. This meant that conversion of an element at either end of the table into one nearer the middle should release energy.

Take uranium 238 as an example. This nucleus breaks down by a series of decays to lead 206. In the process, it emits eight alpha particles. (It also gives off beta particles, but these are so light they can be ignored.) Now the mass of lead 206 is 206.03883, and that of eight alpha particles totals 32.038992. Altogether these products add up to a mass of 238.07782. But the mass of uranium 238, from which they came, is 238.12522. The difference, or loss of mass, is 0.04750. That loss of mass is just enough to account for the energy released when uranium breaks down.

When uranium breaks down to still smaller atoms, as it does in fission, a great deal more energy is released. And when hydrogen is converted to helium, as it is in stars, there is an even larger fractional loss of mass and a correspondingly richer development of energy.

Physicists began to look upon the mass-energy equivalence as a very reliable bookkeeping. For instance, when the positron was discovered in 1934, its mutual annihilation with an electron produced a gamma ray whose energy was just equal to the mass of the two particles. Furthermore, mass could be created out of appropriate amounts of energy. A gamma ray of the proper energy, under certain circumstances, would disappear and give rise to an "electron-positron pair," created out of pure energy. Larger amounts of energy, supplied by cosmic particles or by particles fired out of proton synchrotrons (see Chapter 6), would bring about the creation of more massive particles, such as mesons and anti-protons.

It is no wonder that when the bookkeeping did not balance, as in the surprisingly energetic emission of beta particles, physicists invented the neutrino to balance the energy account rather than tamper with Einstein's equation (see Chapter 6).

If any further proof of the conversion of mass to energy was needed, the atomic bomb provided the final clincher.

PARTICLES AND WAVES

IN THE 1920's dualism reigned supreme in physics. Planck had shown that radiation was particle-like as well as wave-like. Einstein had shown that mass and energy were two sides of the same coin, and that space and time were inseparable. Physicists began to look for other dualisms.

In 1923 the French physicist Louis Victor de Broglie was able to show that, just as radiation had the characteristics of particles, so the particles of matter, such as electrons, should display the characteristics of waves. The waves associated with these particles, he predicted, would have a wavelength inversely related to the mass times the velocity (that is, the momentum) of the particle. The wavelength associated with electrons of moderate speed, de Broglie calculated, ought to be in the X-ray region.

In 1927 even this surprising prediction was borne out. Clinton Joseph Davisson and Lester Halbert Germer of the Bell Telephone Laboratories were bombarding metallic nickel with electrons. As the result of a laboratory accident, which had made it necessary to heat the nickel for a long time, the metal was in the form of large crystals, which were ideal for diffraction purposes, because the spacing between atoms in a crystal is comparable to the very short wavelengths of electrons. Sure enough, the electrons passing through those crystals behaved not as particles but as waves. The film behind the nickel showed interference patterns, alternate bands of fogging and clarity, just as it would have shown if X-rays had gone through the nickel rather than electrons.

Interference patterns were the very thing that Young had used more than a century earlier to prove the wave nature of light. Now they proved the wave nature of electrons. From the measurements of the interference bands, the wavelength associated with the electron could be calculated, and it turned out to be 1.65 angstrom units, almost exactly what de Broglie had calculated it ought to be.

In the same year the British physicist George Paget Thomson, working independently and using different methods, also showed that electrons had wave properties.

De Broglie received the Nobel Prize in physics in 1929, and Davisson and Thomson shared the Nobel Prize in physics in 1937.

This entirely unlooked-for discovery of a new kind of dualism was put to use almost at once in microscopy. Ordinary optical microscopes, as I have mentioned, cease to be useful at a certain point because there is a limit to the size of objects that light waves can define sharply. As objects get smaller, they also get fuzzier, because the light waves begin to pass around them. (For the same reason, the long radio waves give a fuzzy picture even of large objects in the sky.) The cure, of course, is to try to find shorter wavelengths to resolve the smaller objects. Ultraviolet light can define smaller objects than visible light can. X-rays would be better still, but there are no lenses for X-rays. This problem can be solved, however, by using the waves associated with electrons, which have about the same wavelength as X-rays but are easier to manipulate. For one thing, a magnetic field can bend the "electron-rays," because the waves are associated with a charged particle.

Just as the eye can see an expanded image of an object if the light rays involved are appropriately manipulated by lenses, so a photograph can register an expanded image of an object if electron-waves are appropriately manipulated by magnetic fields. And, since the wavelengths associated with electrons are far smaller than those of ordinary light, the resolution obtainable with an "electron microscope" at high magnification is much greater than that available to an ordinary microscope.

A crude electron miscroscope was made in Germany in 1932, but the first really usable one was built in 1937 at the University of Toronto by James Hillier and Albert F. Prebus. Their instrument could magnify an object 7,000 times, whereas the best optical microscopes reach their limit with a magnification of about 2,000. Hillier and others later developed electron microscopes capable of magnifying 100,000 times.

A "proton microscope," if one were developed, would magnify to a far greater extent than does an electron microscope, because the waves associated with protons are shorter. In a sense, the proton synchrotron is a kind of proton microscope, probing the interior of the nucleus with its speeding protons. The greater the speed of a proton, the greater its momentum and the shorter the wavelength associated with it. Protons with an energy of one Mev can "see" the

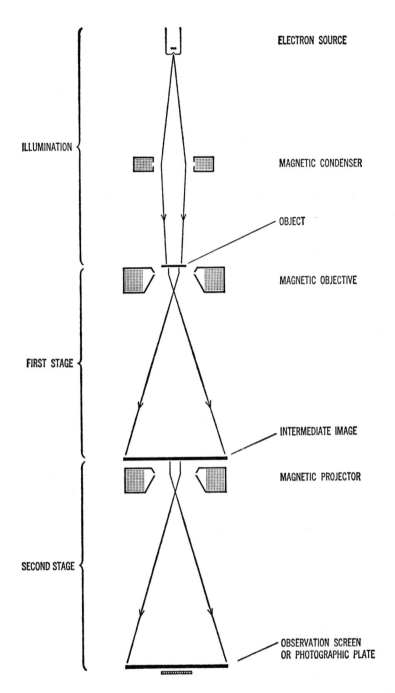

ELECTRON SOURCE

ILLUMINATION

MAGNETIC CONDENSER

OBJECT

MAGNETIC OBJECTIVE

FIRST STAGE

INTERMEDIATE IMAGE

MAGNETIC PROJECTOR

SECOND STAGE

OBSERVATION SCREEN
OR PHOTOGRAPHIC PLATE

DIAGRAM OF ELECTRON MICROSCOPE. *The magnetic condenser directs the electrons in a parallel beam. The magnetic objective functions like a convex lens, producing an enlarged image, which is then further magnified by a magnetic projector. The image is projected on a fluorescent observation screen or a photographic plate.*

nucleus, while at 20 Mev they can begin to "see" detail within the nucleus. This is another reason why physicists are eager to pile more and more electron-volts into their atom smashers — so that they may "see" the ultra-small more clearly.

THE MATTER-WAVES had important consequences for theory, too. For one thing, they cleared up some puzzles about the structure of the atom.

In 1913 Niels Bohr had pictured the atom as consisting of a central nucleus surrounded by electrons circling in fixed orbits around that nucleus. An electron could occupy any of the given orbits, but it could never take a position between them. In jumping from one orbit to another, it absorbed energy if it moved from an inner orbit to an outer one and emitted energy if it moved from an outer orbit to an inner one. This was why an atom could absorb or emit only certain wavelengths of radiation, producing the characteristic lines in spectra. Bohr's scheme was highly successful in explaining the behavior of atoms, and he was awarded the Nobel Prize in physics in 1922 for his theory.

Bohr had no explanation of why the orbits were fixed in the positions they were. He simply chose the orbits that would give the correct results, as far as absorption and emission of the actually observed wavelengths of light were concerned. As the years went on, it became necessary to patch and re-patch the "Bohr atom" to account for the fine details of the spectral lines.

In 1926 the German physicist Erwin Schrödinger decided to take another look at the atom in the light of the de Broglie theory of the wave nature of particles. Considering the electron as a wave, he decided that the electron did not circle around the nucleus as a planet circles around the sun but constituted a wave that curved all around the nucleus, so that it was in all parts of its orbit at once, so to speak. It turned out that, on the basis of the wavelength predicted by de Broglie for an electron, a set of electron-waves would exactly fit the orbits outlined by Bohr. Between the orbits, the waves would join up "out of phase;" thus such orbits could not be stable.

Schrödinger worked out a mathematical description of the atom called "wave mechanics," and this turned out to be a more satisfactory method of looking at the atom than the Bohr system had been. Schrödinger shared the Nobel Prize in physics in 1933 with Dirac (the author of the theory of anti-particles — see Chapter 6), who also contributed to the development of this new picture of the atom.

BY THIS TIME the electron had become a pretty vague "particle." For one thing, as a wave it occupied all parts of an orbit simultaneously! And it soon developed that the electron was even more indefinite than that. Werner Heisenberg of Germany proceeded to raise a profound question which projected particles, and physics itself, almost into a realm of the unknowable.

Heisenberg had presented a model of the atom of his own. He had abandoned all attempts to picture the atom as composed either of particles or of waves. He decided that any attempt to draw an analogy between atomic structure and the structure of the world about us was doomed to failure. Instead, he described the energy levels or orbits of electrons purely in terms of numbers, without a trace of picture. He used a mathematical device called a "matrix" to manipulate his numbers, so his system was called "matrix mechanics."

Heisenberg received the Nobel Prize in physics in 1932 for his contributions to quantum mechanics, but his "matrix" system was less popular with physicists than Schrödinger's wave mechanics, because the latter seemed just as useful as Heisenberg's abstractions, and it is difficult for even a physicist to force himself to abandon all attempts to picture what he is talking about.

Heisenberg went on to consider the matter of describing the position of a particle. How could one determine where a particle was? The obvious answer is: look at it. Well, let us imagine a microscope that could make an electron visible. We must shine a light or some appropriate kind of radiation on it to see it. But an electron is so small that a single photon of light striking it would move it and change its position. In the very act of measuring its position, we would have changed that position.

This is a phenomenon that occurs in ordinary life. When we measure the air pressure in a tire with a gauge, we let a little air out of the tire and change the pressure slightly in the act of measuring it. Likewise, when we put a thermometer in a bathtub of water to measure the temperature, the thermometer's absorption of heat changes the temperature slightly. A meter measuring electric current takes away a little current for moving the pointer on the dial. And so it goes in every measurement of any kind that we make.

However, in all ordinary measurements the change in the subject we are measuring is so small that we can ignore it. The situation is quite different when we come to look at the electron. Our measuring device now is at least as large as the thing we are measuring; there is no conceivable measuring agent smaller than the electron. Consequently our measurement must inevitably have not a negligible but a decisive effect on the object measured. We could stop the electron and so determine its position at a given instant. But in that case we could not know what its motion or velocity was. On the other hand, we might record its velocity, but then we could not fix its position at any given moment.

Heisenberg showed that there is no way of devising a method of pinpointing the position of a subatomic particle unless you are willing to be quite uncertain as to its exact motion. And, in reverse, there is no way of pinpointing a particle's exact motion unless you are willing to be quite uncertain as to its exact position. To calculate both exactly, at the same instant of time, is impossible.

Heisenberg's "uncertainty principle" profoundly affected the thinking of physicists and philosophers. It had a direct bearing on the philosophical question of "causality." But its implications for science are not those that are commonly supposed. One often reads that the principle of indeterminacy removes all certainty from Nature and shows that science after all does not and never can know what is really going on, that scientific knowledge is at the mercy of the unpredictable whims of a universe in which effect does not necessarily follow cause. Whether or not this interpretation is valid from the standpoint of philosophy, the principle of uncertainty has in no way shaken the attitude of scientists toward scientific investigation. If, for instance, the behavior of the individual molecules in a gas cannot be predicted with certainty, nevertheless on the average the molecules do obey certain laws, and their behavior can be predicted on a statistical basis, just as insurance companies can calculate reliable mortality tables even though it is impossible to predict when any particular individual will die.

In most scientific observations, indeed, the indeterminacy is so small compared with the scale of the measurements involved that it can be neglected for all practical purposes. One can determine simultaneously both the position and the motion of a star, of a planet, of a billiard ball or even of a grain of sand, with completely satisfactory accuracy.

As for the uncertainty among the subatomic particles themselves, this does not hinder but actually helps physicists. It has been used to explain facts about radioactivity and about the absorption of subatomic particles by nuclei, as well as many other subatomic events, more reasonably than would have been possible without the uncertainty principle.

The uncertainty principle means that the universe is more complex than was thought, but not that it is irrational

CHAPTER

8

THE
MACHINE

FIRE AND STEAM

THE FIRST LAW of thermodynamics states that energy cannot be created out of nothing. But there is no law against giving Nature a helping hand. The whole civilization of mankind has been built upon finding new sources of energy and harnessing it in ever more efficient and sophisticated ways. In this chapter we shall make a rapid survey of the engines, machines, and instruments that have created modern technology.

It was perhaps half a million years ago that our man-like ancestors "discovered" fire. No doubt they had encountered — and been put to flight by — lightning-ignited brush fires and forest fires before that. But the discovery of its virtues did not come until curiosity overcame fear. Some pre-man may have been attracted to the quietly burning remnants of such a fire and found amusement in playing with it, in feeding it sticks, and in watching the dancing flames. At night he would have appreciated the light and warmth of the fire, and the fact that it kept other animals away. Eventually he would learn to make a fire himself by rubbing dry sticks together, to warm his camp or cave with it, to roast his game to make it easier to chew and better-tasting, and to use its heat for other purposes.

Fire provided man with a practically limitless supply of energy, which is why it is considered the greatest single human discovery — the one that hastened man's rise above the state of an animal. Yet curiously enough, for many thousands of years — in fact, up to the Industrial Revolution — man realized only a small part of its possibilities. He used it for light, to warm his home, to cook his food, to work metals and make glass — and that was about all.

Meanwhile he was discovering other sources of energy. And some of the most important of them were developed during the so-called "Dark Ages." It was in medieval times that man began to burn the black rock called coal in his metallurgical furnaces, to harness the wind with windmills, to use water mills for grinding grain, to employ magnetic energy in the compass, and to use explosives in warfare.

About 670 A.D. a Byzantine named Callinicus is believed to have invented "Greek fire," a primitive incendiary bomb composed of sulfur and naphtha, which was credited with saving Constantinople from its first siege by the Moslems. Gunpowder arrived in Europe in the thirteenth century. Roger Bacon is supposed to have invented it independently about 1280 A.D., but it had been known in Asia for centuries before that and may have been introduced to Europe by the Mongol invasions beginning in 1240 A.D. In any case, artillery powered by gunpowder came into use in Europe in the fourteenth century, and cannons are supposed to have appeared first at the battle of Crecy in 1346 A.D.

The most important of all the medieval inventions is the one credited to Johann Gutenberg of Germany. About 1450 A.D. he cast the first movable type, and thereby introduced printing as a power-

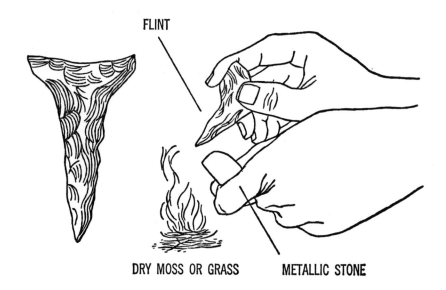

FLINT

DRY MOSS OR GRASS   METALLIC STONE

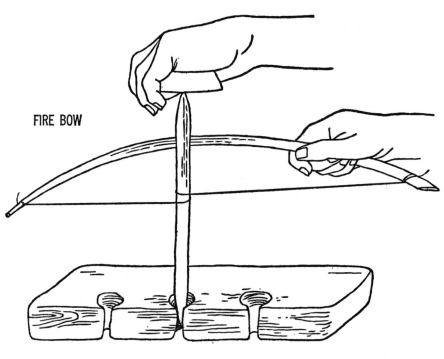

FIRE BOW

SLOTS TREATED WITH RESIN
TO PROMOTE FRICTION

EARLY FIREMAKING METHODS.

ful force in human affairs. Together with the replacement of parchment by paper (which had been invented by the Chinese about 100 A.D.), it made possible the large-scale production and distribution of books and other written material. The recorded knowledge of mankind was no longer buried in royal collections of manuscripts but made accessible in libraries available to all who could read. Pamphlets began to create and give expression to public opinion. (Printing was largely responsible for the success of Martin Luther's revolt against the Papacy, which might otherwise have been nothing more than a private quarrel.) And it was printing that created one of the prime instruments that gave rise to science as we know it. That indispensable instrument is the wide communication of ideas. Science had been a matter of personal communications among a few devotees; now it became a major field of activity which enlisted more and more workers, elicited the prompt and critical testing of theories, and ceaselessly opened new frontiers.

THE GREAT TURNING POINT in man's harnessing of energy came at the end of the seventeenth century. It developed from the simple problem of pumping water out of mines. The old hand pump, you will remember, used a handle to lift a piston in a cylinder, creating a vacuum into which the water then rose through a one-way valve (see Chapter 4). Now it occurred to several inventors: why not use steam instead of muscle power to create the vacuum? Suppose one filled a cylinder (or similar vessel) with water and then forced in steam to push out the water. Now if the vessel was cooled (*e.g.*, by means of cold water played on the outside surface), the steam in the vessel would condense to a few drops of water and leave a virtual vacuum. The water that one wanted to raise (*e.g.*, out of a flooded mine) could then rise through a valve into this evacuated vessel.

The first to translate this idea into a practical working device was an English military engineer named Thomas Savery. His "steam engine" (the word "engine" originally meant any ingenious device, and came from the same Greek root as "ingenious") could be used to pump water out of a mine or a well or to drive a water wheel. But it was dangerous (because the high pressure of the steam might burst the vessels and pipes) and very inefficient (because the heat of the steam was lost each time the container was cooled). Seven years after Savery patented his engine in 1698, an English blacksmith named Thomas Newcomen built an improved engine which operated at low steam pressure; it had a piston in a cylinder and employed air pressure to push down the piston.

Newcomen's engine was not very efficient either, and the steam engine remained a minor gadget for more than 60 years until a Scottish instrument maker named James Watt found the way to make it effective. Hired by the University of Glasgow to fix a model of a Newcomen engine which was not working properly, Watt fell to thinking about the device's wasteful use of fuel. Why, after all, should the steam vessel have to be cooled off each time? Why not keep the steam chamber steam-hot at all times and lead the steam into a separate condensing chamber which could be kept cold? Watt went on to add a number of other improvements: employing steam pressure to help push the piston, hitching the back-and-forth motion of the piston to a shaft that turned a wheel, and so on. By 1782 his steam engine, which got at least three times as much work out of a ton of coal as Newcomen's, was ready to be put to work as a universal work-horse.

Its first application other than as a mere pump was the steamship. In 1787 the American inventor John Fitch built a steamboat that worked, but it failed as a financial venture and Fitch died unknown and unappreciated. Robert Fulton, a more able promoter than Fitch, launched his steamboat, the *Clermont*, in 1807 with so much more fanfare and support that he came to be considered the inventor of the steamship, though actually he was no more the builder of the first such ship than Watt was the builder of the first steam engine.

By the 1830's steamships were crossing the Atlantic and were being driven by the screw-propeller, a considerable improvement over the side paddle-wheels. And by the 1850's the speedy and

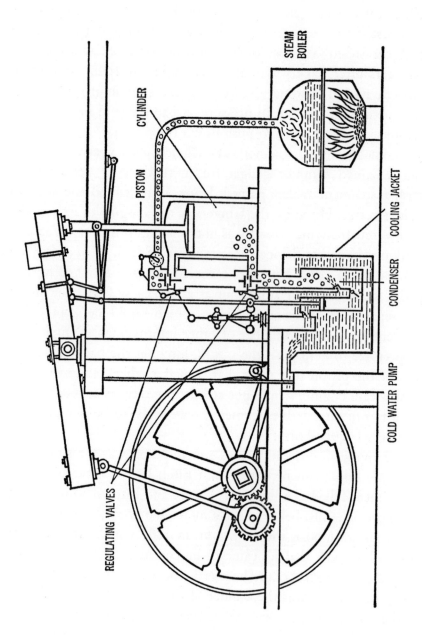

WATT'S STEAM ENGINE.

beautiful Yankee Clippers had begun to furl their sails and to be replaced by steamers in the merchant fleets and navies of the world.

Meanwhile the steam engine had also begun to dominate land transportation. In 1814 the English inventor George Stephenson had built the first practical steam locomotive. For the first time in history land travel became as convenient as sea travel, and overland commerce could compete with sea-borne trade. By 1869 the full width of the United States was spanned by rail.

British inventors also led in introducing the steam engine in factories to run machinery. With the "Industrial Revolution," man completed his graduation from muscle power to mechanical power.

ELECTRICITY

IN THE NATURE OF THINGS, the steam engine is suitable only for large-scale, steady production of power. It cannot efficiently deliver energy in small packages or intermittently at the push of a button: a "little" steam engine, in which the fires were damped down or started up on demand, would be an absurdity. But the same generation that saw the development of steam power also saw the discovery of a means of transforming energy into precisely the form I have mentioned — a ready store of energy which could be delivered anywhere, in small amounts or large, at the push of a button. This form, of course, is electricity.

The Greeks noted that a fossil resin found on the Baltic shores, which we call amber, and they called "elektron," gained the ability to attract feathers, threads or bits of fluff when it was rubbed with a piece of fur. It was William Gilbert of England (the investigator of magnetism — see Chapter 3) who first suggested that this attractive force be called "electricity," from the Greek word "elektron." Gilbert found that in addition to amber, some other materials, such as glass, gained electric properties on being rubbed.

In 1733 the French chemist Charles Francis de Cisternay du Fay discovered that if two amber rods, or two glass rods, were electrified by rubbing, they repelled each other. However, an electrified glass rod attracted an electrified amber rod. If the two were allowed to touch, both lost their electricity.

Benjamin Franklin, who became intensely interested in electricity, suggested that it was a fluid. When glass was rubbed, electricity flowed into it, making it "positively charged;" on the other hand, when amber was rubbed, electricity flowed out of it and it therefore became "negatively charged." And when a negative rod made contact with a positive one, the electric fluid would flow from the positive to the negative until a neutral balance was achieved.

This was a remarkably shrewd speculation. If we substitute the word electrons for Franklin's "fluid," and reverse the direction of flow (actually electrons flow from the amber to the glass) his guess was essentially correct.

A French inventor named J. T. Desaguliers suggested in 1740 that substances through which the electric fluid traveled freely (*e.g.*, metals) be termed "conductors," and those through which it did not move freely (*e.g.*, glass and amber) be called "insulators."

Experimenters found that a large electric charge could gradually be accumulated in a conductor if it was insulated from loss of electricity by glass or a layer of air. The most spectacular device of this kind was the "Leyden jar," first used in 1745 at the University of Leyden in Holland. The charge is built up on tinfoil coating a glass jar, via a brass chain stuck into the jar through a stopper. When you touch the charged jar, you get a startling electric shock. The Leyden jar can also produce a spark. Naturally, the greater the charge on a body, the greater its tendency to escape. The force driving the electrons away from the region of highest excess (the "negative pole") toward the region of greatest deficiency (the "positive pole") is the "electromotive force" (EMF). If the electric potential becomes high enough, the electrons will even jump an insulating gap between the negative and positive poles. Thus they will leap across an air gap, producing a bright spark and a crackling noise. The light of the spark is caused by the radiation resulting from the

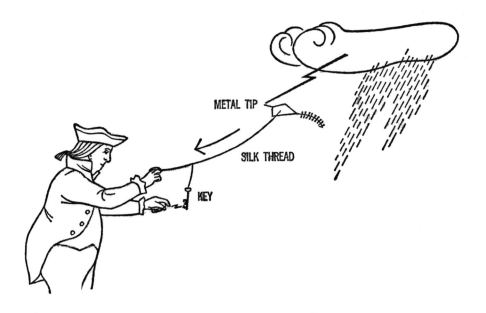

METAL TIP

SILK THREAD

KEY

FRANKLIN'S EXPERIMENT.

collisions of innumerable electrons with air molecules, and the noise arises from the expansion of the quickly heated air, followed by the clap of cooler air rushing into the partial vacuum momentarily produced.

Naturally one wondered whether lightning and thunder were the same phenomenon, on a vast scale, as the little trick performed by a Leyden jar. This question prompted Benjamin Franklin's famous experiment in 1752. The kite he flew in a thunderstorm had a pointed wire, to which he attached a silk thread which could conduct electricity down from the thunderclouds. When Franklin put his hand near a metal key tied to the silk thread, the key sparked. Thus Franklin demonstrated that the thunderclouds were charged with electricity, and that thunder and lightning were indeed the effect of a Leyden-jar-in-the-sky in which the clouds formed one pole and the earth another.

The luckiest thing about the experiment, from Franklin's personal standpoint, was that he survived. Others who tried it were killed, because the induced charge on the kite's pointed wire accumulated to the point of producing a fatally intense discharge.

Franklin's experiment had two electrifying (if you'll pardon the pun) effects. In the first place, the world at large suddenly became interested in electricity. Secondly, it put the American colonies on the map, culturally speaking. For the first time an American had actually displayed sufficient ability as a scientist to impress the cultivated Europeans of the Age of Reason. When, a quarter-century later, Franklin represented the infant United States at Versailles and sought assistance, he won respect not only as the simple envoy of a new republic but also as a mental giant who had tamed the lightning and brought it humbly to earth. That flying kite contributed more than a little to the cause of American independence.

WHAT WE HAVE BEEN LOOKING AT is, of course, "static electricity." The discovery of electric currents, or "dynamic electricity," began with Luigi Galvani of Italy, and every high-school student of physics is familiar with that story: how Galvani discovered that touching a frog's leg with two different metals (brass and iron) made the leg twitch, how Alessandro Volta found that two metals in contact generated a flow of electricity, how he proceeded to use this knowledge to invent the electric battery, etc.

But the generation of electricity on a large scale had to wait for Michael Faraday's "dynamo-electric machine," or "dynamo" (from the Greek word for "power"). As we saw in Chapter 4, Faraday succeeded in producing an electric current in a wire coil or a metal wheel by moving it across a magnet's lines of force. In this way the energy of motion was converted into electrical energy. To generate more current, a stronger magnet was needed, and in 1845 the British physicist Charles Wheatstone achieved this by replacing the permanent magnet with an "electromagnet" developed by the American physicist Joseph Henry — a piece of iron wrapped in many turns of insulated wire, which enabled a current to crowd many lines of magnetic force into the iron.

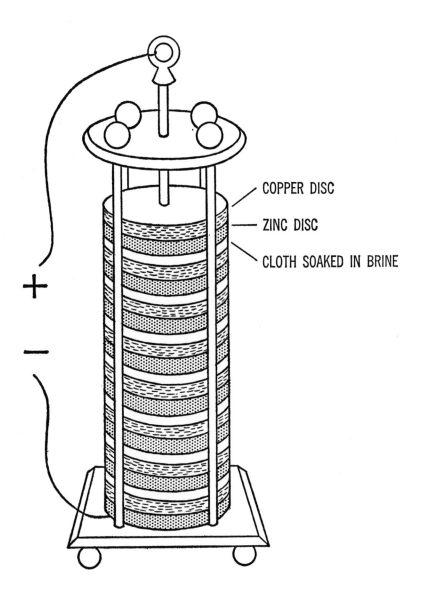

COPPER DISC

ZINC DISC

CLOTH SOAKED IN BRINE

$+$

$-$

VOLTA'S BATTERY. *The two different metals in contact give rise to a flow of electrons, which are conducted from one "cell" to the next by the salt-soaked cloth.*

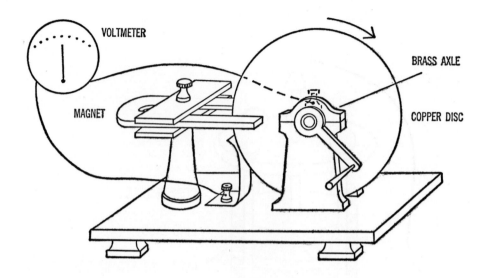

FARADAY'S "DYNAMO." *The rotating copper disc cuts the magnet's lines of force, inducing a current detected on the voltmeter.*

Once an effective dynamo had been developed, the rest was easy. Steam power or a waterfall could provide the energy to turn a turbine and thus generate huge quantities of electric current.

For the next step — putting electricity to work — the world is considerably indebted to Joseph Henry. Henry, a native of Albany, N. Y., who became professor of natural philosophy at Princeton University, then served as the first secretary of the new Smithsonian Institution, and was largely responsible for the founding of the United States Weather Bureau, was a scientist who has been insufficiently honored in his own country. His work paralleled that of Faraday: he discovered the induction of electricity and other important principles at about the same time as Faraday, and his name is less known only because Faraday published first.

Henry's first application of electricity was the invention of telegraphy. He devised a system of relays which made it possible to transmit an electric current over miles of wire. The strength of a current declines fairly rapidly as it travels along the resisting wire;

what Henry's relays did was to use the dying signal to activate a small electromagnet which operated a switch that turned on a boost in power from stations placed at appropriate intervals. Thus a message consisting of coded pulses of electricity could be sent for a considerable distance. Henry actually built a telegraph that worked.

Because he was an unworldly man who believed that knowledge should be shared with the world and therefore did not patent his discoveries, Henry again got no credit for this invention. The credit fell to the artist (and eccentric religious bigot) Samuel Finley Breese Morse. With Henry's help, freely given, Morse built the first practical telegraph in 1844. Morse's main original contribution to telegraphy was the system of dots and dashes known as the "Morse Code."

Henry's most important development in the field of electricity

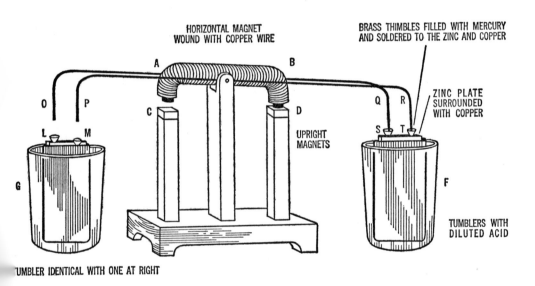

HENRY'S MOTOR. *The upright bar magnet* B *attracts the wire-wound magnet* B, *pulling the long metal probes* Q *and* R *into the brass thimbles* S *and* T, *which act as terminals for the wet cell* F. *Current flows into the horizontal magnet, producing an electromagnetic field that pulls* A *and* C *together. The whole process is then repeated on the opposite side. Thus the horizontal bars oscillate up and down.*

321

was the electric motor. He showed that electric current could be used to turn a wheel, just as the turning of a wheel can generate current in the first place. And an electrically driven wheel (or motor) could be used to run machinery. The motor could be carried anywhere; it could be turned on or off at will (without waiting to build up a head of steam); and it could be made as small as one wished.

The catch was that electricity had to be transported from the generating station to the place where the motor was to be used. Some way had to be found to cut down the loss of electrical energy (taking the form of dissipated heat) as it traveled over wires.

One answer was the "transformer." The experimenters with currents found that electricity suffered far less loss if it was transmitted at a low rate of flow. So the output from the generator was stepped up to a high voltage by means of a transformer which, while multiplying the voltage, say, three times, reduces the current (rate of flow) to one-third. At the receiving station, the current can be stepped up again for use in motors.

The transformer works by using the "primary" current to induce a current at high voltage in a secondary coil. This induction requires varying the magnetic field through the second coil. Since a steady current will not do this, the current used is a continually changing one which builds up to a maximum and then drops to zero and starts building in the opposite direction — in other words, an "alternating current."

Alternating current (ac) did not win out over direct current (dc) without a struggle. Thomas Alva Edison, the greatest name in electricity in the final decades of the nineteenth century, championed dc and fought ac on the ground that it was more dangerous (pointing out, for instance, that it was used in electric chairs). He was bitterly opposed by Nikola Tesla, a Croatian engineer who had worked for Edison and been shabbily treated. Tesla developed a successful system of ac. In 1893 George Westinghouse, also a believer in ac, won a crucial victory over Edison by obtaining for his electric company the contract to develop the Niagara Falls power plants on an ac basis. In the following decades the German-born electrical engineer

Charles Proteus Steinmetz, working for the General Electric Company, established the theory of alternating currents on a firm mathematical basis. Today alternating current is all but universal in systems of power distribution.

ELECTRICAL GADGETS

ONE OF THE FIRST ELECTRICAL GADGETS (after telegraphy) was the telephone, patented by the Scottish-born inventor Alexander Graham Bell in 1876. In the telephone mouthpiece, the speaker's sound waves strike a thin steel diaphragm and make it vibrate in accordance with the pattern of the waves. The vibrations of the diaphragm in turn set up an analogous pattern in an electric current, by way of carbon powder. When the diaphragm presses on the carbon powder, the powder conducts more current; when the diaphragm moves away, it conducts less. Thus the electric current strengthens and weakens in exact mimicry of the sound waves. At the telephone receiver the fluctuations in the strength of the current actuate an electromagnet which makes a diaphragm vibrate and reproduce the sound waves.

In 1877, a year after the invention of the telephone, Edison patented his "phonograph." The first records had the grooves scored on tinfoil wrapped around a rotating cylinder; then Emile Berliner introduced wax-coated disks; and in 1925 recordings began to be made by means of electricity through the use of a "microphone," which translated sound into a mimicking electric current via a piezo-electric crystal instead of a metal diaphragm — the crystal allowing a better quality of reproduction of the sound. In the 1930's the use of radio tubes for amplification was introduced. Then, in the post-World War II era, came the long-playing record, "hi-fi," and "stereophonic" sound, which have had the effect, as far as the sound itself is concerned, of practically removing all mechanical barriers between the orchestra or singer and the listener!

"Tape-recording" of sound, oddly enough, is actually older than radio; it was invented in 1898 by a Danish electrical engineer named Valdemar Poulsen but had to await certain technical advances to become practical. An electromagnet, responding to an electric current carrying the sound pattern, magnetizes a powder coating on a tape or wire moving past it, and the playback is accomplished through an electromagnet which picks up this pattern of magnetism and translates it again into a current which will reproduce the sound.

OF ALL THE TRICKS performed by electricity, certainly the most popular was its turning night into day. Mankind had fought off the daily crippling darkness-after-sundown with the campfire, the torch, the candle, whale oil, kerosene, and gas. Now electricity brought to pass a far better kind of lighting — safer, more convenient, and as brilliant as one could wish.

The problem was to heat a filament by electricity to an incandescent glow. It seemed simple, but many tried and failed to produce a durable lamp. Even in the best available vacuum the filament would melt, burn up or break down. In 1878 Thomas Edison, fresh from his triumph in creating the phonograph, announced that he would tackle the problem. He was only 31, but such was his reputation as an inventor that his announcement caused the stocks of gas companies to tumble on the New York and London stock exchanges.

After hundreds of experiments and fabulous frustrations, Edison finally found a material that would serve as the filament — a scorched cotton thread. On October 21, 1879, he lit his bulb. It burned for 40 continuous hours. On the following New Year's Eve Edison put his lamps on triumphant public display by lighting up the main street of Menlo Park, N. J., where his laboratory was located. He quickly patented his lamp and began to produce it in quantity.

Yet Edison was not the sole inventor of the incandescent lamp. At least one other inventor had about an equal claim — Joseph Swan of England, who exhibited a carbon-filament lamp at a meeting of the Newcastle-on-Tyne Chemical Society on December 18, 1878, but did not get his lamp into production until 1881.

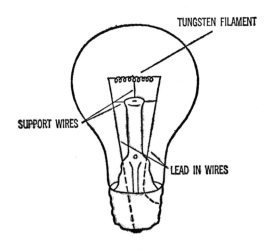

INCANDESCENT LAMP.

Edison proceeded to work on the problem of providing homes with a steady and sufficient supply of electricity for his lamps — a task which took as much ingenuity as the invention of the lamp itself. Two major improvements were later made in the lamp. In 1910 William David Coolidge of the General Electric Company adopted the heat-resisting metal tungsten as the material for the filament, and in 1913 Irving Langmuir introduced an inert gas (nitrogen or argon) in the lamp to prevent the evaporation and breaking of the filament that occurred in a vacuum.

Other kinds of electric lamps have, of course, been developed. The so-called "neon lights" are tubes in which an electric discharge excites atoms of neon gas to emit a bright, red glow. The "sunlamp" contains mercury vapor, which when excited by a discharge yields radiation rich in ultraviolet light; this can be used not only to produce a tan but also to kill bacteria or generate fluorescence. And the latter in turn leads to fluorescent lighting. Here the ultraviolet light from mercury vapor excites fluorescence in a "phosphor" coating the inside of the tube. Since this cool light wastes little energy in heat, it consumes less electric power.

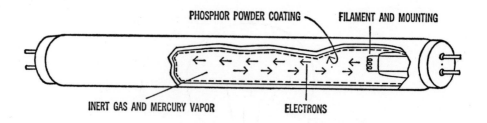

FLUORESCENT LAMP. *A discharge of electrons from the filament excites the mercury vapor in the tube, producing ultraviolet radiation. The ultraviolet makes the phosphor glow.*

The latest promising development is a method that converts electricity directly into light without the prior formation of ultraviolet light. In 1936 the French physicist George Destriau discovered that an intense alternating current could make a phosphor glow. Electrical engineers are now using this phenomenon, called "electroluminescence," to develop glowing panels. Thus a luminescent wall or ceiling could light a room, bathing it in a soft, colored glow. The project is still in the laboratory and demonstration stage.

PROBABLY NO INVENTION involving light has given mankind more enjoyment than photography. It was originated in the year 1839 by a Frenchman, Louis Jacques Mandé Daguerre, and an Englishman, Fox Talbot.

In essence, photography depends mainly on chemistry. The image is focused by a lens upon an "emulsion" (a jellied suspension — from the Latin word for "milk") of a silver compound. The light produces a chemical change in the compound, the amount of change being proportional to the intensity of the light at any given point. In the developing process, the chemical developer converts those parts changed by the light into metallic silver, again to an extent proportional to the intensity of light. The unaffected silver compound is then dissolved away, leaving a "negative" on which the image appears as a pattern of blackening in various degrees. Light projected through the negative reverses the light and dark spots and forms the positive image.

Through the nineteenth century the process was gradually made faster and simpler. The American inventor George Eastman developed dry plates (in place of the original moist emulsion) and then adopted plastic film as the backing for the emulsion. More sensitive emulsions were created, so that faster shots could be made and the subject did not need to "pose."

Since World War II picture-taking has been further simplified by means of the "Land camera," invented by Edwin H. Land of the Polaroid Corporation. It uses two films on which the negative and positive are developed automatically by chemicals incorporated in the film.

In 1936 a practical process of color photography was made generally available. It was based on the observation by Maxwell and von Helmholtz that any color in the spectrum could be produced by combining red, green, and blue light. On this principle, the color film is composed of emulsions in three layers, one sensitive to the red, one to the green, and one to the blue components of the image. Three separate but superimposed pictures are formed, each reproducing the intensity of light in its part of the spectrum as a pattern of black-and-white shading. The film is then developed in three successive stages, using red, blue, and green dyes to deposit the appropriate colors on the negative. Each spot in the picture is a specific combination of red, green, and blue, and the brain interprets these combinations to reconstitute the full range of color.

In 1959 Land presented a new theory of color vision. The brain, he maintained, does not require a combination of three colors to create the impression of full color. All it needs is two different wavelengths, or sets of wavelengths, one longer than the other by a certain minimum amount. For instance, one of the sets of wavelengths may be the entire spectrum, or white light. Because the average wavelength of white light is in the yellow-green region, it can serve as the "short" wavelength. Now a picture reproduced through a combination of white light and red light (serving as the long wavelength) comes out in full color. Land has also made pictures in full color with filtered green light and red light and with other appropriate dual combinations. Just why this method should work is not yet clearly understood, but it does work and it has upset the older theories of color vision.

The invention of motion pictures came from an observation first made by the English physician Peter Mark Roget in 1824. He noted that the eye forms a persistent image which lasts for an appreciable fraction of a second. After the inauguration of photography, many experimenters, particularly in France, made use of this fact to create the illusion of motion by showing a series of pictures in rapid succession. Everyone is familiar with the parlor gadget consisting of a series of picture cards which, when riffled rapidly, make a figure seem to move and perform acrobatics. If a series of pictures, each slightly different from the one before, is flashed on a screen at intervals of about one-sixteenth of a second apart, the persistence of the successive images in the eye will cause them to blend together and so give the impression of continuous motion.

It was Edison who produced the first "movie." He photographed a series of pictures on a strip of film and then ran the film through a projector, which showed each in succession with a burst of light. The first motion picture was put on display for public amusement in 1894, and in 1914 theaters showed the first full-length motion picture, *The Birth of a Nation.*

To the silent movies, a sound track was added in 1927. The "sound track" also takes the form of light: the wave pattern of music and the actors' speech is converted into a varying current of electricity by a microphone, and this current lights a lamp which is photographed along with the action of the motion picture. When the film, with this track of light at one side, is projected on the screen, the brightening and dimming of the lamp in the pattern of the sound waves is converted back to an electric current by means of a "phototube," using the photoelectric effect, and the current in turn is reconverted to sound.

Within two years after the first "talking picture," *The Jazz Singer*, silent movies were a thing of the past, and so, almost, was vaudeville. By the late 1930's the "talkies" had added color, and now we seem to be in for the "smellies" — movies that literally have an odor.

INTERNAL-COMBUSTION ENGINES

WHILE PETROLEUM gave way to electricity in the field of artificial illumination, it became indispensable for another technical development which revolutionized modern life as deeply, in its way, as did the introduction of electrical gadgetry. This development was the internal-combustion engine.

Actually, some internal-combustion engines were built at the beginning of the nineteenth century, before petroleum came into common use. They burned turpentine vapors or hydrogen as fuel. But it was only with gasoline, the one vapor-producing liquid that is both combustible and obtainable in large quantities, that such an engine could become more than a curiosity.

In 1876 the German technician Nikolaus August Otto built a "four-cycle" engine. First a piston fitting tightly in a cylinder is pushed outward, so that a mixture of gasoline and air is sucked into the vacated cylinder. Then the piston is pushed in again to compress the vapor. At the point of maximum compression the vapor is ignited and explodes. The explosion drives the piston outward, and it is this powered motion that drives the engine. It turns a wheel which pushes the piston in again to expel the burned residue or "exhaust" — the fourth and final step in the cycle. Now the wheel moves the piston outward to start the cycle over again.

A Scottish engineer named Dugald Clerk almost immediately added an improvement. He hooked up a second cylinder, so that its piston was being driven while the other was in the recovery stage: this made the power output steadier. Later the addition of more cylinders (eight is now the most common number) increased the smoothness and power of this "reciprocating engine."

The ignition of the gasoline-air mixture at just the right moment presented a problem. All sorts of ingenious devices were used, but by 1923 it became common to depend on electricity. The supply comes from a "storage battery." This is a battery which, like any other, delivers electricity as the result of a chemical reaction. But it can be recharged by sending an electric current through it in the direction opposite to the discharge; this current reverses the chemical reaction and allows the chemicals to produce more electricity. The reverse current is provided by a small generator driven by the engine.

The most common type of storage battery has plates of lead and lead oxide in alternation with cells of concentrated sulfuric acid. It was invented by the French physicist Gaston Planté in 1859 and was put into its modern form in 1881 by the American electrical engineer Charles Francis Brush. More rugged and more compact storage batteries have been invented since, but none can compete with the lead battery in economy.

The electric current supplied by the storage battery is raised in voltage by means of a transformer called an "induction coil," and this stepped-up voltage provides the ignition spark, created across the gap in the familiar spark plugs.

Once an internal-combustion engine starts firing, inertia will keep it moving between power strokes. But outside energy must be supplied to start the engine. At first it was done by hand (*e.g.*, the automobile crank), and outboard motors and power lawn mowers are still started by yanking a cord. The "self-starter" in modern automobiles is powered by the storage battery, which supplies the energy for the first few turns of the engine.

THE FIRST PRACTICAL "horseless carriage" was built in 1885 by the German engineer Gottlieb Daimler. But what really made the automobile, as a common conveyance, was the invention of "mass production."

The prime originator of this technique was Eli Whitney, who merits more credit for it than for his more famous invention of the cotton gin. In 1798 Whitney received a contract from the Federal Government to make guns for the army. Up to that time guns had been manufactured individually, each from its own fitted parts. Whitney conceived the notion of making the parts uniform, so that a given part would fit any gun. This single, simple innovation — manufacturing standard, interchangeable parts for a given type of article — was perhaps as responsible as any other factor for the creation of modern mass-production industry. When power tools came in, they made it possible to stamp out standard parts in practically unlimited numbers.

It was Henry Ford who first exploited the concept to the full. He had built his first automobile (a two-cylinder job) in 1892, then had gone to work for the Detroit Automobile Company in 1899 as chief engineer. The company wanted to produce custom-made cars, but Ford had another notion. He resigned in 1902 to produce cars on his own — in quantity. In 1909 he began to turn out the Model T Ford on the Whitney plan — car after car, each just like the one before and all made with the same parts.

Ford saw that he could speed up production by using human workers as one used machines, performing the same small job over and over with uninterrupted regularity. So he set up the "assembly line," with workers adding parts to the construction as it passed them on moving belts until the finished car rolled off at the end of the line. Two economic advances were achieved by this system: high wages for the workers and cars that could be sold at amazingly low prices.

In 1892 the German mechanical engineer Rudolf Diesel introduced a modification of the internal-combustion engine which was simpler and more economical of fuel. He put the fuel-air mixture under high pressure, so that the heat of compression alone was enough to ignite it. The "Diesel engine" made it possible to use higher-boiling fractions of petroleum, which do not knock. Because of the higher compression used, the engine must be more solidly constructed and is therefore considerably heavier than the gasoline engine. But it has gained favor for trucks, tractors, buses, ships, and locomotives.

THE GREATEST TRIUMPH of the internal-combustion engine came, of course, in the air. By the 1890's man had achieved the age-old dream — older than Daedalus and Icarus — of flying on wings. Gliding had become an avid sport of the aficionados, though its first important practitioner, the German engineer Otto Lilienthal, was killed in 1896 during a glider flight. Now there was a violent urge to take off in powered flight.

The American physicist and astronomer Samuel Pierpont Langley tried in 1902 and 1903 to fly a glider powered by an internal-combustion engine and came within an ace of succeeding. Had his money not given out, he might have got into the air on the next try. As it was, the honor was reserved for the brothers Orville and Wilbur Wright, bicycle-manufacturers who had taken up gliders as a hobby.

On December 17, 1903, at Kitty Hawk, N. C., the Wright brothers got off the ground in a propeller-driven glider and stayed in the air for 59 seconds, flying 852 feet. It was the first airplane flight in history — and it went almost completely unnoticed by the world at large.

There was considerably more public excitement after the Wrights had achieved flights of 25 miles and more, and when, in 1909, the French engineer Louis Blériot crossed the English Channel in an airplane. The air battles and exploits of World War I further stimulated the imagination. But the airplane remained more or less a curiosity — merely a new and more horrible instrument of war and a plaything of stunt flyers and thrill-seekers. Aviation did not come into its own until Charles Augustus Lindbergh in 1927 flew nonstop from New York to Paris. The world went wild over the feat, and the development of bigger and safer airplanes began.

Two major innovations have been effected in the airplane engine since it was established as a means of transportation. The first was the adoption of the gas-turbine engine. In this engine the hot, expanding gases of the fuel drive a wheel by their pressure against its blades, instead of driving pistons in cylinders. The engine is simple, cheaper to run, and less vulnerable to trouble, and it needed only the development of alloys that could withstand the high temperatures of the gases to become a practicable affair. Such alloys were devised by 1939. Since then "turbo-prop" planes, using a turbine engine to drive the propellers, have become increasingly popular.

But they are now being superseded, at least for long flights, by the second major development — the jet plane. In principle the driving force here is the same as the one that makes a toy balloon dart forward when its mouth is opened and the air escapes. This is action-and-reaction: the motion of the expanding, escaping air in one direction results in equal motion, or thrust, in the opposite direction, just as the forward movement of the bullet in a gun barrel makes the gun kick backward in recoil. In the jet engine the burning of the fuel produces hot, high-pressure gases which drive the plane forward with great force as they stream backward through the exhaust. A rocket is driven by exactly the same means, except that it carries its own supply of oxygen to burn the fuel.

Patents for "jet propulsion" were taken out by a French engineer, René Lorin, as early as 1913, but at the time it was a completely impractical scheme for airplanes. Jet propulsion is economical only at speeds of more than 400 miles an hour. After World War II, military jets were developed to speeds approaching 2,000 miles per hour. The jetliners now in use by commercial airlines regularly cruise at 500 to 600 miles per hour.

RADIO

IN 1888 HEINRICH HERTZ conducted the famous experiments that detected radio waves, predicted 20 years earlier by James Clerk Maxwell (see Chapter 7). What he did was to set up a high-voltage

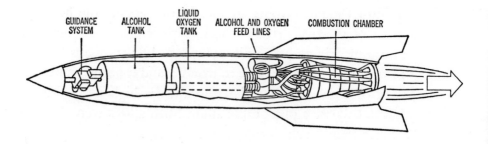

GUIDANCE SYSTEM ALCOHOL TANK LIQUID OXYGEN TANK ALCOHOL AND OXYGEN FEED LINES COMBUSTION CHAMBER

A SIMPLE LIQUID-FUELED ROCKET.

alternating current which surged into first one then another of two metal balls separated by a small air gap. Each time the potential reached a peak in one direction or the other, it sent a spark across the gap. Under these circumstances, Maxwell's equations predicted, electromagnetic radiation should be generated. Hertz used a receiver consisting of a simple loop of wire with a small air gap at one point to detect that energy. Just as the current gave rise to radiation in the first coil, so the radiation ought to give rise to a current in the second coil. Sure enough, Hertz was able to detect small sparks jumping across the gap in his detector coil, placed across the room from the radiating coil. Energy was being transmitted across space.

By moving his detector coil to various points in the room, Hertz was able to tell the shape of the waves. Where sparks came through brightly the waves were at peak or trough. Where sparks did not come through at all, they were midway. Thus he could calculate the wavelength of the radiation. He found that the waves were tremendously longer than those of light.

In the decade following, it occurred to a number of people that the "Hertzian waves" might be used to transmit messages from one place to another, for the waves were long enough to go around obstacles. In 1890 the French physicist Édouard Branley made an improved receiver by replacing the wire loop with a glass tube filled with metal filings to which wires and a battery were attached. The filings would not carry the battery's current unless a high-voltage

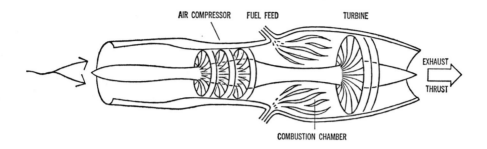

AIR COMPRESSOR   FUEL FEED   TURBINE

EXHAUST

THRUST

COMBUSTION CHAMBER

A TURBOJET ENGINE. *Air is drawn in, compressed, and mixed with fuel, which is ignited in the combustion chamber. The expanding gases power a turbine and produce thrust.*

alternating current was induced in the filings, as Hertzian waves would do. With this receiver he was able to detect Hertzian waves at a distance of 150 yards. Then the English physicist Oliver Joseph Lodge (who later gained a dubious kind of fame as a champion of spiritualism), modified this device and succeeded in detecting signals at a distance of half a mile and in sending messages in Morse Code.

The Italian inventor Guglielmo Marconi discovered that he could improve matters by connecting one side of the generator and receiver to the ground and the other to a wire, later called an "antenna" (because it resembled, I suppose, an insect's feeler). By using powerful generators, Marconi was able to send signals over a distance of nine miles in 1896, across the English Channel in 1898, and across the Atlantic in 1901. Thus was born what the British still call "wireless telegraphy" and the Americans named "radiotelegraphy," or "radio" for short.

Marconi worked out a system for excluding "static" from other sources and tuning in only on the wavelength generated by the transmitter. For his inventions Marconi shared the Nobel Prize in physics in 1909 with the German physicist Karl Ferdinand Braun, who also contributed to the development of radio.

The American physicist Reginald Aubrey Fessenden proceeded to develop a special generator of high-frequency alternating currents (doing away with the spark-gap device) and to devise a system of "modulating" the radio wave so that it carried a pattern mimicking sound waves. What was modulated was the amplitude (or height) of the waves; consequently this was called "amplitude modulation," now known as AM radio. On Christmas Eve, 1906, music and speech came out of a radio receiver for the first time.

The early radio enthusiasts had to sit over their sets with earphones on. Some means of strengthening, or "amplifying," the signal was needed, and the answer was found in a discovery that Edison had made — his only discovery in "pure" science.

In one of his experiments, looking toward improving the electric lamp, Edison sealed a metal wire into a light bulb near the hot filament. To his surprise, electricity flowed from the hot filament to the metal wire across the air gap between them. Because this phenomenon had no utility for his purposes, Edison, a practical man, merely wrote it up in his notebooks and forgot it. But the "Edison effect" became very important indeed when the electron was discovered and it became clear that current across a gap meant a flow of electrons.

In 1904 the English electrical engineer John Ambrose Fleming put the Edison effect to brilliant use. He surrounded the filament in a bulb with a cylindrical piece of metal (called a "plate"). Now this plate could act in either of two ways. If it was positively charged, it would attract the electrons boiling off the heated filament, and so would create a circuit that carried electric current. But if the plate was negatively charged, it would repel the electrons and thus prevent the flow of current. Suppose, then, that the plate was hooked up to a source of alternating current. When the current flowed in one direction, the plate would get a positive charge and pass current in the tube; when the alternating current changed direction, the plate would acquire a negative charge and no current would flow in the tube. Thus the plate would pass current in only one direction: in effect, it would convert alternating to direct current. Because such a tube acts as a valve for the flow of current, the British logically call it a "valve." In the United States it is vaguely called a "tube."

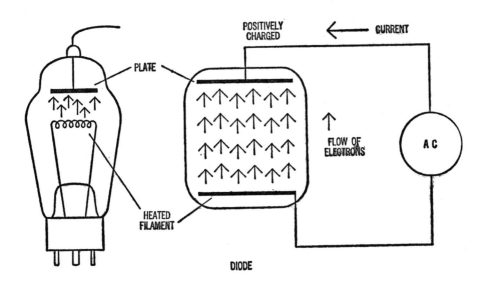

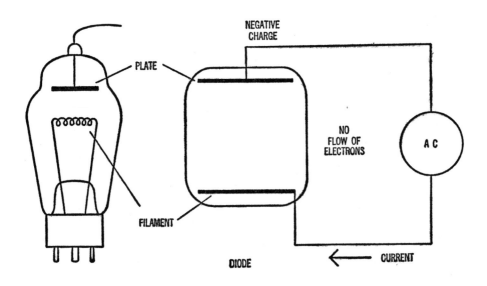

PRINCIPLE OF THE VACUUM-TUBE DIODE.

337

Scientists took to calling it a "diode," because it has two electrodes, the filament and the plate.

The diode serves in a radio set as a "rectifier," changing alternating current to direct where necessary. In 1907 the American inventor Lee De Forest went a step farther. He inserted a third electrode in the tube, making a "triode" out of it. The third electrode is a perforated plate ("grid") between the filament and the plate. The grid attracts electrons and speeds up the flow from the filament to the plate (through the holes in the grid). A small increase in the positive charge on the grid will result in a large increase in the flow of electrons from the filament to the plate. Consequently even the small charge added by weak radio signals will increase the current flow greatly, and this current will mirror all the variations imposed by the radio waves. In other words, the triode acts as an "amplifier." Triodes and even more complicated modifications of the tube have become essential equipment not only for radio sets but for all sorts of electronic equipment.

One more step was needed to make radio sets completely popular. During World War I the American electrical engineer Edwin Howard Armstrong developed a device for lowering the frequency of a radio wave. This was intended, at the time, for detecting aircraft, but after the war it was put to use in radio receivers. Armstrong's "superheterodyne receiver" made it possible to tune in clearly on an adjusted frequency by the turn of a dial, where previously it had been a complicated task to adjust reception over a wide range of possible frequencies. With the control of sound level and station tuning reduced to the turn of a dial, radio sets became hugely popular.

There remained the problem of static. The systems of tuning introduced by Marconi and his successors minimized "noise" from thunderstorms and other electrical sources but did not eliminate it. Again it was Armstrong who found an answer. In place of amplitude modulation, which was subject to interference from the random amplitude modulations of the noise sources, he substituted frequency modulation. That is, he kept the amplitude of the radio carrier wave constant and superimposed a variation in frequency on it. Where the

James Watt's steam engine.

JOHN FITCH'S STEAMBOAT.

GEORGE STEPHENSON'S STEAM LOCOMOTIVE.

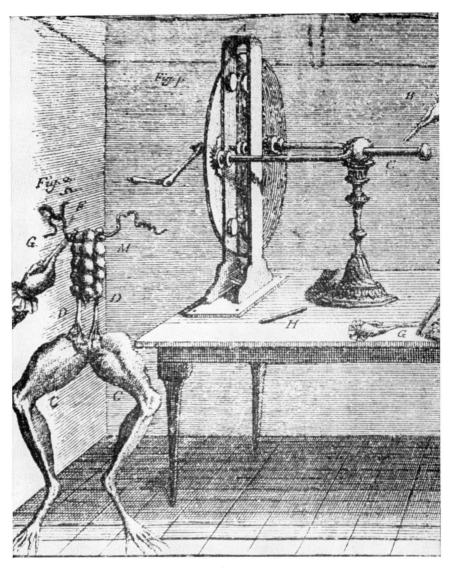

GALVANI'S EXPERIMENT, *which led to the discovery of electric currents. Electricity from his static-electricity machine made the frog's leg twitch; he found that touching the nerve with two different metals also caused the leg to twitch.*

A JET PLANE *that flew at a record altitude of 103,395 feet.*

THE X-15 ROCKET PLANE, *which set a speed record of 2,150 miles per hour and flew to an altitude of 131,500 feet.*

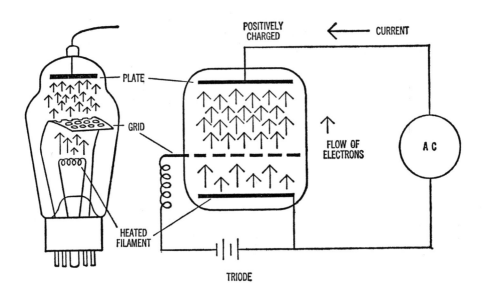

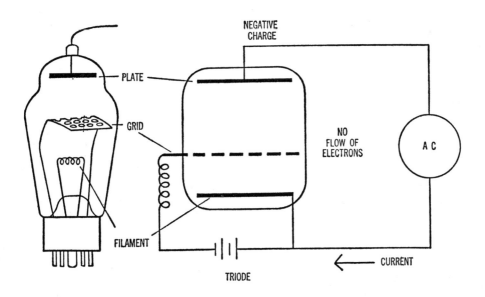

PRINCIPLE OF THE TRIODE.

339

sound wave was high in amplitude, the carrier wave was made low in frequency, and vice versa. Frequency modulation (FM) virtually eliminated static, and FM radio came into popularity after World War II for programs of serious music. Unfortunately FM will work only for carrier waves of high frequency, and these cannot be transmitted much beyond the horizon. The area of reception for a given FM transmitting station is therefore limited.

TELEVISION was an inevitable sequel to radio, just as talking movies were to the silents. The technical forerunner of television was the transmission of pictures by wire. This entailed translating a picture into an electric current. A narrow beam of light passed through the picture on a photographic film to a phototube behind. Where the film was comparatively opaque, a weak current was generated in the phototube; where it was clearer, a large current was formed. The beam of light swiftly "scanned" the picture from left to right line by line and produced a varying current representing the entire picture. The current was sent over wires and at the destination reproduced the picture on film by a reverse process. Such "wirephotos" were transmitted between London and Paris as early as 1907.

Television is the transmission of a "movie" instead of still photographs — either "live" or from a film. The transmission must be extremely fast, which means that the action must be scanned very rapidly. The light-dark pattern of the image is converted into a pattern of electrical impulses by means of a camera using, in place of film, a coating of metal which emits electrons when light strikes it.

The first practical television camera was the "iconoscope," patented in 1938 by the Russian-born American inventor Vladimir Kosma Zworykin. In the iconoscope the rear of the camera is coated with a large number of tiny cesium-silver droplets. Each emits electrons as the light beam scans across it, in proportion to the brightness of the light. The iconoscope was later replaced by the "image orthicon" — a refinement in which the cesium-silver screen is thin enough so that the emitted electrons can be sent forward to strike a thin glass plate which emits more electrons. This "amplification" increases the sensitivity of the camera to light, so that strong lighting is not necessary.

The television receiver is a variety of cathode-ray tube. A stream of electrons shot from a filament ("electron-gun") strikes a screen coated with a fluorescent substance, which glows in proportion to the intensity of the electron stream. Pairs of electrodes controlling the direction of the stream cause it to sweep across the screen from left to right in a series of hundreds of horizontal lines, each slightly below the one before, and the entire "painting" of a picture on the screen in this fashion is completed in a thirtieth of a second. The beam goes on painting successive pictures at the rate of 30 per second. At no instant of time is there more than one dot on the screen (bright or dark, as the case may be), yet, thanks to the persistence of vision, we see not only complete pictures but an uninterrupted sequence of movement and action.

Experimental television was broadcast in the 1920's, but television did not become practical in the commercial sense until 1947. Since then it has virtually taken over the field of entertainment.

In the mid-1950's two refinements were added. By the use of three types of fluorescent materials on the television screen, designed to react to the beam in red, blue, and green colors, color television was introduced. And "video tape," a type of recording similar to the sound track on a movie film, made it possible to reproduce recorded programs or events with better quality than could be obtained from motion-picture film.

THE VACUUM TUBE, the heart of all the electronic devices, eventually became a limiting factor. Usually the components of a device are steadily improved in efficiency as time goes on — which means that they are stepped up in power and flexibility and reduced in size and mass. (This is sometimes called "miniaturization.") But the vacuum tube became a bottleneck in the road to miniaturization. And then, quite by accident, an unexpected solution turned up.

In the 1940's several scientists at the Bell Telephone Laboratories grew interested in the substances known as "semi-conductors." These substances, such as silicon and germanium, conduct electricity only moderately well, and the problem was to find out how they conducted it. The Bell Lab investigators discovered that such conductivity as they possessed was due to traces of impurities mixed with the element in question.

Let's consider a crystal of pure germanium. Each atom has four electrons in its outermost shell, and in the regular array of atoms in the crystal each of the four electrons pairs up with an electron of a neighboring germanium atom, so that all the electrons are paired in stable bonds. If, however, a little bit of arsenic is introduced into this contented family of atoms, the picture grows complicated. Arsenic has five electrons in its outermost shell. An arsenic atom taking the place of a germanium atom in the crystal will be able to pair four of its five electrons with the neighboring germanium atoms, but the fifth can find no electron to pair with. It is left "on the loose." Now if an electric voltage is applied to this crystal, the loose electron will wander in the direction of the positive electrode. It will not move as freely as would electrons in a conducting metal, but the crystal will conduct electricity better than a non-conductor such as sulfur or glass.

This is not very startling, but now we come to a case which is somewhat more odd. Let us add a bit of boron, instead of arsenic, to the germanium. The boron atom has only three electrons in its outermost shell. These three can pair up with the electrons of three neighboring germanium atoms. But what happens to the electron of the boron atom's fourth germanium neighbor? That electron is paired with a "hole!" The word "hole" is used advisedly, because this site, where the electron would find a partner in a pure germanium crystal, does in fact behave like a vacancy. If a voltage is applied to the boron-contaminated crystal, the next neighboring electron, attracted toward the positive electrode, will move into the hole. In doing so, it leaves a hole where it was, and the electron next farther away from the positive electrode moves into *that* hole. And so the hole, in effect, travels steadily toward the negative electrode, moving exactly like an electron but in the opposite direction. In short, it has become a conveyor of electric current.

To work well, the crystal must be almost perfectly pure with just the right amount of the specified impurity (*i.e.*, arsenic or boron).

The germanium-arsenic semi-conductor, with a wandering electron, is said to be "*n*-type" — *n* for "negative." The germanium-boron semi-conductor, with a wandering hole which acts as if it were positively charged, is "*p*-type" — *p* for "positive."

Now suppose we make a germanium crystal with one half *p*-type and the other half *n*-type. If we connect the *n*-type side to a negative electrode and the *p*-type side to a positive electrode, the electrons on the *n*-type side will move across the crystal toward the positive electrode, while the holes on the *p*-type side will travel in the opposite direction toward the negative electrode. Thus a current flows through the crystal. Now let us reverse the situation — that is, connect the *n*-type side to the positive electrode and the *p*-type to the negative electrode. This time the electrons of the *n* side travel toward the positive electrode — which is to say, away from the *p* side — and the holes of the *p* side similarly move in the direction away from the *n* side. As a result, the border regions at the junction between the *n* and *p* sides lose their free electrons and holes. This amounts to a break in the circuit, and no current flows.

In short, we now have a setup that can act as a rectifier. If we hook up an alternating current to this dual crystal, the crystal will pass the current in one direction but not in the other. Therefore alternating current will be converted to direct current. The crystal serves as a diode, just as a vacuum tube (or "valve") does.

With this device, electronics returned full circle to the first type of rectifier used for radio — namely, the crystal with a "cat's whisker." But the new type of crystal was far more effective and versatile. And it had impressive advantages over the vacuum tube. It was lighter, much less bulky, stronger, invulnerable to shocks, and it did not heat up — all of which gave it a much longer life than the tube. The new device was named, at the suggestion of John R. Pierce of

UNBIASED P-N JUNCTION

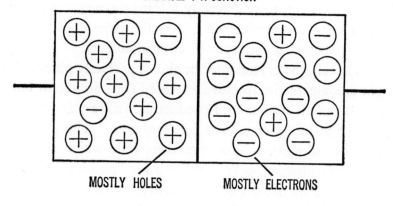

MOSTLY HOLES   MOSTLY ELECTRONS

ELECTRONS   HOLES

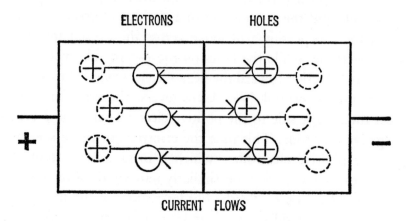

CURRENT FLOWS

P-TYPE   N-TYPE

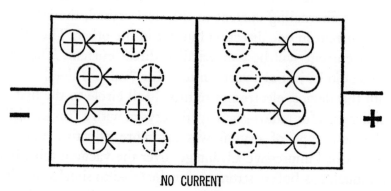

NO CURRENT

PRINCIPLE OF THE JUNCTION TRANSISTOR.

the Bell Lab, the "transistor," because it *trans*ferred a signal across a re*sistor*.

In 1948 William Shockley, Walter H. Brattain, and John Bardeen at the Bell Lab went on to produce a transistor which could act as an amplifier. This was a germanium crystal with a thin *p*-type section sandwiched between two *n*-type ends. It was in effect a triode with the equivalent of a grid between the filament and the plate. By controlling the positive charge in the *p*-type center, holes could be sent across the junctions in such a manner as to control the electron flow. Furthermore, a small variation in the current of the *p*-type center would cause a large variation in the current across the semi-conductor system. The semi-conductor triode could thus serve as an amplifier, just as a vacuum tube triode did. Shockley and his co-workers Brattain and Bardeen received the Nobel Prize in physics in 1956.

By 1953 tiny transistors were being used in hearing-aids, making them so small that they could be fitted inside the ear. In short order the transistor — steadily developed so that it could handle higher frequencies, resist heat, and be reduced to minuscule size — took over many functions of the vacuum tube. Perhaps its most notable use is in electronic computers, which it has greatly reduced in size and improved in reliability. We are, in a way, entering a "transistor age."

CHAPTER

9

THE
REACTOR

FISSION

THE RAPID ADVANCES in technology in the twentieth century have been bought at the expense of a stupendous increase in our consumption of the earth's energy resources. As the underdeveloped nations, with their billions of people, join the already industrialized countries in high living, the rate of consumption of fuel will jump even more spectacularly. Where will mankind find the energy supplies needed to support his civilization?

We have already seen a large part of the earth's timber disappear. Wood was man's first fuel. By the beginning of the Christian era, much of Greece, northern Africa, and the Near East had been ruthlessly deforested, partly for fuel, partly to clear the land for animal herding and agriculture. The uncontrolled felling of the forests was a double-barreled disaster. Not only did it destroy the wood supply, but the drastic uncovering of the land meant a more or less permanent destruction of fertility. Most of these ancient regions, which once supported man's most advanced cultures, are sterile and unproductive now, populated by a ground-down and backward people.

The Middle Ages saw the gradual deforestation of western Europe, and modern times have seen the much more rapid deforestation of the North American continent. Almost no great stands of virgin timber remain in the world's temperate zones except in Canada and Siberia.

It seems unlikely that man will ever be able to get along without wood. Building lumber and paper will always be necessities.

As for fuel, coal and oil have taken wood's place. But these "fossil fuels" cannot be replaced once they are used up. With respect to coal and oil, man is living on his capital at an extravagant rate.

The oil, particularly, is going fast. The world is now burning a million barrels of oil each hour, and the rate of consumption is rising rapidly. Although well over a trillion barrels remain in the earth, it is estimated that by 1980 oil production will reach its peak and begin to decline. The coal reserve is much larger, but not all of it is easy to mine. By the twenty-fifth century or sooner, coal may become an expensive commodity.

We can expect new finds. Perhaps surprises in the way of coal and oil await us in Australia, in the Sahara, even in Antarctica. Moreover, improvements in technology may make it economical to exploit thinner and deeper coal seams, to plunge more and more deeply for oil, and to extract oil from oil shale and from sub-sea reserves.

No doubt we shall also find ways to use our fuel more efficiently. The process of burning fuel to produce heat to convert water to steam to drive a generator to create electricity wastes a good deal of energy along the way. Most of these losses could be side-stepped if heat could be converted directly into electricity. A hopeful current development is the "thermoelectric cell." It employs a transistor arrangement (see Chapter 8). Heating one end of a semi-conductor

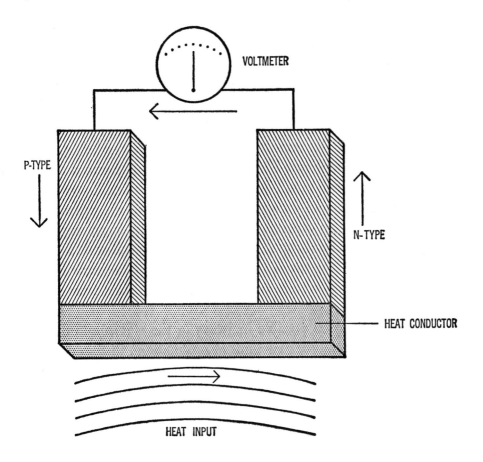

P-TYPE

VOLTMETER

N-TYPE

HEAT CONDUCTOR

HEAT INPUT

THE THERMOELECTRIC CELL. *Heating the conductor causes elec-trons to flow toward the cold end of the* n-*type semi-conductor and from the cold to the warm region of the* p-*type. If a circuit is formed, current flows in the direction shown by the arrows. Thus heat is converted to electrical energy.*

creates an electric potential in the material: in a *p*-type semi-conduc-tor the cold end becomes negative; in an *n*-type it becomes positive. Now if these two types of semi-conductors are joined in a U-shaped structure, with the *n*-*p* junction at the bottom of the U, heating the bottom will cause the upper end of the *p* branch to gain a negative charge and the upper end of the *n* branch to acquire a positive charge. As a result current will flow from one end to the other, and it will be generated as long as the temperature difference is maintained.

The over-all efficiency of such a cell has not yet reached that of a steam plant; the cell so far converts only 10 per cent of the applied heat to electricity, whereas 30 to 40 per cent of the heat of steam is converted. But improvements in efficiency can be expected. In 1959 the Westinghouse Electric Corporation announced a thermoelectric cell which could deliver three times as much power per pound as those previously constructed. In any case, the thermoelectric cell, requiring no expensive generator or bulky steam engine, is portable and could be set up in isolated areas as a small-scale supplier of electricity. All it needs as an energy source is a kerosene heater. Such devices are reported to be used routinely in rural areas of the Soviet Union.

Notwithstanding all possible increases in the efficiency of using fuel and the likelihood of new finds of coal and oil, these sources of energy are definitely limited. The day will come, and not far in the future, when neither coal nor oil can serve as an important large-scale energy source.

And yet man's energy needs will continue and even be far larger than those of today. What's to be done?

ONE POSSIBILITY is to make increasing use of renewable energy sources: to live on the earth's energy income rather than its capital. Wood can be such a resource if forests are grown and harvested as a crop, though wood alone could not come anywhere near meeting all our energy needs. We could also make much more use of windpower and waterpower, though these again could never be more than subsidiary sources of energy. The same must be said about certain other potential sources of energy in the earth, such as tapping the heat of the interior (*e.g.*, in hot springs) or harnessing the ocean tides.

Far more important, for the long run, is the possibility of directly tapping some of the vast energy pouring on the earth from the sun. Already schemes are being tested for heating houses with sunlight; solar furnaces have been built; and so on. At the moment the most promising device under development is the "solar battery." This, like the thermoelectric cell, makes use of the endlessly versatile transistor.

As developed by the Bell Telephone Laboratories, the solar battery is a flat sandwich of n-type and p-type semi-conductors. Sunlight striking the plate knocks some electrons out of place. The transistor is connected, as an ordinary battery would be, in an electric circuit. The freed electrons move toward the positive pole and holes move toward the negative pole, thus constituting a current. The solar

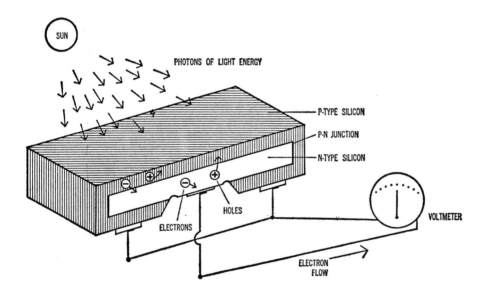

A SOLAR BATTERY CELL. *Sunlight striking the thin wafer frees electrons, thus forming electron-hole pairs. The p-n junction acts as a barrier, or electric field, separating electrons from holes. A potential difference therefore develops across the junction, and current then flows through the wire circuit.*

351

battery can develop electric potentials of up to half a volt, and up to nine watts of power, from each square foot exposed to the sun. This is not much, but the beauty of the solar battery is that it has no liquids, no corrosive chemicals, no moving parts — it just keeps on generating electricity indefinitely merely by lying in the sun.

The artificial satellite Vanguard I, launched by the United States on March 17, 1958, was the first to be equipped with a solar battery to power its radio signals. Those signals are still being heard after years of operation, and should continue to be heard for years into the future.

The amount of energy falling upon one acre of a generally sunny area of the earth is 9,400,000 kilowatt-hours per year. If substantial areas in the earth's desert regions, such as Death Valley and the Sahara, were covered with solar batteries and electricity-storing devices, they could provide the world with its electricity needs for an indefinite time — for as long, in fact, as the human race is likely to endure, even if it does not commit suicide.

BUT THE TAPPING OF SOLAR ENERGY, it seems, is not likely to be achieved on any great scale in this generation or the next. Fortunately we have an immense source of energy, here on the earth, which can tide us over for hundreds of years after we run out of inexpensive coal and oil. It is the energy in the atomic nucleus.

Nuclear energy is commmonly called "atomic energy," but that is a misnomer. Strictly speaking, atomic energy is the energy yielded by chemical reactions, such as the burning of coal and oil, because they involve the behavior of the atom as a whole. The energy released by changes in the nucleus is of a totally different kind and vastly greater in magnitude.

Soon after the discovery of the neutron by Chadwick in 1932, physicists realized that they had a wonderful key for unlocking the atomic nucleus. Since it had no electric charge, the neutron could easily penetrate the charged nucleus. Physicists immediately began to bombard various nuclei with neutrons to see what nuclear reactions they could bring about, and among the most ardent investigators with this new tool was Enrico Fermi of Italy.

Fermi and his associates discovered that they got better results if they slowed down the neutrons by passing them through water or paraffin first. Bouncing off protons in the water or paraffin, the neutrons are slowed just as a billiard ball is by hitting other billiard balls. When a neutron is reduced to "thermal" speed (the normal speed of motion of atoms), it has a greater chance of being absorbed by a nucleus, because it remains in the vicinity of the nucleus longer. Another way of looking at it is to consider that the wavelength of the wave associated with the neutron is longer, for the wavelength is inversely proportional to the momentum of the particle. As the neutron slows down, its wavelength increases. To put it metaphorically, the neutron grows fuzzier and takes up more volume. It therefore hits a nucleus more easily, just as a bowling ball has more chance of hitting a ten-pin than a golf ball would have.

The probability that a given species of nucleus will capture a neutron is called its "cross-section." This term, metaphorically, pictures the nucleus as a target of a particular size. It is easier to hit the side of a barn with a baseball than it is to hit a foot-wide board at the same distance. The cross-sections of nuclei under neutron bombardment are reckoned in trillion-trillionths of a square centimeter (10^{-24} square centimeter). That unit, in fact, was named a "barn" by physicists.

When a nucleus absorbs a neutron, its atomic number is unchanged (because the charge of the nucleus remains the same), but its mass number goes up by one unit. Hydrogen 1 becomes hydrogen 2, oxygen 17 becomes oxygen 18, and so on. The energy delivered to the nucleus by the neutron as it enters may "excite" the nucleus—that is, increase its energy content. This surplus energy is then emitted as a gamma ray.

The new nucleus often is unstable. For example, when aluminum 27 takes in a neutron and becomes aluminum 28, one of the neutrons in the new nucleus soon changes to a proton (by emitting an electron). This increase in the positive charge of the nucleus transforms the aluminum (atomic number 13) to silicon (atomic number 14).

Now, because neutron bombardment is an easy way of converting an element to the next higher one, Fermi decided to bombard uranium to see if he could form an artificial element — number 93. In the products of the bombardment of uranium he and his co-workers did find signs of new radioactive substances. They thought they had made element 93, and called it "uranium X." But how could the new element be identified positively? What sort of chemical properties should it have?

Well, element 93, it was thought, should fall under rhenium in the periodic table, so it ought to be chemically similar to rhenium. (Actually, though no one realized it at the time, element 93 belonged in a new rare-earth series, which meant that it would resemble uranium, not rhenium — see Chapter 5. Thus the search for its identification got off on the wrong foot entirely.) If it was like rhenium, perhaps the tiny amount of "element 93" created might be identified by mixing the products of the neutron bombardment with rhenium and then separating out the rhenium by chemical methods. The rhenium would act as a "carrier," bringing out the chemically similar "element 93" with it. If the rhenium proved to have radioactivity attached to it, this would indicate the presence of element 93.

The German physicist Otto Hahn and the Austrian physicist Lise Meitner, working together in Berlin, pursued this line of experiment. Element 93 failed to show up with the rhenium. Hahn and Meitner then went on to try to find out whether the neutron bombardment had transformed uranium into other elements near it in the periodic table. At this point, in 1938, Germany occupied Austria and Miss Meitner, who until then, as an Austrian national, had been safe despite the fact that she was Jewish, was forced to flee from Hitler's Germany to the safety of Stockholm. Hahn continued his work with the German physicist Fritz Strassmann.

Several months later Hahn and Strassmann found that barium, when added to the bombarded uranium, carried off some radioactivity. They decided that this radioactivity must belong to radium,

FISSION OF A URANIUM ATOM. *The white streak in the middle of this photographic plate represents the tracks of the two atoms flying apart from the central point where the uranium atom split in two. The plate was soaked in a uranium compound and bombarded with neutrons, which produced the fission caught in this picture. The other white dots are randomly developed silver grains. The picture was made in the Eastman Kodak Research Laboratories.*

RADIOACTIVITY MADE VISIBLE. *On the tray is some tantalum made radioactive in the Brookhaven reactor; the glowing material is shielded here under several feet of water. The radioactive tantalum will be placed in the pipe shown and then transferred to a large lead container for use as a 1,000-curie source of radioactivity for industrial purposes.*

DRAWING OF THE FIRST CHAIN REACTOR, *built under the Chicago football stadium.*

THE CHICAGO REACTOR UNDER CONSTRUCTION. *This was the only photograph made during the building of the reactor. The rods in the holes are uranium, and the reactor's nineteenth layer, consisting of solid graphite blocks, is in process of being laid on.*

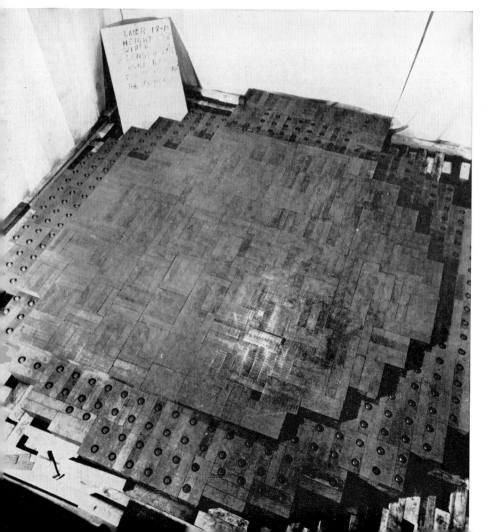

THE FIRST HYDROGEN BOMB, *exploded at Bikini on March 1, 1954.*

THE REACTOR CORE *of one of the first nuclear power plants, built in Shippingport, Pennsylvania.*

the element below barium in the periodic table. The conclusion was, then, that the neutron bombardment of uranium changed some of it to radium.

But this radium turned out to be peculiar stuff. Try as they would, Hahn and Strassmann could not separate it from the barium. In France, Irène Joliot-Curie and her co-worker P. Savitch undertook a similar task and also failed.

And then Meitner, the refugee in Scandinavia, boldly cut through the riddle. In a letter published in the British journal *Nature* in January of 1939, she suggested that the "radium" could not be separated from the barium because no radium was there. The supposed radium was actually radioactive barium: it was barium that had been formed in the neutron bombardment of uranium. This radioactive barium decayed by emitting a beta particle and formed lanthanum. (Hahn and Strassmann had found that ordinary lanthanum added to the products brought out some radioactivity which they assigned to actinium; actually it was radioactive lanthanum.)

But how could barium be formed from uranium? Barium was only a middleweight atom. No known process of radioactive decay could transform a heavy element into one only about half its weight. Meitner made so bold as to suggest that the uranium nucleus had split in two. The absorption of a neutron had caused it to undergo "fission." The two elements into which it had split, she said, were barium and element 43, the element above rhenium in the periodic table. A nucleus of barium and one of element 43 (later named technetium) would make up a nucleus of uranium.

Niels Bohr, attending a conference on theoretical physics in Washington the same month that Meitner's letter was published in *Nature*, told physicists what he had heard of the fission suggestion in Denmark. In high excitement, the physicists went back to their laboratories to test the hypothesis, and within a month half a dozen experimental confirmations were announced.

And so began the work that led to the most terrible weapon of destruction ever devised.

355

THE ATOM BOMB

THE FISSION REACTION released an unusual amount of energy, vastly more than ordinary radioactivity did. But it was not solely the additional energy that made fission so portentous a phenomenon. More important was the fact that it released two or three neutrons. Within two months after the Meitner letter, the awesome possibility of a "nuclear chain reaction" had occurred to a number of physicists.

The expression "chain reaction" has acquired an exotic meaning, but actually it is a very common phenomenon. The burning of a piece of paper is a chain reaction. A match supplies the heat required to start it, and once the burning has begun, this supplies the very agent, heat, needed to maintain and spread the flame. Burning brings about more burning on an ever-expanding scale.

That is exactly what happens in a nuclear chain reaction. One neutron fissions a uranium atom; this releases two neutrons which can produce two fissions which release four neutrons which can produce four fissions, and so on. The first atom to fission yields 200 Mev of energy; the next step yields 400 Mev, the next 800 Mev, the next 1,600 Mev, etc. Since the successive stages take place at intervals of about a millionth of a second, you can see that within a single second a staggering amount of energy will be released. The fission of one ounce of uranium produces as much energy as the burning of 90 tons of coal or of 2,000 gallons of fuel oil. Peacefully used, uranium fission could relieve all our immediate worries about vanishing fossil fuels and man's mounting consumption of energy.

But the discovery of fission came just before the world was plunged into an all-out war. The fissioning of an ounce of uranium, physicists estimated, would yield as much explosive power as 600 tons of TNT. The thought of the consequences of a war fought with such weapons was horrible, but the thought of a world in which Nazi Germany laid its hands on such an explosive before the Allies did was even more horrible.

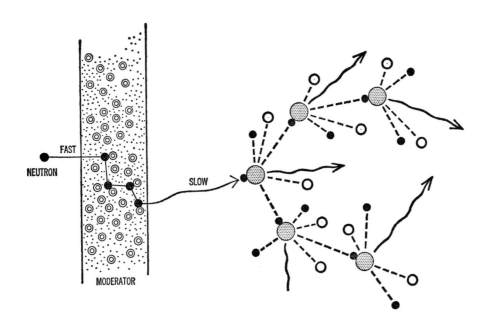

NUCLEAR CHAIN REACTION IN URANIUM. *The gray circles are ura-nium nuclei, the black dots neutrons, the wavy arrows gamma rays, and the small circles fission fragments.*

In the summer of 1939 Leo Szilard and other physicists prevailed upon the gentle and pacific Einstein to write a letter to President Franklin Delano Roosevelt, pointing out the potentialities of uranium fission and suggesting that every effort be made to develop such a weapon before the Nazis managed to do so. Although it was difficult at first for civilians or the military to take the scientists' astounding statements seriously, eventually the United States Government organized the huge "Manhattan Engineering Project" to make an atom bomb.

As was to be expected, practice did not by any means follow easily from theory. It took a bit of doing to arrange a uranium chain reaction. In the first place, you had to have a substantial amount

357

of uranium, refined to extreme purity so that neutrons would not be wasted in absorption by impurities. Uranium is a rather common element in the earth's crust, averaging about two grams per ton of rock, which makes it 400 times as common as gold. But it is well spread out, and there are few places in the world where it occurs in rich ores or even in reasonable concentration. Furthermore, before 1939 uranium had had almost no uses, and no methods for its purification had been worked out. Less than an ounce of uranium metal had been produced in the United States.

The laboratories at Iowa State College, under the leadership of F. H. Spedding, went to work on the problem of purification and in 1942 began to produce reasonably pure uranium metal.

That, however, was only a first step. Now the uranium itself had to be broken down to separate out its more fissionable fraction. The isotope uranium 238 has an even number of protons (92) and an even number of neutrons (146). Nuclei with even numbers of nucleons are more stable than those with odd numbers. The other isotope in natural uranium — uranium 235 — has an odd number of neutrons (143). Bohr therefore predicted that it would fission more readily than uranium 238. This was quickly found to be true. U-238 fissions only when struck by fast neutrons of more than a certain energy, but U-235 would undergo fission upon absorbing neutrons of any energy, all the way down to simple thermal neutrons.

The trouble was that in purified natural uranium only one atom in 140 is U-235, the rest being U-238. This meant that most of the neutrons released by fissions of U-235 would be captured by U-238 atoms without producing fission. Even if the uranium was bombarded with neutrons fast enough to split U-238, the neutrons released by the fissioning U-238 would not be energetic enough to carry on a chain reaction in the remaining atoms of this more common isotope. In other words, the presence of U-238 would cause the chain reaction to damp and die. It would be like trying to burn wet leaves.

There was nothing for it, then, but to try to separate the U-235 from the U-238, or at least remove enough U-238 to effect a substantial enrichment of the U-235 content in the mixture. The physicists attacked this problem by several methods, each of them offering only thin prospects of success. The one that eventually worked out best was "gaseous diffusion."

The uranium-235 atom is 1.3 per cent less massive than the uranium-238 atom. Consequently if the atoms were in the form of a gas, the U-235 atoms would move about slightly faster than the U-238 atoms. This meant they might be separated by reason of their faster diffusion through a series of filtering barriers. But first uranium had to be converted to a gas. About the only way to get it in this form was to combine it with fluorine and make uranium hexafluoride, a volatile liquid composed of one uranium atom and six fluorine atoms. In this compound a molecule containing U-235 would be less than 1 per cent lighter than one containing U-238 — but that difference proved to be sufficient to make the method work.

The uranium hexafluoride gas was forced through porous barriers under pressure. At each barrier the molecules containing U-235 got through a bit faster, on the average, and so with every passage through the successive barriers the advantage in favor of U-235 grew. To obtain sizable amounts of almost pure uranium-235 hexafluoride required thousands of barriers, but well-enriched concentrations of U-235 could be achieved with a much smaller number of barriers.

By 1942 it was reasonably certain that the gaseous diffusion method (and one or two others) could produce "enriched uranium" in quantity, and separation plants were built at Oak Ridge, Tenn.

Meanwhile the physicists were calculating the "critical size" that would be needed to maintain a chain reaction in a lump of enriched uranium. If the lump was small, too many neutrons would escape from its surface before being absorbed by U-235 atoms. To minimize this loss by leakage, the volume of the lump had to be large in proportion to its surface. At a certain "critical size," enough neutrons would be intercepted by U-235 atoms to keep a chain reaction going.

The physicists also found a way to make efficient use of the available neutrons. "Thermal" (*i.e.*, slow) neutrons, as I have mentioned, are more readily absorbed by uranium 235 than fast ones are. The experimenters therefore used a "moderator" to slow the neutrons from the rather high speeds they had on emerging from the fission reaction. Ordinary water would have been an excellent slowing agent, but unfortunately the nuclei of ordinary hydrogen hungrily snap up neutrons. Deuterium (hydrogen 2) fills the bill much better; it has practically no tendency to absorb neutrons. Consequently the fission experimenters became very interested in preparing supplies of heavy water. (There is a thrilling story of Joliot-Curie managing to smuggle France's supply of heavy water out of the country ahead of the invading Nazis in 1940.) Still, heavy water had drawbacks: it might boil away when the chain reaction got hot, and it would corrode the uranium. The scientists seeking to create a chain-reacting system in the Manhattan Project decided to use carbon, in the form of very pure graphite, as the moderator.

Now let us imagine a chain reaction. We start things off by sending a triggering stream of neutrons into the assembly of moderator and enriched uranium. A number of uranium-235 atoms undergo fission, releasing neutrons which go on to hit other uranium-235 atoms. They in turn fission and turn loose more neutrons. Some neutrons will be absorbed by atoms other than uranium 235; some will escape from the pile altogether. But if from each fission one neutron, and exactly one, takes effect in producing another fission, then the chain reaction will be self-sustaining. If the "multiplication factor" is more than one, even very slightly more (*e.g.*, 1.001), the chain reaction will rapidly build up to an explosion. This is good for bomb purposes but not for experimental purposes. Some device had to be worked out to control the rate of fissions. That could be done by sliding in rods of a substance such as cadmium, which has a high cross-section for neutron capture. The chain reaction develops so rapidly that the damping cadmium rods could not be slid in fast enough, were it not for the fortunate fact that the fissioning uranium atoms do not emit all their neutrons instantly. About one neutron in 150 is delayed a few minutes in emerging from the fission fragment that emits it. When the multiplication factor is only slightly above one, this delay is sufficient to give time for applying the controls.

IN 1941, EXPERIMENTS WERE CONDUCTED with uranium-graphite mixtures, and enough information was gathered to lead physicists to decide that even without enriched uranium, a chain reaction might be set up if only the lump of uranium were made large enough. Columbia University was then working with eight-foot and even larger cubes of material, containing seven tons or more of uranium oxide. (I was a student at Columbia at the time and heard rumors of the uranium experiments. When I mentioned these casually to Professor Harold Urey, who was teaching me thermodynamics, he snapped at me with a vehemence that surprised me, but I gathered enough of my wits together to keep my mouth shut thereafter, although I drew my own private conclusions and was somewhat less than surprised when the news of the atomic bomb broke in 1945.)

The Manhattan Project in 1942 set out to build a uranium chain-reactor of critical size at the University of Chicago. By that time some six tons of pure uranium were available; this was eked out with uranium oxide. Alternate layers of uranium and graphite were laid down one on the other, with holes through them for insertion of the cadmium control rods. The structure was called a "pile" — a non-committal code name which did not give away its function. (During World War I the newly designed armored vehicles on caterpillar treads were referred to as "tanks" for the same purpose of secrecy. The name "tank" stuck, but "atomic pile" fortunately gave way eventually to the more descriptive name "nuclear reactor.")

The Chicago pile, built under the football stadium, measured 30 feet wide, 32 feet long and 21½ feet high. It weighed 1,400 tons and contained 52 tons of uranium, as metal and oxide. On December 2, 1942, the cadmium control rods were slowly pulled out. At 3:45 P.M. the multiplication factor reached one — a self-sustaining fission reaction was under way. At that moment mankind (without knowing it) entered the "atomic age."

The physicist in charge was Enrico Fermi (justly so, for he had started the whole thing by his bombardment of uranium with neutrons in 1934). A telegram announcing the success was immediately sent to Washington, in these words: "The Italian navigator has entered the new world." The Office of Scientific Research and Development wired back: "How were the natives?" and the answer came at once, "Very friendly."

It is curious that the first Italian navigator discovered one new world in 1492, and the second discovered another in 1942; those who value the mystic interplay of numbers make much of this coincidence.

MEANWHILE ANOTHER FISSIONABLE FUEL had turned up. Uranium 238, upon absorbing a thermal neutron, forms uranium 239, which breaks down quickly to neptunium 239, which in turn breaks down almost as quickly to plutonium 239.

Now the plutonium 239 nucleus has an odd number of neutrons (145) and is more complex than uranium 235, so it should be highly unstable. It seemed a reasonable guess that plutonium, like uranium 235, might undergo fission with thermal neutrons. In 1941 this was confirmed experimentally. Still uncertain whether the preparation of uranium 235 would prove practical, the physicists decided to hedge their bets by trying to make plutonium in quantity.

Special reactors were built in 1943 at Oak Ridge and at Hanford, in the State of Washington, for the purpose of manufacturing plutonium. These reactors were a great advance over the first pile in Chicago. For one thing, the new reactors were designed so that the uranium could be removed from the pile periodically. The plutonium produced could be separated from the uranium by chemical methods, and the fission products, some of them strong neutron absorbers, could be removed. Secondly, the new reactors were water-cooled to prevent overheating. (The Chicago pile could operate only for short periods, because it was cooled merely by air.)

By 1945 enough purified uranium 235 and plutonium 239 was available for the construction of bombs.

For bomb purposes it was desirable to make the nuclear chain reaction mount as rapidly as possible. This called for making the reaction go with fast neutrons, to shorten the intervals between fissions, so the moderator was omitted. The bomb was also enclosed in a massive casing to hold the uranium together long enough for a large proportion of it to fission.

Since a critical mass of fissionable material would explode spontaneously (sparked by stray neutrons from the air), the bomb fuel was divided into two or more sections. The triggering mechanism was an ordinary explosive (TNT?) which drove these sections together when the bomb was to be detonated. One arrangement was called "the thin man" — a tube with two pieces of uranium 235 at its opposite ends. Another, "the fat man," had the form of a ball in which a shell composed of fissionable material was "imploded" toward the center, making a dense critical mass held together momentarily by the force of the implosion.

To test such a device on a minor scale was impossible. The bomb had to be above critical size or nothing. Consequently the first test was the explosion of a full-scale fission bomb. On July 16, 1945, at Alamogordo, N. M., a bomb was exploded with truly horrifying effect. The physicist I. I. Rabi, on being asked later what he had witnessed, is reported to have said mournfully, "I can't tell you, but don't expect to die a natural death." (It is only fair to add that the gentleman so addressed by Rabi did die a natural death some years later.)

Two more fission bombs were prepared. One was dropped on Hiroshima on August 6, 1945, the second on Nagasaki a few days later. With the bombing of Hiroshima, the "atomic age," already nearly three years old, broke on the consciousness of the world.

For four years after that, Americans lived under the delusion that there was an "atom-bomb secret" which could be kept from other nations forever if only security measures were made tight enough. Actually the facts and theories of nuclear fission had been matters of public record since 1939, and the Soviet Union was fully engaged in research on the subject in 1940. If World War II had not occupied her lesser resources to a far greater extent than it occupied the greater resources of the uninvaded United States, the U.S.S.R. might have made an atomic bomb by 1945 as we did. As it was, the Soviet Union exploded her first atomic bomb on September 22, 1949, to the dismay and unnecessary amazement of most Americans. On October 3, 1952, Great Britain became the third atomic power by exploding a test bomb, and on February 13, 1960, France joined the "club" as the fourth member, setting off an atomic bomb in the Sahara.

MEANWHILE THE FISSION BOMB had been reduced to triviality. Man had succeeded in setting off another energetic nuclear reaction which made superbombs possible.

In the fission of uranium, 0.1 per cent of the mass of the uranium atom is converted to energy. But in the fusion of hydrogen atoms to form helium, fully 0.5 per cent of their mass is converted to energy. At temperatures in the millions of degrees, the energy of protons is high enough to allow them to fuse. Thus two protons may unite and, after emitting a positron and a neutrino (a process which converts one of the protons to a neutron) become a deuterium nucleus. A deuterium nucleus may then fuse with a proton to form a tritium nucleus, which can fuse with still another proton to form helium 4. Or deuterium and tritium nuclei will combine in various ways to form helium 4.

Because such nuclear reactions take place only under the stimulus of high temperatures, they are referred to as "thermonuclear reactions." In the 1930's the one place where the necessary temperatures were believed to exist was at the center of stars. In 1938 the German-born physicist Hans Albrecht Bethe (who had left Hitler's Germany for the United States in 1935) proposed that fusion reactions were responsible for the energy that the stars radiated. It was the first completely satisfactory explanation of stellar energy since Helmholtz had raised the question nearly a century earlier.

Now the uranium fission bomb provided the necessary temperatures on the earth. It could serve as a match hot enough to ignite a fusion chain reaction in hydrogen. For a while it looked very doubtful that the reaction could actually be made to work in the form of a bomb. For one thing, the hydrogen fuel had to be condensed to a dense mass, which meant that it had to be liquefied and kept at a temperature only a few degrees above absolute zero. In other words, what would be exploded would be a massive refrigerator. Furthermore, even assuming a hydrogen bomb could be made, what purpose would it serve? The fission bomb was already devastating enough to knock out cities; a hydrogen bomb would merely pile on destruction and wipe out whole civilian populations.

Nevertheless, despite the unappetizing prospects, the United States and the Soviet Union felt compelled to go on with it. The United States Atomic Energy Commission proceeded to produce some tritium fuel, set up a 65-ton fission-fusion contraption on a coral atoll in the Pacific, and on November 1, 1952, produced the first thermonuclear explosion on our planet. It fulfilled all the ominous predictions: the explosion yielded the equivalent of three million tons of TNT (three "megatons") — 150 times the energy of the Hiroshima bomb. The blast wiped out the atoll.

The Russians were not far behind: on August 12, 1953, they also produced a successful thermonuclear explosion.

Meanwhile a scheme for generating a thermonuclear chain reaction in a simpler way and packing it into a portable bomb had been conceived. The key to this reaction was the element lithium. When the isotope lithium 6 absorbs a neutron, it splits into nuclei of helium and tritium, giving forth 4.8 Mev of energy in the process. Suppose, then, that a compound of lithium and hydrogen (in the form of the heavy isotope deuterium) is used as the fuel. This compound is a solid, so there is no need for refrigeration to condense the fuel. A fission trigger would provide neutrons to split the lithium. And the heat of the explosion would cause the fusion of the deuterium present in the compound and of the tritium produced by the splitting of lithium. In other words, several energy-yielding reactions would

3 6 5

take place: the splitting of lithium, the fusion of deuterium with deuterium, and the fusion of deuterium with tritium.

Now besides releasing tremendous energy, these reactions would also yield a great number of surplus neutrons. It occurred to the bomb builders: why not use the neutrons to fission a mass of uranium? Even common uranium 238 could be fissioned with fast neutrons (though less readily than U-235). The heavy blast of fast neutrons from the fusion reactions might fission a considerable number of U-238 atoms. Suppose one built a bomb with a U-235 core (the igniting match), a surrounding explosive charge of lithium deuteride, and around all this a blanket of uranium 238 which would also serve as explosive. That would make a really big bomb. The U-238 blanket could be made almost as thick as one wished, because there is no critical size at which uranium 238 will undergo a chain reaction spontaneously.

The bomb was built; it was exploded at Bikini in the Marshall Islands on March 1, 1954; and it shook the world. The energy yield was around 15 megatons. Even more dramatic was a rain of radioactive particles that fell on 23 Japanese fishermen in a fishing boat named *The Lucky Dragon*. The radioactivity destroyed the cargo of fish, made the fishermen ill, and did not exactly improve the health of the rest of the world.

Since 1954, fission-fusion-fission bombs have become items in the armaments of the United States, the Soviet Union, and Great Britain.

NUCLEAR POWER

THE DRAMATIC USE of nuclear power in the form of unbelievably destructive bombs has done more to present the scientist in the role of an ogre than anything else that has occurred since the beginnings of science.

In a way this portrayal has its justifications, for no arguments or rationalizations can change the fact that scientists did indeed construct the atomic bomb, knowing from the beginning its destructive powers and that it would probably be put to use.

It is only fair to add that this was done under the stress of a great war against ruthless enemies, and with an eye to the frightful possibility that a man as maniacal as Adolf Hitler might get such a bomb first. It must also be added that, on the whole, the scientists working on the bomb were deeply disturbed about it and that many opposed its use, while some even left the field of nuclear physics afterward in what can only be described as remorse. Far fewer pangs of conscience were felt by most of the political and military leaders who made the actual decision to use the bombs.

Furthermore, we cannot and should not subordinate the fact that in releasing the energy of the atomic nucleus scientists put at man's disposal a power which can be used constructively as well as destructively. It is important to emphasize this in a world and at a time in which the threat of nuclear destruction has put science and scientists on the shamefaced defensive, and in a country like the United States, which has a rather strong Rousseauan tradition against book-learning as a corrupter of the simple integrity of man in a state of nature.

Even the explosion of an atomic bomb need not be purely destructive. Like the lesser chemical explosives long used in mining and in the construction of dams and highways, nuclear explosives could be vastly helpful in construction projects. In the United States, "Project Plowshare" (named from Isaiah's moving prophecy that the day would come when the nations "shall beat their swords into plowshares") is already exploring peaceful uses of such explosions. A harbor in Alaska is to be excavated. Oil-bearing rock is to be shattered and its oil content made available. There are even studies of the possibility of producing reservoirs of heat (by underground explosions creating pools of molten salt) which could be tapped to make steam and electricity. But the pursuit and success of such studies will depend on the nuclear powers reaching an agreement to carry on underground tests of nuclear explosions, not for the purpose of developing weapons but for peaceful uses.

The brightest hope for the constructive use of nuclear power lies in the kind of chain reaction that was born under the football stadium at the University of Chicago. A controlled nuclear reactor can develop huge quantities of heat, which of course can be drawn off by a "coolant," such as water or even molten metal, to produce electricity or heat a building.

Experimental nuclear reactors that produced electricity were built in Great Britain and the United States within a few years after the war. As everyone knows, the United States now has a fleet of nuclear-powered submarines, the first of which, the *U.S.S. Nautilus*, was launched in January 1954. This vessel, as important for its day as Fulton's *Clermont* was in its time, introduced engines with a virtually unlimited source of power which now permit submarines to travel entirely around the world under water, and at speeds formerly impossible. The *Nautilus* gave a dramatic demonstration by making an underwater crossing of the Arctic Ocean (and the North Pole) in 1958, and the *U.S.S. Triton*, the world's largest submarine, circumnavigated the globe under water along Magellan's route in 84 days between February and May in 1960. About three dozen nuclear-powered submarines have been built or are under construction or authorized in the United States.

The Soviet Union has not made known (up to this writing) whether it has or is building such submarines, but in December 1957 it launched the first nuclear-powered surface vessel, the *Lenin*, an ice-breaker. Shortly before that the United States had laid the keel for a nuclear-powered surface vessel, and in July 1959 the *U.S.S. Long Beach* (a cruiser) and the *Savannah* (a merchant ship) were launched. The *Long Beach* is powered by two nuclear reactors. Under construction is an aircraft carrier, the *U.S.S. Enterprise*, which will be powered by eight nuclear reactors. There may be 300 nuclear-powered ships of all sorts in operation throughout the world by 1975. Both the United States and the Soviet Union are experimenting with nuclear-powered aircraft as well, and even nuclear-powered spaceships are not being neglected. Perhaps nuclear-powered locomotives may some day be added to the list.

The first nuclear reactor built for the production of electric

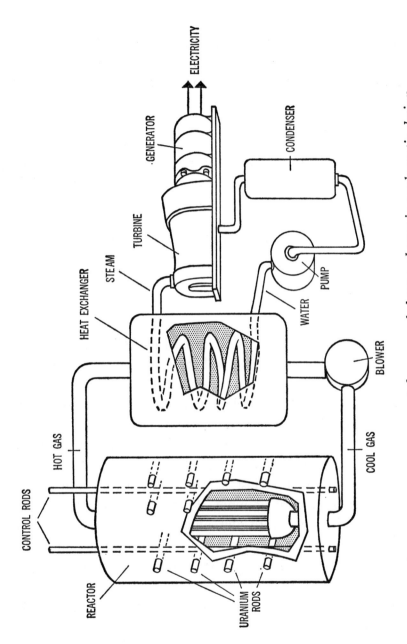

A NUCLEAR POWER PLANT of the gas-cooled type, shown in a schematic design. The reactor's heat here is transferred to a gas, which may be a vaporized metal, circulating through it, and the heat is then used to convert water to steam.

power for civilian use was put into action in the Soviet Union in June of 1954. It was a small one, with a capacity of not more than 5,000 kilowatts. By the end of 1956 Great Britain had its "Calder Hall" plant in operation, with a capacity of more than 50,000 kilowatts. The United States was third in the field. On May 26, 1958, Westinghouse completed a small nuclear reactor for the production of civilian power at Shippingport, Pa. All three nations are building larger reactors, and many other countries are preparing to harness nuclear power.

So far the electricity produced by nuclear power cannot compete with coal-produced electricity except in regions where coal is scarce and expensive indeed. That situation may prevail for some time, but it is hoped that advances in technique will eventually allow nuclear power to become economical. As it is, by 1963 the world is expected to have nuclear reactors with a total capacity of 1,300,-000 kilowatts of electricity.

IF FISSION eventually replaces coal and oil as the world's chief source of energy, how long will the new fuel last? Not very long, if we have to depend entirely on the scarce fissionable material uranium 235. But fortunately man can create other fissionable fuels with uranium 235 as a starter.

We have seen that plutonium is one of these man-made fuels. Suppose we build a small reactor with enriched uranium fuel and omit the moderator, so that fast neutrons will stream into a surrounding jacket of natural uranium. These neutrons will convert uranium 238 in the jacket into plutonium. If we arrange things so that few neutrons are wasted, from each fission of a uranium-235 atom in the core we may get more than one plutonium atom manufactured in the jacket. In other words, we will breed more fuel than we consume. Such a reactor was built at Arco, Idaho, in 1951. It was called EBR-1 (Experimental Breeder Reactor-1). Besides proving the workability of the breeding principle, it produced electricity. Large-scale breeder reactors are now being built.

SOVIET EXPERIMENTS IN FUSION. *Russian workers are shown install-ing ALFA, an apparatus with a doughnut-shaped chamber in which they conducted experiments with plasmas, looking toward produc-ing thermonuclear reactions.*

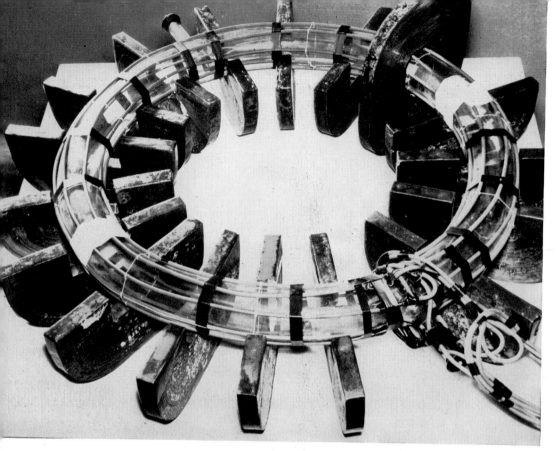

LOS ALAMOS EXPERIMENTS IN FUSION. *This is a tube of the "Perhapsatron," one of the American devices for studying pinch effects on plasmas. The pieces of iron are the halves of the magnetic cores (one is complete) that will ring the tube.*

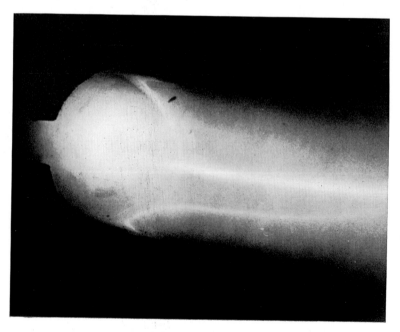

PINCHED PLASMA *in the Perhapsatron tube.*

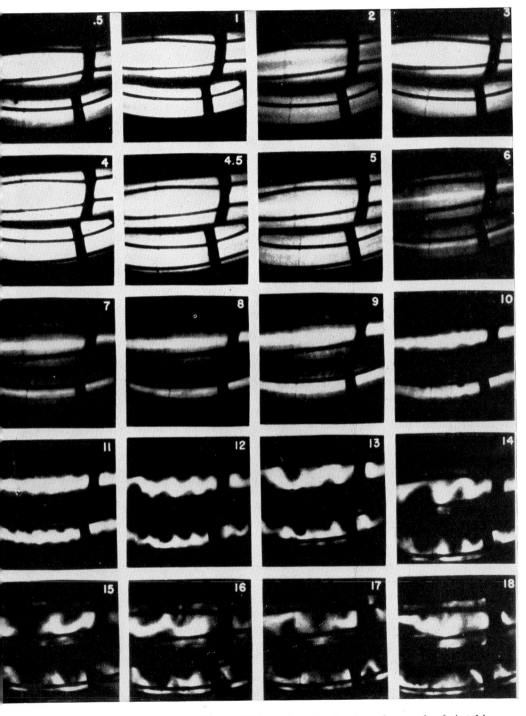

THE LIFE AND DEATH OF A PINCH. *This series of pictures shows the brief history of a wisp of plasma in the magnetic field of the Perhapsatron. Each photograph gives two views of the plasma, one from the side and one from below through a mirror. The pinch broke down in millionths of a second; the number on each picture is the time in microseconds.*

THE BELL SOLAR BATTERY, *here used to furnish power to a telephone lin*

A THERMOELECTRIC CELL *for converting heat directly into electricity. Th heat of sunlight is focused by the concave mirror at the right on a disk o semiconducting material where it produces a flow of electrons. These exper. ments were performed at the Westinghouse Research Laboratories.*

Breeding could multiply the fuel supply from uranium many times, because all of the common uranium 238 would become potential fuel.

The element thorium is another potential source of fissionable fuel. Upon absorbing fast neutrons, it is changed to the artificial isotope thorium 233, which soon decays to uranium 233. Now uranium 233 is fissionable by slow neutrons, and will maintain a self-sustaining chain reaction. Thus thorium can be added to the fuel supply, and thorium appears to be about five times as abundant as uranium in the earth.

All in all, the total amount of power conceivably available from the uranium and thorium supplies of the earth is about 20 times that available from the coal and oil we have left. But it seems that only a small part of the uranium and thorium can be extracted from the earth at less than prohibitive cost. This may limit the practical supply of energy from fissionable fuels to a few centuries.

RADIOACTIVITY

THE ARRIVAL OF THE ATOMIC AGE brought to man a hazard almost entirely new to his experience. The unlocking of the nucleus released floods of nuclear radiations. To be sure, life on the earth had always been exposed to natural radioactivity and cosmic rays. But man's concentration of naturally radioactive substances, such as radium, which ordinarily exist as greatly diluted traces in the earth's crust, vastly compounded the danger. Some early workers with X-rays and radium even received lethal doses: Marie Curie and her daughter Irène Joliot-Curie both died of leukemia from their exposures, and there is the famous case of the watch-dial painters in the 1920's who died as the result of pointing their radium-tipped brushes with their lips. The coming of fission added new force to the danger. Whether in bombs or in power reactors, it unleashes radioactivity on a scale that could make the entire atmosphere, the oceans, and everything we eat, drink or breathe dangerous to human life. Fission has introduced a form of pollution which will tax man's ingenuity to control.

When the uranium or plutonium atom splits, its "fission products" take various forms. Sometimes the two fragments are barium and technetium, sometimes one of a number of other possible pairs. All told, some 200 different radioactive fission products have been identified. All of these are dangerous in varying degrees, depending on the energy and nature of the radiation. Alpha particles taken into the body, for instance, are more dangerous than beta particles. The rate of decay also is important: a "nuclide" (species of nucleus) that breaks down rapidly will bombard the receiver with more radiation per second or per hour than one that breaks down slowly.

The rate of breakdown of a radioactive nuclide is something that can be spoken of only when large numbers of the nuclide are involved. An individual nucleus may break down at any time — the next instant or a billion years hence or any time in between — and there is no way of predicting when it will. Each radioactive species, however, has an average rate of breakdown, so if a large number of atoms is involved, it is possible to predict with great accuracy what proportion of them will break down in any unit of time. For instance, let us say that experiment shows that, in a given sample of an atom we shall call X, the atoms are breaking down at the rate of one out of two per year. At the end of a year, 500 of every 1,000 original X atoms in the sample would be left as X atoms; at the end of two years, 250; at the end of three years, 125; and so on. The time it takes for half of the original atoms to break down is called that particular atom's half-life, so the half-life of atom X is one year. Every radioactive nuclide has its own characteristic half-life, which never changes under ordinary conditions. (The only kind of outside influence that can change it is bombardment of the nucleus with a particle or the extremely high temperature in the interior of a star — in other words, a violent event capable of attacking the nucleus *per se*.)

The half-life of uranium 238 is 4.5 billion years. It is not surprising, therefore, that there is still uranium 238 left in the Universe, despite the decay of uranium atoms. A simple calculation will show that it will take a period more than six times as long as the half-life to reduce a particular quantity of a radioactive nuclide to 1 per cent of its original quantity. Even 30 billion years from now there will still be two pounds of uranium left from each ton of it now in the earth's crust.

Although the isotopes of an element are practically identical chemically, they may differ greatly in their nuclear properties. Uranium 235, for instance, breaks down six times as fast as uranium 238; its half-life is only 710 million years. It can be reasoned, therefore, that in eons gone by, uranium was much richer in uranium 235 than it is today. Six billion years ago, for instance, uranium 235 would have made up about 70 per cent of natural uranium. Mankind is not, however, just catching the tail end of the uranium 235. Even if he had been delayed another million years in discovering fission, the earth would still have 99.9 per cent as much uranium 235 then as it has now.

Clearly any nuclide with a half-life of less than 100 million years would have declined to the vanishing point in the long lifetime of the Universe. This explains why we cannot find more than traces of plutonium today. The longest-lived plutonium isotope, plutonium-244, has a half-life of only 70 million years.

The uranium, thorium, and other long-lived radioactive elements thinly spread through the rocks and soil produce small quantities of radiation which is always present in the air about us. Man is even slightly radioactive himself, for all living tissue contains traces of a comparatively rare unstable isotope of potassium (potassium 40) which has a half-life of 1.3 billion years.

All this makes up what is called "background radiation" (to which cosmic rays also contribute). The constant exposure to natural radiation probably has played a part in evolution by producing mutations and may be partly responsible for the affliction of cancer. But living organisms have lived with it for millions of years. Nuclear radiation has become a serious hazard only in our own time, first as man began to experiment with radium, and then with the coming of fission and nuclear reactors.

By the time the atomic-energy project began, physicists had learned from painful experience how dangerous nuclear radiation was. The workers in the project were therefore surrounded with elaborate safety precautions. The "hot" fission products and other radioactive materials were placed behind thick shielding walls, and looked at only through lead glass. Instruments were devised to handle the materials by remote control. Each person was required to wear strips of photographic film or other detecting devices to "monitor" his accumulated exposure. Extensive animal experiments were carried out to estimate the "maximum permissible exposure." (Mammals are more sensitive to radiation than are other forms of life, but man is averagely resistant, for a mammal.)

Despite everything, accidents happened, and a few nuclear physicists died of "radiation sickness" from massive doses. Yet there are risks in every occupation, even the safest; the nuclear-energy workers have actually fared better than most, thanks to increasing knowledge of what the hazards are and care in avoiding them.

But a world full of nuclear power reactors, spawning fission products by the ton and the thousands of tons, will be a different story. How will all that deadly material be disposed of?

A great deal of it is short-lived radioactivity which fades away to harmlessness within a matter of weeks or months; it can be stored for that time and then dumped. Most dangerous are the nuclides with half-lives of one year to 30 years. They are short-lived enough to produce intense radiation, yet long-lived enough to be hazardous for generations. A nuclide with a 30-year half-life will take two centuries to lose 99 per cent of its activity.

Fission products can be put to good use. As sources of energy, they can power small devices or instruments. For example, there have been demonstrations of a small transistor-generator, producing electricity directly from heat, which uses short-lived nuclides to provide the heat. This device, called SNAP ("Systems for Nuclear Auxiliary Power"), can be as light as five pounds, generates two and a half watts, and weight for weight produces ten times as much power as could an ordinary chemical battery. It lasts much longer, too.

Radionuclides also have large potential uses in medicine (*e.g.*, for treatment of cancer), in killing bacteria and preserving food, and in many fields of industry, including chemical manufacturing. For instance, the Hercules Powder Company has designed a reactor to use radiation in the production of the anti-freeze ethylene glycol.

Yet when all is said and done, no conceivable uses could employ more than a small part of the vast quantities of fission products that power reactors will discharge. It is estimated that every 200,000 kilowatts of nuclear-produced electricity will involve the production of a pound and a half of fission products per day. What to do with it?

Already the United States has stored millions of gallons of radioactive liquid underground. Both the United States and Great Britain have dumped concrete containers of fission products at sea. There have been proposals to drop the radioactive wastes in oceanic abysses, to store them in old salt mines, to incarcerate them in molten glass and bury the solidified material. But there is always the nervous thought that in one way or another the radioactivity will escape in time and contaminate the soil or the seas. One particularly haunting nightmare is the possibility that a nuclear-powered ship might be wrecked and spill its accumulated fission products into the ocean.

IF RADIOACTIVE POLLUTION by peaceful nuclear energy is a potential danger, at least it will be kept under control, and probably successfully, by every possible means. But there is a pollution which has already spread over the world and which, indeed, in a nuclear war might be broadcast deliberately. This is the fallout from atomic bombs.

Fallout is produced by all nuclear bombs, even those not fired in anger. Because fallout is carried around the world by the winds and brought to earth by rainfall, it is virtually impossible for any nation to explode a nuclear bomb in the atmosphere without detection. In the event of a nuclear war, fallout in the long run might produce more casualties and do more damage to living things in the world at large than the fire and blast of the bombs themselves would wreak on the countries attacked. The huge output of fission products from fission-fusion-fission superbombs would be carried via the stratosphere over a whole hemisphere, falling eventually on the attacker as well as the attacked.

The intensity of the fallout from the first superbomb, exploded in the Pacific on March 1, 1954, caught scientists by surprise. They had not expected the fallout from a fusion bomb to be so "dirty." But the reason became clear when they learned that the fusion core was supplemented with a blanket of uranium 238 which was fissioned by the neutrons. Not only did this multiply the force of the explosion, but it gave rise to a vastly greater cloud of fission products than a simple fission bomb of the Hiroshima type.

The fallout from the bomb tests to date has added only a small amount of radioactivity to the earth's background radiation. But even a small rise above the natural level may increase the incidence of cancer, cause genetic damage, and shorten the average life expectancy slightly. The most conservative estimators of the hazards agree that by increasing the mutation rate (see Chapter 12 for a discussion of mutations), fallout is storing up a certain amount of trouble for future generations.

One of the fission products is particularly dangerous for human life. This is strontium 90 (half-life, 28 years). Strontium 90 falling on the soil and water is taken up by plants and thereafter incorporated into the bodies of those animals (including man) that feed directly or indirectly on the plants. Its peculiar danger lies in the fact that strontium, because of its chemical similarity to calcium, goes to the bones and lodges there for a long time. The minerals in bone have a slow "turnover;" that is, they are not replaced nearly as rapidly as are the substances in the soft tissues. For that reason strontium 90, once absorbed, may remain in the body for a major part of a person's lifetime.

Strontium 90 is a brand-new substance in our environment; it did

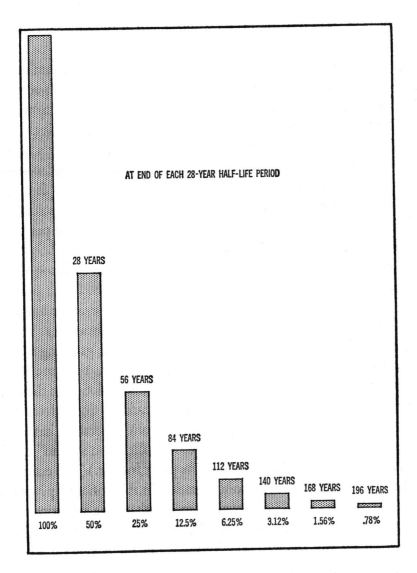

AT END OF EACH 28-YEAR HALF-LIFE PERIOD

28 YEARS

56 YEARS

84 YEARS

112 YEARS

140 YEARS 168 YEARS 196 YEARS

100%   50%   25%   12.5%   6.25%   3.12%   1.56%   .78%

DECAY OF STRONTIUM 90 *over approximately 200 years.*

not exist on the earth in any detectable quantity until man fissioned the uranium atom. But today, within less than a generation, some strontium 90 has become incorporated in the bones of every human being on earth, and indeed in all vertebrates. And considerable quantities of it are still floating in the stratosphere, sooner or later to add to the concentration in our bones.

The strontium-90 concentration is measured in "strontium units" (S.U.). One S.U. is one micromicrocurie of strontium 90 per gram of calcium in the body. A "curie" is a unit of radiation (named in honor of the Curies, of course) originally meant to be equivalent to that produced by a gram of radium in equilibrium with its breakdown product, radon. It is now more generally accepted as meaning 37 billion disintegrations per second. A micromicrocurie is a trillionth of a curie, or 2.12 disintegrations per minute. A strontium unit would therefore mean 2.12 disintegrations per minute per gram of calcium present in the body.

The concentration of strontium 90 in the human skeleton varies greatly from place to place and among individuals. Some persons have been found to have as much as 75 times the average amount. Children average at least four times as high a concentration as adults, because of the higher turnover of material in their growing bones. Estimates of the averages themselves vary, because they are based mainly on estimates of the amounts of strontium 90 found in the diet. (Incidentally, milk is not a particularly hazardous food, from this point of view, because calcium obtained from vegetables has more strontium 90 associated with it. The cow's "filtration system" eliminates some of the strontium it gets in its plant fodder.) The estimates of the average strontium-90 concentration in the bones of people in the United States in 1959 ranged from less than one strontium unit to well over five strontium units. (The "maximum permissible" was established by the International Commission on Radiation Protection at 67 S.U.) But the averages mean little, particularly since strontium 90 may collect in "hot spots" in the bones and reach a high enough level there to initiate leukemia or cancer.

Many eminent scientists firmly believe that the fallout from the bomb tests represents an important peril to the human race. The chemist Linus Pauling has argued that the fallout from a single superbomb may lead to 100,000 deaths from leukemia and other diseases in the world, and he has pointed out that radioactive carbon 14, produced by the neutrons from a nuclear explosion, constitutes a genetic danger. On the other hand, some scientists, including spokesmen for the United States Atomic Energy Commission, have minimized the seriousness of the fallout hazard. All agree, however, that a resumption of nuclear-bomb testing in the atmosphere should be avoided.

In the fall of 1958 the United States, the U.S.S.R., and Great Britain suspended bomb-testing by a gentleman's agreement. (This did not prevent France from exploding her first atomic bomb in the spring of 1960.) Up to this writing, the major nuclear powers had stood by that tacit understanding, although they had failed to reach an agreement to make the bomb-testing ban permanent. It seemed clear that these nations would not go back to exploding test bombs in the air. Nor were they far apart on the question of banning tests underground (except for joint experiments on the use of nuclear explosions for peaceful purposes). There was still considerable dispute between the United States and the Soviet Union as to whether one side or the other might cheat by setting off small bombs underground and muffling the explosion, but the scientists of both sides seemed to agree that by cooperative research it would be possible eventually to develop a reliable detection system.

FUSION POWER

FOR MORE THAN 20 YEARS nuclear physicists have had in the back of their minds a dream even more attractive than turning fission to constructive uses. It is the dream of harnessing fusion energy. Fusion, after all, is the engine that makes our world go round: the fusion reactions in the sun are the ultimate source of all our forms of energy and of life itself. If somehow we could reproduce such reactions on the earth under control, all our energy problems would be solved. Our fuel supply would be as big as the ocean, for the fuel would be hydrogen. And fusion power would be immensely more convenient than fission power. Pound for pound, a fusion reactor would deliver about five to ten times as much power as a fission reactor. Furthermore, fusion produces no radioactive ashes.

The specific primary fuel would be deuterium (hydrogen 2), which fuses much more readily than ordinary hydrogen. Although only 15 out of every 100,000 hydrogen atoms in nature are deuterium, the oceans contain enough deuterium to supply 100 million times as much power as all the minable coal and oil in the earth. Nuclear "burning" of the deuterium would take care of all of mankind's conceivable energy needs for millions of years.

Now that we have made a hydrogen bomb, why can't we make a hydrogen power reactor? The main reason is the extremely high temperatures involved. But perhaps a small part of the reason also is that the fusion-power problem has so far not had nearly as urgent or massive attention as was devoted to the nuclear bomb projects. There are ideas, at least, about how to go about harnessing fusion reactions, but work on these ideas is receiving only mild support and proceeding in comparatively leisurely fashion.

The fusion problem is twofold: (1) to produce the temperature necessary to ignite a fusion chain reaction — perhaps 350 million degrees; (2) to hold the fire, burning at this sort of temperature, in any kind of working system.

The first problem looks to be the less difficult. Obviously we can't ignite the engine with a fission bomb. But heavy currents of electricity or high-energy sound waves can heat a gas to very high temperatures: they have produced temperatures as high as 15,000° C. for considerable periods and as high as a million degrees very briefly. There is every reason to hope that the necessary temperature will eventually be attained.

Containing the hot gas is an altogether different sort of problem, calling for entirely new ideas. Obviously no material container could hold a gas at anything like the explosive temperature of 350 million degrees. The first step toward a solution is to reduce the density of the gas to far below normal pressure; this cuts down the heat content, though the energy of the particles remains high. The second step

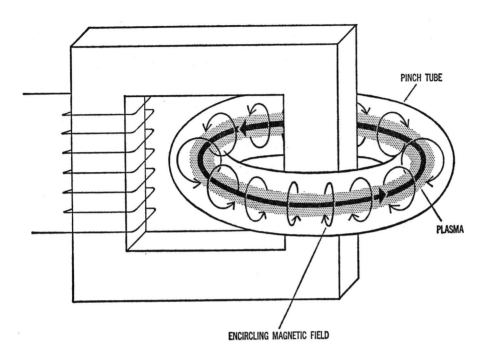

PINCH TUBE

PLASMA

ENCIRCLING MAGNETIC FIELD

MAGNETIC BOTTLE designed to hold a hot gas of hydrogen nuclei (a plasma). The ring is called a "torus."

was a concept of great ingenuity. A gas at very high temperature has all the electrons stripped off its atoms; it is a "plasma" made up of electrons and bare nuclei. Since it consists entirely of charged particles, why not use a strong magnetic field, taking the place of a material container, to hold it? The "magnetic bottle" idea was tried, and it worked — but only for the briefest instant. The wisps of plasma "pinched" in the bottle immediately writhed like a snake, broke up, and died out.

Experimenters have made a good deal of progress in shaping magnetic fields in ways that keep the plasma alive slightly longer. The most promising developments are a doughnut-shaped field ("torus") and a combination of longitudinal and ringing magnetic fields. Several laboratories in the United States are engaged in the project — an activity under the Atomic Energy Commission called Project Sherwood — and laboratories in Great Britain and the Soviet Union have been at least as active. So far, apparently, no verified thermonuclear chain reaction has been achieved in such a bottle. The telltale evidence of such a reaction will be the production of neutrons, but neutrons are not decisive proof, because they may arise in other ways.

There is some faint hope that the necessary temperature can be lowered by using tritium to help in the reaction. A deuterium atom will fuse with a tritium atom at as low a temperature as 45 million degrees. Although tritium would not be a practicable fuel for a fusion reactor, because it would have to be manufactured at great expense, it might serve as the sparkplug to start a deuterium chain reaction.

The List of Illustrations, Index of Names,
and Index of Subjects will be found
at the end of Volume Two.